THE NEGRO'S STRUGGLE FOR SURVIVAL

THE NEGRO'S STRUGGLE FOR SURVIVAL

A STUDY IN HUMAN ECOLOGY

BY

S. J. HOLMES

PROFESSOR OF ZOÖLOGY IN THE UNIVERSITY
OF CALIFORNIA

KENNIKAT PRESS, INC./PORT WASHINGTON, N. Y.

CONTENTS

LIST OF FIGURES

[iii]

LIST OF FIGURES

LIST OF TABLES

[v]

LIST OF TABLES— *(Continued)*

LIST OF TABLES—(*Concluded*)

APPENDIX

LIST OF TABLES

[ix]

APPENDIX TABLES—(*Concluded*)

PREFACE

THE BIOLOGICAL TREND of the American Negro cannot fail to have an important influence upon the people of the United States in many ways. No comprehensive treatment of the subject has appeared since Dr. F. L. Hoffman's paper, "Race Traits and Tendencies of the American Negro," published in 1896, and since then many aspects of the problem have greatly changed. In the present volume I have endeavored to bring together the principal data available on the vital fortunes of our Negro population. No attempt is made to predict what will happen to the Negroes in the distant future. I have kept pretty close to facts and have confined myself mainly to the discussion of present trends in the conviction that it is only through the study of contemporary changes in the endeavor to ascertain their causes that we can obtain any basis for deductions as to the future, and then only for a short time.

Being a biologist, I have treated my theme from the viewpoint of one who observes the competition of two rival species inhabiting the same territory. That I happen to belong to one of the contending groups has not prevented me, I trust, from maintaining throughout a detached and objective attitude. The struggle for survival enters into different phases as time goes on and environmental conditions change. How it works out, depends not only on the character of the competitors, but also on the influences to which they are exposed. Now the one contestant may prevail and now the other, according to the nature of the environment in which the struggle goes on. In many localities whites have supplanted Negroes, and in others Negroes have supplanted whites. It is not the physical environment alone that decides the issue: an even greater influence is often exerted by social, economic, and psychological factors.

For several reasons which are discussed in the following pages the rates of natural increase of whites and blacks in the United States have come to be more nearly equal than they were in previous decades. It is not impossible that in the near future the Negroes may be increasing more rapidly than the whites. A study of the problem inevitably leads to the investigation of birth rates, death rates, infant mortality, immunity and susceptibility to disease, the causes and biological effects of migration, the results of race mixture, and the influence of the various other forces which affect the natural increase of peoples. Unfortunately, one cannot arrive at valid conclusions on such topics without compiling and analyzing a large amount of statistical data. But I have endeavored to spare the reader, who may not care to be interrupted more than necessary by arrays of figures, by consigning several of the statistical tables to an appendix.

In compiling statistical material and in making calculations based thereon I have been assisted by Dr. H. J. Ralston, who has relieved me of much tedious arithmetic. The studies here described have been aided by a grant made by the President of the University of California upon the recommendation of the Board of Research of that institution. The results of some of these studies are embodied in a number of previous papers. A large part of Chapter V appeared in an article on "Differential Mortality in the American Negro," which was published in *Human Biology* for February and May, 1931. I am indebted to the editor for permission to reproduce it here in a somewhat modified form. To Dr. E. F. Penrose, who has read the entire manuscript, I am grateful for several helpful criticisms and suggestions.

S. J. H.

THE NEGRO'S STRUGGLE FOR SURVIVAL

CHAPTER I

THE INTERRACIAL STRUGGLE FOR EXISTENCE

ALL LIVING CREATURES tend to multiply without stint and to replenish the earth with their kind. When two species occupy the same territory and depend upon the same means of subsistence, each tends to supplant the other. Human beings are no exception to this rule. It matters not whether the two groups engage in actual conflict or vie with each other in the offices of brotherly love, competition for the means of subsistence is bound to go on. Even though they may interbreed and eventually fuse into a single hybrid stock, the two groups will, in the meantime, inevitably engage in a struggle for numerical supremacy.

The struggle for existence in human beings as well as in lower organisms usually goes on quite unobtrusively and in ways difficult to detect. Several years ago, the common clam of the Atlantic seaboard was accidentally introduced into San Francisco Bay along with the eastern oysters which were planted in that locality. The environment seemed peculiarly suitable to the clams from the east coast, and they multiplied so rapidly that most of the native species of clam were virtually exterminated. Now, anything like an actual conflict between clams is quite unthinkable. These creatures spend their lives burrowing in the mud and drawing in water which contains the microscopic plants and animals that supply their food. By attending strictly to their own business of assimilating nutriment and reproducing their kind, the clams of one species came to prevail over and exterminate their rivals.

This is but one illustration of the general fact that throughout nature the struggle for existence is, as a rule, a rather orderly and peaceful procedure. It is often difficult to explain just how and why one species succeeds in exterminating another. The dandelions may kill out the grass on the lawn, or, as some Russian investigators have recently shown, one variety of dandelion may exterminate another, but what peculiarities of the dandelions enable them to achieve success we do not know. In the animal world varieties are continually supplanting other varieties, but it is only rarely that success can be attributed to greater prowess in battle or to any other advantage that can be clearly perceived. Conflict is a relatively rare manifestation of the struggle for existence. And although it has been a very conspicuous feature of the history of our own species, it has probably played a much less important rôle in evolution than have the bloodless battles which are carried on in times of peace.

There is no way of avoiding the conclusion that biologically Negroes and whites in the United States are rivals for the possession of a common territory. To what extent actual conflicts between the races may arise in the future no one can tell. In any event, they will probably play a very minor rôle in the struggle for racial supremacy. Throughout human history, stocks have continually been replaced, peacefully or otherwise, by their successful rivals. Even relatively stable populations represent but a temporary retardation in the general course of racial change. What is of greater importance than military prowess in the biological fortunes of peoples is the more obscure factors which affect the balance of births and deaths. Among rival groups, the one with the greater preponderance of births over deaths, or the greater net fertility, will naturally prevail. The victories won through high fertility or a low death rate are just as fatal to the losing competitor as a war of extermination.

A population consisting of different racial elements is inevitably in a condition of unstable equilibrium. It is out of the question to suppose that the present proportions of Negroes and whites in the United States will continue indefinitely. But considering this as one possibility, there are four ways in which the racial struggle may conceivably work out:

1. We may all become black;
2. We may all become white;
3. Whites and blacks may fuse into a hybrid stock; or
4. We may become permanently biracial, either mingled together, or occupying different local areas.

One can make reasonable forecasts of the probable future trend of population growth only by a study of the changes which are now going on and by endeavoring to ascertain the causes by which these changes are brought about. The purely biological effects of the contact of different races vary greatly with time and place, to say nothing of the native characteristics of the races concerned. The tendency of one race to supplant another arises out of the fact that races are composed of organisms, and it is a characteristic of all organisms to increase, so far as means of subsistence will permit, and to crowd out all competitors. In this tendency we have a primary force which is always to be reckoned with, and which is bound to express itself regardless of whatever other relations between the races may develop.

If the relation of one race to another were purely antagonistic, its influence upon the biological fortunes of its rivals would present a much simpler problem. But along with competition growing out of the natural increase of numbers, we have in organized society the development of mutual services between human beings, so that the presence of one's fellows becomes an aid as well as a hindrance to success in the struggle for existence. Societies in animals and human beings are based upon mutual aid. It is quite possible for members of distinct races to work into such relations that, within certain limits, the presence of the one may be of positive advantage to the other. A social group functions in many ways like a single organism in which the parts work together to their common advantage. If our complex social and economic organization should suddenly cease to function, a great many of us would die of starvation within a few weeks. It is quite possible for Negroes and whites to be distributed in occupational groups in such a way that the very life of each race would be dependent upon the other. Nevertheless, even in this extreme, the fundamental factor of competition would continue, and in periods of a general shortage of food or other necessities of life it might become acute. Among such imperfectly socialized creatures as human beings, the relations of individuals are as a matter of fact partly symbiotic and partly antagonistic. In certain localities of the Southwest we have had the spectacle of Mexican laborers driving out certain elements of the population, both white and Negro, from one occupation after another. The remaining native population then comes to depend upon the Mexicans. The competing invaders now constitute an organic part of our social and economic order. But this mutually advantageous arrangement does not prevent the Mexicans and the white population from being biological rivals.

In our social life, competition and coöperation often work
gether in curious ways. The degree in which different racial
ments of a community compete or coöperate is subject to m
variation, as is shown by the very different effects resulting from
contact of races in different parts of the world. What happens
primitive race when it is brought into association with one of n
highly developed culture depends, of course, upon many cat
but one factor of great importance is how the more primitive
adjusts itself to a more highly developed social order. Several tr
of American Indians, for example, proved to be little amenabl
the institutions of the white man. To the whites, they were sin
in the way—and they disappeared. Several other tribes have dv
dled in numbers; a few have increased. The American Indians,
like the Negroes, have remained, in large part, a sort of fore
element in our population, never really incorporated into our so
life. The few tribes which have increased in numbers have b
artificially shielded in reservations or they have worked into
vantageous economic relations with the whites.

To many primitive peoples the white man has proved a dea
scourge. The Tasmanians are completely gone. The natives of *A*
tralia are a dwindling remnant, having a status more or less c
parable to that of the rest of the mammalian fauna. The Maori
New Zealand rapidly decreased after the advent of the whi
Throughout Polynesia and Melanesia a widespread depopulat
has been going on, which has threatened with extinction the nati
of many islands of the Pacific. There is no doubt that the white n
has been mainly responsible for this decrease in numbers. He
brought diseases which have at times decimated the ranks of the
tive populations. It is estimated that in 1875 40,000 out of 120,
Fijians died of an epidemic of measles. At various times, large nt
bers of natives have perished from influenza. The colds introdu
by the whites and their sequelae, bronchitis and pneumonia, h
been potent causes of death. Tuberculosis, almost unknown bef
the visits of the white man, has become widely spread through
the Pacific area, and smallpox, syphilis, and the common infecti
diseases of childhood increased the total mortality. Many of th
diseases, introduced amid populations previously almost entir
free from them, and consequently unprotected by the developm

of a partial immunity which has been slowly acquired by the white race, have raged with unusual severity. The readiness to fall victim to these diseases was doubtless further increased by changes in native customs made by the whites, and especially by the unhygienic habit of wearing clothes, which the Reverend W. J. Burrat designates as the greatest of all the curses introduced by civilization. Another evil which has been increased by the whites is the use of alcohol, which, in certain parts of Melanesia, according to Rivers, "has exerted and is still exerting a most deleterious influence," as it certainly has done among native peoples in various other parts of the world.

A common effect of the invasion of the whites is the decline of the native birth rate. In part, this results from the spread of venereal disease. In many places, it is due in part to the barbarous custom of forcibly recruiting adult males, and occasionally also females, as laborers and deporting them to other localities. As Rivers has remarked, "this custom forms one of the blackest of civilization's crimes," and it is a crime which has been frequently committed wherever the whites have come into contact with native races. Moreover, under white domination, the natives are often led to reduce their birth rate voluntarily. "Why," remarked an intelligent Melanesian, "should we bring children into the world, only to work for the white man?"

Through warfare, disease, exploitation, oppression, the break-up of native customs, and the general demoralization of native character, the white man has wrought frightful havoc among many primitive peoples who have been subjected to his influence. But he is far from proving an unmitigated curse. In many ways, his relations to his less enlightened fellow humans have been decidedly beneficial. If he has introduced disease, he has, through hygiene and sanitation, checked the spread of epidemics and greatly reduced the death rate among native peoples. If he has subjected natives to a ruthless economic exploitation, he has, by developing natural resources and the introduction of new forms of industry, greatly increased the wealth of many regions and thereby enabled them to support a much larger native population. On several occasions, the influence of the whites has resulted in the prevention of internecine wars and the institution of improved forms of government. The great Pacific area, where so many interesting movements of peoples have been taking place, affords many illustrations of the changing relationships of white and native races. The relations of different peoples inhabiting the same areas, being partly antagonistic and partly symbiotic, naturally change with time. At first they are apt to be mainly antagonistic. For this there are several causes, some of which have been already mentioned. But with the advent of industrial development, the improvement of political administration, the education of native children, and better hygiene and sanitation, the natives come to reap many advantages from the presence of the whites. In many parts of the Pacific area the course of depopulation has been stayed, and now, for some years, the native peoples have in general been on the increase. In 1856, Featherstone wrote that "the Maoris are dying out; and nothing can save them." In 1884, Sir William Buller predicted that, "in all probability five and twenty years hence, there would only be a remnant left." Nevertheless, in spite of a decline which has often caused them to be cited as an illustration of a disappearing race, since 1896, when their numbers reached about their lowest point, the Maoris have been on the upgrade. In fact, the yearbook of New Zealand for 1931 states that "during the last few years the natural increase of the Maori population has exceeded that of the Europeans." This is true for both the pure Maoris and the half-caste population, although the latter has been increasing at the more rapid rate. The Maoris are gradually adapting themselves to the economic and social institutions of the whites and are thereby coming to secure some of the advantages of contact with a more highly developed civilization.

In Hawaii the native population has long been decreasing in numbers. The development of the agricultural resources has brought large numbers of aliens to the islands, which are now inhabited by a conglomerate collection of Chinese, Portuguese, Japanese, Filipinos, Hindus, Porto Ricans, Negroes, and Pacific Islanders of various kinds. The Hawaiians have intermarried with several of these stocks, and the mixed breeds have increased much more rapidly in number than the pure native inhabitants. But notwithstanding the rapid growth of the alien peoples, even the native Hawaiians have now begun to multiply more rapidly. The unmixed Hawaiians, however, are still decreasing, although less rapidly than formerly; but if half mixed Hawaiians were counted as pure Hawaiians the latter would show an increase in the past two decades. In other words, Hawaiian germ plasm is increasing in quantity.

The natives of Fiji, who have been for a long time decreasing, have begun to show a small surplus of births over deaths, and this in spite of an extensive invasion of Hindus, who now constitute about two-fifths of the population of the islands. The downward trend of population has been turned also in the Tonga Islands, the Admiralty Islands, the Carolines, Samoa, New Britain, and in many smaller islands. Mr. Roberts, in his volume, *Population Problems of the Pacific,* estimates that out of the total island population of the Pacific area, 35 per cent is increasing, 39 per cent is stationary, and 25.5 per cent is decreasing, with 0.16 per cent faced with imminent extinction. These figures relate only to the endemic peoples of the islands. How long the Polynesians and Melanesians will continue to increase is problematical. They may be overrun later by more sturdy migrants from Asia who will drive the native inhabitants to the wall. Just now, the natives seem to be the favorites of fortune.

Similar changes are occurring among primitive peoples in other parts of the world. The statistical data available on the native population of the Union of South Africa show an increase of the indigenous Bantu inhabitants, as well as an increasing number of mixed breeds and incomers from Asia. The first effects of the invasion by whites in southern and central Africa were notoriously unfavorable to the increase of native peoples. Through war, the recruiting of slaves, the introduction of diseases, and the demoralization of native customs, the Negroes suffered heavy losses; in some parts white occupancy still exercises a baneful influence on the black population. As General Smuts remarked in his Rhodes lecture (1930) : "It is unfortunately the fact that throughout much of the African continent, the native population is not increasing, and in some parts, like Angola and the Congo, it is definitely declining. The part of Africa in which the native population is increasing most rapidly within the last six years is the Union of South Africa, and that fact is a great tribute to the blessings of a settled European government, to the favorable economic conditions which render such an expansion possible, and to the medical care and welfare work carried on among the natives."

In other parts of Africa the bad effects of the white invasion still predominate. According to a recent report on labor conditions in the Belgian Congo, the birth rate of the natives has fallen off to such a degree that it threatens the loss of man power needed for the industrial development of the region. The methods in vogue for recruiting labor are severely criticized in this report, and a plea is made for a more humane and intelligent management of the Negro population in order to prevent the gradual loss of this valuable financial asset. The report is of interest for its somewhat belated recognition of the value of policies which have elsewhere proved effective in conserving the supply of labor.

The British administration of India has led to a rapid growth of the native population, the last census showing an increase of some 30,000,000 in the preceding decade. Since 1800, the indigenous population of Java has increased over tenfold under the administration of the Dutch. The Filipinos have about doubled in number since the United States came into control of the islands in 1898. The growth of the population in the West Indies is, in large measure, the result of the development of the resources of these islands under the guidance of the whites. In respect of racial replacement, these islands have an interesting history. The inhabitants of Jamaica, Haiti, Guadaloupe, Martinique, and Barbados are now mainly blacks. The ruthless exploitation of the Spaniards greatly reduced the native population of these islands, and the African slaves who were imported as a substitute for the natives were more successful in adjusting themselves to the economic régime of their masters. They throve under white control, and absorbed or replaced most of the natives who remained. The biological victory is clearly in the hands of the black man. The Caribbean has now become a great spawning area of black humanity from which numerous immigrants migrate into Mexico, Brazil, Venezuela, Colombia, and Central America, where they contribute to deepen the shade of the mixed inhabitants of these countries. Many thousands have come into the United States, and, unless this influx is checked, it will probably continue to increase in volume.

The prediction of the future increase or decrease of primitive peoples on the basis of mere numerical statistics is a dangerous proceeding. One might plot curves of population increase or decrease, find an equation expressing the observed changes with a fair degree of approximation, and then calculate the expected number of individuals at any future period. Such a procedure applied to the peoples of the Pacific area twenty years ago would have availed us little. I think it would be of little value also in forecasting the probable future of our own Negro population. What one most needs to know are the causes upon which the balance of births and deaths depends, and how these causes are being modified with the lapse of time. These causes are many. They are in part biological, but they are also economic, political, and especially psychological. They are affected by social status, education, religion, and various other things besides. The problem is one of great complexity, and it is never twice the same. The increase of native populations in the Pacific area and in other parts of the globe, after a period of decline, is very probably owing to the changing relationship between natives and whites. Will our own colored population take on a new lease of life after its period of slackening increase? The answer to this question will depend in large part upon how the relationships of the two races come to be adjusted. Purely biological factors, such as hereditary differences in resistance to disease, will play a very important rôle. But, as is shown by the present increase of many peoples whom we have been accustomed to regard as members of a dying race, the factor of adjustment to a new social and economic order may play a rôle of even greater importance.

Chapter II

THE GROWTH OF THE NEGRO POPULATION

THE NEGRO POPULATION of the United States had its origin in the importation of a cargo of African slaves by a Dutch trader in 1619. Negro laborers proved to be much more tractable and satisfactory than the American Indians whom the thrifty colonists attempted to press into service on their farms and plantations. Consequently many cargoes of Negro slaves were imported up to the abolition of the slave trade in 1808. After this time, a goodly number were doubtless smuggled in until the emancipation in 1863 destroyed the last vestige of the slave trade in this country.

The earliest trustworthy record of the number of Negroes in the United States is in the report of the first United States census, which was taken in 1790. In the three decades following this date, the Negro population increased from 757,208 to 1,771,656, or by something over a million, an appreciable part of this increase resulting from the importation of slaves. After 1808, the increase was mainly through the excess of births over deaths. Between 1820 and 1850 the number of Negroes more than doubled, and by 1890, forty years later, it more than doubled again. After 1880, the multiplication of the Negroes became less rapid. The increase between 1910 and 1920 was the least of all, namely, 6.5 per cent, or a somewhat higher figure if allowance is made for the undercount of Negroes in 1920. The last census (1930) shows an increasing rate of growth, the significance of which will be discussed later.

While the increase of Negroes in the United States has been mainly due to their favorable birth rate, a small number of Negro immigrants have come in from various foreign countries, chiefly the West Indies, Central America, and Canada. The number of foreign-born Negroes in the United States is given in table 1. The population of the United States from 1790 to 1930 is given by color or race in Table II of the Appendix.

The numbers of foreign-born Negroes given in the census returns for 1850 and 1860 are too low, since the place of birth was stated for free Negroes only. All slaves were regarded as native born, and hence those who may have been smuggled in were not recorded as of foreign origin.

Most of the foreign-born Negroes go into the Northern States. Over half of the Negro immigrants come from the West Indies. Many come from Central America and Canada; a smaller number come from the islands of the Atlantic (exclusive of the West Indies), and from Mexico and South America; only a very few come

TABLE 1

NUMBER AND PERCENTAGE OF FOREIGN-BORN NEGROES IN THE UNITED STATES

Date	Number	Percentage	Date	Number	Percentage
1850	4,067	0.1	1900	20,336	0.2
1860	4,363	0.1	1910	40,339	0.4
1870	9,645	0.2	1920	73,803	0.7
1880	14,017	0.2	1930	98,620	0.8
1890	19,979	0.3			

from Africa. In 1929, for example, of the 1,254 Negro immigrants, 1,197 came from America, 42 came from Europe, 2 from Asia, 12 from Africa, and 1 from the Pacific islands. Of those coming from America, 155 came from Canada, 14 from Mexico, 215 from Central America, 73 from South America, 115 from Cuba, and 615 from other parts of the West Indies. These figures do not include the uncertain numbers coming from Porto Rico or other possessions of the United States. Up to the time when visa fees and literacy tests were imposed, Negro immigration had been rapidly increasing. According to the reports of the Commissioner General of Immigration, the number of Negroes admitted in 1899 was only 412. By 1910, the number had increased to 4,966, and by 1923 it had reached the maximum of 12,243. The official records for departures date from 1908, and the figures show a general, if somewhat irregular, increase from 889 in 1908 to the maximum number of 2,183 in 1922, after which the number gradually declined. After the check which Negro immigration received in 1924, the influx has again increased fairly steadily up to 1930. From 1911 to 1920, admissions exceeded departures by 52,427, and between 1921 and 1929 by 28,761. These latter amounted to 37,461 between 1920 and 1930.

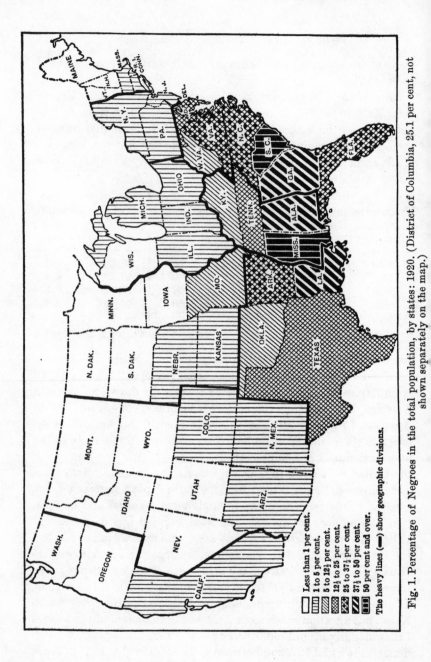

Fig. 1. Percentage of Negroes in the total population, by states: 1920. (District of Columbia, 25.1 per cent, not shown separately on the map.)

Less than 1 per cent.
1 to 5 per cent.
5 to 12½ per cent.
12½ to 25 per cent.
25 to 37½ per cent,
37½ to 50 per cent.
50 per cent and over.

The heavy lines (▬) show geographic divisions.

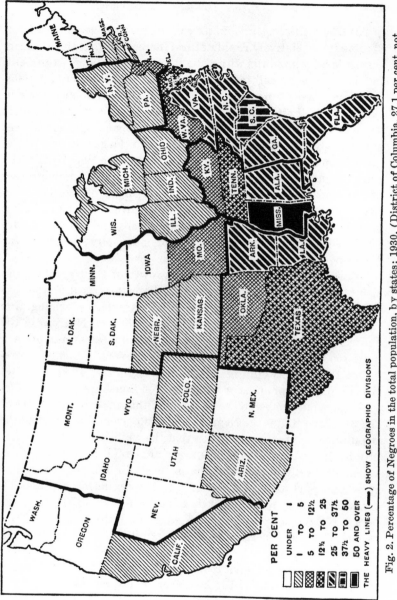

Fig. 2. Percentage of Negroes in the total population, by states: 1930. (District of Columbia, 27.1 per cent, not shown separately on the map.)

PER CENT

UNDER I
1 TO 5
5 TO 12½
12½ TO 25
25 TO 37½
37½ TO 50
50 AND OVER

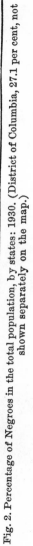

THE HEAVY LINES (━━) SHOW GEOGRAPHIC DIVISIONS

[13]

The composition of this influx with respect to age and sex is favorable for a relatively rapid natural increase in that the incomers consist largely of adults with a slight excess of females. At present, immigration is a small factor in the growth of our colored population, but it is quite possible that it may play a much larger rôle in the future if limitations are not imposed upon immigration from the Western Hemisphere. There is now nothing except the visa fees and literacy tests to prevent the incoming of large numbers of Negroes from the West Indies and other parts of the New World. The causes which, a few years ago, greatly increased the immigration of Mexicans may come to induce a larger influx of Negroes from nonquota countries. That this influx will continue to increase seems very probable. Although the reservoirs from which it is drawn are not large, they are capable in time of materially increasing the Negro population of the United States.

Opinions concerning the probable growth of the Negro population have varied greatly. Some of the estimates based on the rate of increase up to 1880 gave figures which were truly alarming. One writer predicted that there would be 200,000,000 Negroes in the United States by 1980. A more reasonable but, as events proved, quite too liberal estimate was that of Professor Gilliam, who predicted that there would be 12,000,000 Negroes by 1900. The fact that in Mississippi and, for a long time in South Carolina, the Negroes have outnumbered the whites, and that in several counties of the Southern States the Negroes constitute over 90 per cent of the population, led to the conclusion that the white man might eventually be driven out of extensive areas of the South. Haiti and Jamaica afford illustrations of what seemed in a fair way to happen in a large part of the United States. One circumstance which increased the alarm was the fact that in the census of 1870 large numbers of Negroes were not enumerated; indeed, the discrepancy was estimated to be something over half a million. Consequently the census of 1880 made the increase for the immediately preceding decade seem greater than it really was. The enumeration of Negroes in 1890 is also considered to be defective, but not to so extreme a degree, the shortage being estimated as something over 200,000.

The rate of growth of the Negro population has materially decreased since 1880. This decrease has not only allayed alarm over

Moreover, the mortality from these diseases is on the increase among the colored, and on the decrease among the whites. In consequence, the natural increase in the colored population will be less from decade to decade and in the end a decrease must take place. It is sufficient to know that in the struggle for race supremacy the black race is not holding its own; and this fact once recognized, all danger from a possible numerical supremacy of the race vanishes. Its extreme liability to consumption alone would suffice to seal its fate."

In a book, *The Ultimate Solution of the American Negro Problem,* Edward Eggleston concluded that there is a decided tendency toward a more or less complete elimination of the American Negro as an unfit element of the population, and that "the causes operating to bring about this solution of the Negro problem will persist and ultimately, and within the present century, so reduce the relative numerical strength of that race, as to have removed the Negro problem from the field of serious questions."

A still more recent pronouncement comes from one of our most prominent vital statisticians, Dr. Raymond Pearl. In his discussion of the vital prospects of the Negro he tells us that "the Negro is biologically a less fit animal, in the American environment, physical, social, and general, than the white. Under conditions as they are, Nature by the slow but dreadfully sure processes of biological evolution is apparently solving the Negro problem in the United States, in a manner which, when finished, will be, like all Nature's solutions, final, complete, and absolutely definite. Just in proportion as the Negro becomes anything but an agricultural laborer in the Southern States does he hasten the time of his final extinction in this country."

Another feature of the interracial struggle which is reassuring the whites is the fact that the white population has been increasing much more rapidly than its black competitor. In fact, ever since the first census in 1790 the proportion of whites to Negroes has become steadily greater. In 1790 Negroes comprised 19.3 per cent of the population, but in 1920 the percentage sank to 9.94 and in 1930 to 9.7. Even in the Southern States the whites have been increasing more rapidly than the blacks. Between 1880 and 1890, for example, the whites in the Southern States increased by 23.91 per cent, the Negroes by only 13.4 per cent.

the possibility of the whites' being swamped by the blacks, but
has given rise to predictions that the Negroes are actually on
road to extinction, or at least to becoming a negligible element

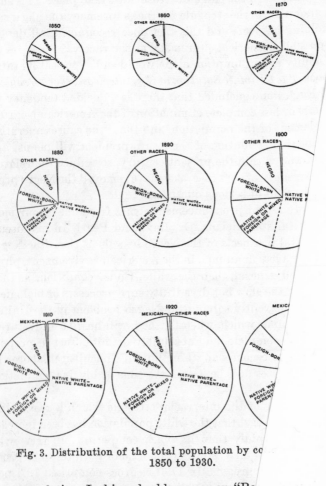

Fig. 3. Distribution of the total population by co
1850 to 1930.

our population. In his valuable paper on "Ra
encies of the American Negro," published in
man states that ". . . the Negro is subject to
all ages, but especially so at the early age p
the result of an inordinate mortality from

The more rapid growth of the white population was, in large measure, the result of an increasingly large immigration from Europe. For a few years just preceding the Great War, the annual influx from Europe was over a million. As was shown in the studies made by the Immigration Commission, and later by the birth statistics, the fertility of immigrant women was markedly higher than that of white women of native parentage; and the second generation of immigrants, although less prolific than their parents, had a higher birth rate than the older American stock. Directly and indirectly, therefore, the phenomenal growth of the white population received a marked impetus from the millions of immigrants coming mainly from Europe. One cannot estimate precisely how rapidly the white population of the United States would have grown had it not received these substantial annual additions from abroad. Certainly, its rate of increase would have approached much more nearly that of the Negroes.

But, aside from immigration, the growth of the white population of the United States has been unusually rapid. The abundant natural resources of a sparsely settled country favored a high birth rate. As population pressure became greater, however, the birth rate declined, and although the death rate fell at the same time, there was, nevertheless, a falling off in the rate of natural increase.

Among the Negroes, the birth rate and the death rate have also fallen. Although the Negro birth rate in the Registration Area for Birth is higher than that of the whites, the net increase of the Negroes, owing to the relatively high death rate, is less rapid than that of their white competitors. However, the diminishing death rate of the Negroes, and especially the rapid decline of their infant mortality, is gradually tending to equalize the net reproductive rates of the two races. This tendency toward equalization is favored by the restriction of the European invasion, which prevents the American whites from being continually recruited by an exceptionally prolific stock. As time goes on, the natural increase of the entire white population will approach more nearly the reproductive rate of our native population of native parentage. Over extensive areas of our Northern and Eastern States, this latter element of our population is not sufficiently fertile to maintain itself with the present balance of births and deaths. We may look forward to a further decline in the birth rate of our native white population, partly as a result of those factors which have caused a reduced birth rate throughout most civilized countries of the world and partly as a consequence of the restriction of immigration. If, as seems likely, immigration will be subject to still further restriction, if not prohibited altogether, the increase of our white population will be reduced still more rapidly.

In the light of these tendencies, the returns of the 1930 census are of especial interest. Between 1920 and 1930, the whites increased from 94,820,915 to 108,864,207, or by 14.8 per cent, and the Negroes increased from 10,463,131 to 11,891,143, or 13.6 per cent. In this decade, the additions to our white population through immigration were relatively small, and partly as a result of this fact the percentages of increase of the two races in this interval are more nearly equal than they were before 1920. Between 1910 and 1920, the increase of the whites exceeded that of the Negroes by 9.5 per cent; between 1920 and 1930 the white excess was only 1.2 per cent. But this tendency toward equalization of the rates of increase in the two races is owing not only to the slow increase of the whites; if we can accept the returns of the census, there has also been a rather striking increase in the propagation of the Negroes. The Negro rate of increase had been falling for several decades until it had reached the low figure of 6.5 per thousand. Instead of sinking still lower in the last intercensus period, the Negro rate of increase has turned rather sharply upward. Does this represent a real change in the biological trend of our Negro population? It is an important question. Can the census figures be relied upon? We have already alluded to the large undercount of Negroes in the census of 1870 and the defective enumeration in 1890. These undercounts are admitted by the census authorities. Was there an undercount also in 1920, so that the falling rate of increase from 1910 to 1920 was made to seem greater than it really was and, at the same time, the increase of the Negro population between 1920 and 1930 was exaggerated? It is not surprising that the accuracy of the returns of the 1920 census has been called in question. Populations commonly show fairly consistent trends in a given direction, and irregular ups and downs in census returns are usually taken to indicate inaccuracies in the count. Soon after the 1920 returns on the Negro population were published, Professor Kelly Miller challenged their accuracy on the ground that they indicated too great a reduction in numbers. The essential accuracy of the census returns was defended by Mr. Beales, who attributed the slow increase of the Negroes mainly to the decline of their birth rate and the influence of the great epidemic of influenza in 1918. When the results of the 1930 census were published, Professor Miller again returned to the charge and contended that the later enumeration confirmed his previous conclusion of the inadequacy of the 1920 count of the Negro population. According to Professor Miller, the Negroes, in 1920, owing to their recent extensive migrations, "were crowded in improvised huts and shanties, or packed away in garrets and basements, or hidden in the darkened nooks where the census takers could not get at them. Something of the same conditions prevailed as obtained in 1870, producing an obvious undercount." Commenting on the irregular rate of increase shown by successive censuses, Professor Miller asks, "Why, in the name of all the statisticians at once, should this increase register 11.2 per cent from 1900 to 1910, then drop to 6.5 during the next decade, and then, presto, jump to 13.6 from 1920 to 1930. If we make reasonable corrections for these suspected censuses of 1870, 1890, and 1920, it will appear that the Negro population has obeyed closely the expected statistical law. The increase from 1910 to 1920 was 2,063,650. To ascribe about 1,000,000 increment to each of the consecutive decades would certainly be a more rational distribution than to award 635,000 to the former and 1,428,000 to the latter." Here the implication is plain that if the data do not fit into a certain regular "expected statistical law," they must be wrong.

Everyone must concede that there is a good deal of inaccuracy in all census returns on population. These inaccuracies are probably much greater in some census returns than in others. If we grant that the undercount of Negroes in 1920 was greater than it was in 1910 or in 1930, the question of chief interest is whether or not the shortage is sufficiently great to account for the apparent change in the trend of our Negro population during the past two decades. In the Summary on Population issued by the Bureau of the Census, the statement is made that "The increase in the number of Negroes between 1920 and 1930, as indicated by the 1930 census, is so much greater than the increase during the previous census decade that some question has been raised as to the completeness of the enumeration of persons of this race in 1920. A study of the figures for the Negro population as returned in 1910, 1920, and 1930, by age, in connection with available figures for Negro death rates would indicate that, while there may have been some shortage in the 1920 enumeration, as compared with that of 1910 or 1930, it would not appear to exceed 150,000."

Recognizing the fact that, recently, among many native peoples a decrease of population has been followed by an actual increase, one is not justified in rejecting on purely *a priori* grounds the evidence of a somewhat similar change in our own colored population. The facts mentioned in Chapter I should make it evident that, when two or more races are intermingled and subject to changing relationships, it is very unsafe to assume that the more primitive peoples are bound to increase or decrease according to any uniform "statistical law." In attempting to interpret the significance of the data on the Negro population of the United States, several facts should be borne in mind. The decline in the Negro birth rate was doubtless in part the cause of the small increase shown by the Negro population in 1920. The Negro migration of the World War period, with its dislocation of large numbers of Negroes, naturally led to a marked reduction of the prolificacy of the migrants; and a minor factor was the influenza epidemic of 1918, which not only swept away many Negroes but prevented the birth of many more. How far the unsettled condition of the northern migrants contributed to the undercount is a matter of mere conjecture. In general, censuses are considerably less accurate than is commonly supposed. There are some chronic sources of inaccuracy which are matters of frequent comment by students of population statistics. There is always an underenumeration of children under 5 years, and particularly of children under 1 year of age. As is stated in the report of the 1930 census on Age Distribution, "the number of children in the age group 10–14, in six out of the last eight censuses, was greater than the number in the age group under 5 years old at the census taken 10 years earlier. In the Negro population, it is probable that the under-enumeration of children under 5 has usually amounted to 10 per cent or more."

It is perfectly evident that in a population in which there has not been extensive immigration or emigration, the number of children in age group 10–14 should be less than that in age group 0–4 of the previous census by the number in the latter group who have died within the decade. If the 1920 census of Negroes is more inadequate than the censuses of 1910 or 1930, owing to the extensive migration of Negroes during or just after the war period, one would expect to find that the undercount was relatively greatest for persons in the ages characteristic of the migrating groups, namely, in the wage-earning period of life. In order to answer this question, one has to make a comparative study of the statistical data on age grouping. The procedure I have adopted with this end in view is as follows. Assuming for the sake of the argument that the returns of the 1910 and 1930 censuses are substantially correct, let us take the several age groups in 1910 and follow them through to 1930 with the aim of ascertaining if the numbers in these groups in 1920 are what might reasonably be expected in the light of probable losses by death. The age group 10–14, for example, in 1910 would be the 20–24 age group in 1920, and the 30–34 age group in 1930. We should expect that this group, as it gets older, will become steadily reduced in numbers. Since it will not be greatly affected by the small number of Negroes who migrate into or out of the United States, we should also expect that the cohorts would lose a larger percentage between 1920 and 1930 than between 1910 and 1920, for the reason that the death rate is higher in the thirties than it is in the twenties. If, in 1920, age group 20–24 is less by a reasonable number than age group 10–14 in 1910, and considerably greater in number than age group 30–34 in 1930, we may conclude that for this group the returns of the 1920 census are probably not far wrong, or at least that they are consistent with the returns of the previous and the following censuses. Taking the cohort in ages 10–14 in 1910, which consisted of 1,155,266 Negroes, we find that it was reduced to 1,054,847 in 1920, and to 864,514 in 1930, thus losing 100,419 in the first decade and 190,333 in the second. All things considered, this result is not unreasonable. But passing to the next two age groups, we find some curious results. The 15–19 age group, consisting of 1,060,416 Negroes in 1910, was reduced to 909,739 in 1920 and to 890,900 in 1930, losing 150,677 in the first decade and only 18,839 in the second. These figures are simply incredible. Surely a group cannot lose over 14 per cent in deaths in one decade and less than 2 per cent when it is ten years older.

A similar anomaly is found in the next age group, 20–24, which lost 332,920 between 1910 and 1920, and only 10,442 between 1920 and 1930. The next age group lost 107,296 between 1910 and 1920 and 143,880 between 1920 and 1930, a result much more in accordance with expectations. Other age groups show losses between 1920 and 1930 which are much greater than would be expected in comparison with the losses sustained in the previous decade. Undoubtedly the source of a large part of these discrepancies is to be sought in errors in reporting ages. People are notoriously prone to lie concerning their ages, and many uneducated persons do not know how old they really are. Census returns show a marked excess of ages which are some multiple of five. Thus in all our recent censuses there have been many more persons aged 25, 30, 35, and 40 than of the ages immediately preceding or following these numbers. An exception is age 15, which for some reason is an unpopular age. In most of our censuses there have been fewer people aged 15 than either 14 or 16, and this occurs in both sexes and in both whites and Negroes. As a result of misstating ages, our cohorts cannot be considered as always including the same persons who were in the age group ten years younger at the time of the previous census.

If the discrepancies I have mentioned arise from misstatements, willful or otherwise, in reporting ages, it occurred to me that similar discrepancies, though perhaps to a less degree, would be met with also in the white population. In order to test the matter I chose the native white population of native parentage, a group which, like the Negroes, is little affected by immigration or emigration. In following through the age groups I met with various highly improbable changes in the numerical composition of the cohorts. The improbable changes in the Negro age groups 15–19 and 20–24 have their counterparts in equally improbable changes in the same age groups of the whites. In general, there is a marked parallelism in the anomalous changes in the age groups of the two races. Apparently, the causes, whatever they are, which lead Negroes to misstage their ages, have a potent influence also upon the reported ages of the whites.

On the whole, the discrepancies one finds in following through the age groups from 1910 to 1930 are apt to neutralize one another in the total aggregate. There is evidence, however, that there was an actual undercount in the wage-earning period of life, but this undercount probably did not exceed 75,000.

The method employed by the Bureau of the Census in estimating the extent of the undercount of Negroes in 1920 is based on the assumption that the censuses of 1910 and 1930 are substantially correct, barring the usual underenumeration of young children. The number of Negroes 10 years of age and over in 1920 may be obtained by subtracting from the number enumerated in 1910 the number of Negroes living at that time who died between 1910 and 1920. The number of Negroes in all age groups in 1920 may be derived also by adding to those in the several age groups over 10 in 1930 the number of Negroes living in 1920 that died between 1920 and 1930.

The number of Negroes 10 years of age in 1920 may be calculated, therefore, in two ways: (1) by working forward from the census of 1910, and (2) by working backward from the census of 1930. In fact, the estimates arrived at by these two methods, each of which affords a check on the other, are in fair agreement (with a difference of about 30,000), and they indicate that the undercount of Negroes over 10 years old in 1920 was probably not more than 60,000.

In addition to the undercount of Negroes aged 10 years and over in 1920, one must consider the possible omission of children under 10 years of age. Taking the ages under 5 we find the following numbers for the last five censuses:

1890	1900	1910	1920	1930
1,047,574	1,215,655	1,263,288	1,143,699	1,230,206

These figures show that children under 5 were increasing in number up to 1910; the 1920 census shows a decrease of 119,589 over the previous decade. There was an increase of 86,507 in 1930, although the number in 1930 was less than in 1910. If we take the mean between the numbers in the age groups 0–4 in 1910 and 1930, namely, 1,246,747, we find that it was 102,048 greater than the number in this group given in the 1920 census. Similarly, the mean of the 5–9 age groups of 1910 and 1930 is 41,260 greater than the num-

ber in the 5–9 age group in 1920. Evidently the Negro population
under 10 years of age in 1920 was considerably below what would
be expected if this population followed any consistent trend in the
last two decades. According to all the data in our possession, there
was no uniform trend in this period toward either an increase or
a decrease in numbers. Sometime in this 20-year interval, and probably in the early part of it, there was a change from an increasing
to a decreasing population in the 0–4 age group. This change was
quite evidently due mainly to the decline of the birth rate. It is
noteworthy that a similar change occurred in the number of children under 5 in the native-born white population, which had been
increasing up to 1920, when it reached the highest number yet
recorded.

The extensive Negro migration during the war period and the
influenza epidemic of 1918–19 which swept away many young children and caused a marked decline in the birth rate, would naturally
reduce greatly the number of children who were in the 0.4 age
group in 1920. One may arrive at an approximate estimate of the
size of this group at that time by adding to the number of Negroes
aged 10–14 in 1930 the probable number belonging to this cohort
who had died between 1920 and 1930. The volumes on Mortality
Statistics between 1920 and 1930 afford a fairly satisfactory basis
for such an estimate, although of course they permit of no very
exact calculation. If we reckon the deaths at 65,000, and add this
number to the 1,251,542 Negroes aged 10–14 in 1930, we obtain
1,316,542 as the approximate number of Negroes in the 0–4 age
group in 1920. This is 172,843 in excess of the actual enumeration.
Allowing for the few foreign-born Negroes aged 10–14 in 1930
(probably not more than from 2,000 to 3,000), the 1920 count of
children under 5 was probably about 170,000 short of the actual
number. This represents the actual undercount, but since there is
always an undercount of children under 5, the omissions relative
to those of other census years must have been much less. It is the
relative rather than the actual omissions which chiefly concern us
in the study of population increase. In the light of estimates of the
amount of the undercount of children under 5 in 1910 and 1930,
the undercount in 1920 was probably not more than 100,000 greater
than in the other census years.

All things considered, I am inclined to believe that the undercount of Negroes in 1920 was not more than 200,000 greater than the undercount of 1910 or 1930. The estimate of the Census Bureau, which I have had the opportunity of carefully checking over, makes the shortage 150,000, but this is done on the assumption that there was an excess of about 50,000 Negro deaths that were unrecorded in the influenza epidemic in 1918. It is probable that death registration during this epidemic was less accurate than at other times, but the excess of unrecorded deaths can hardly be assumed to be as great as 50,000. Possibly a safer figure for the undercount in 1920 would be 200,000 instead of 150,000.

If we concede that in 1920 some 200,000 Negroes were left out of the reckoning, how would it affect our conclusion concerning the recent trend of our Negro population? Adding 200,000 Negroes to the 10,463,131 Negroes enumerated in 1920 would make the increase during the decade 1910–1920 8.5 per cent instead of 6.5 per cent. The rate of increase between 1920 and 1930 would accordingly be reduced from 13.6 per cent to 11.52 per cent. Hence, after making a reasonable allowance for the deficiencies of the 1920 census, there is still a marked change in the trend of our Negro population within the last twenty years. Even if we assume the undercount in 1920 to be 300,000, the rate of increase from 1920 to 1930 (10.48 per cent) would still be somewhat greater than that between 1910 and 1920 (9.52 per cent). There can be no reasonable doubt, therefore, that the vital prospects of the American Negro have taken a turn for the better. How long this good fortune will last is another matter.

The conclusion which I would emphasize in this chapter is that it is quite unwarranted to assume that the rate of increase of our Negro population must have been changing in any uniform way. According to the available statistical data the rate of increase, which had been falling between 1910 and 1920, had risen somewhat in the decade from 1920 to 1930. Since a decreased rate of population growth has been followed by a more rapid increase in a number of peoples elsewhere in the world, there is nothing inherently improbable in the occurrence of a similar change in the Negro population of the United States. In fact, various present influences would tend to bring about such an effect.

CHAPTER III

THE STABILIZED RATE OF NATURAL INCREASE AMONG THE NEGRO POPULATION

STUDENTS OF POPULATION CHANGES must, of necessity, make frequent use of statistics in drawing conclusions. But in the interpretation of statistics, one cannot always take facts at their face value. Sometimes the data are wrong, as we found reason to believe in respect to the count of Negroes in the 1920 census. More frequently the source of error is not in the statistics, but in the conclusions which they seem to support.

Nothing can be simpler and more obvious than the fact that, in a population not subjected to gains or losses through migration, the rate of increase must be determined by the extent to which births outnumber deaths. In 1920, the birth rate for the white population in the Registration Area for Births was 23.5 per thousand, and the death rate was 12.8 per thousand. Hence, barring the effect of migration, the white population must have been increasing at the rate of 10.7 per thousand. At the same time, the Negro birth rate in this area was 26.3 per thousand, and the death rate 18.4, leaving a net increase of 7.9 per thousand. If the figures are correct, there is no way of escaping from the conclusion that in the Registration Area for Births in 1920 the whites were increasing much more rapidly than the Negroes. Let us suppose, however, that women should continue to be exactly as fertile as they were in 1920 and that the incidence of death should also remain precisely the same. Would the races continue to increase at the same relative rates? Clearly they would not. The actual prolificacy of any population depends in part upon its age composition. If, to take an improbable illustration, the females of a population were all in age groups 0–5 and 35 and older, there might be a fair number of births. In the same population ten years later, when the 0–5 group was from 10 to 15 years old, and the women formerly over 35 were all over 45, there would be almost no births, because the young group, with rare exceptions, would not be old enough to have babies, and the older group, also with rare exceptions, would be too old to have them.

We have an illustration of the same principle in our foreign-born population, whose rate of propagation has been rapidly decreasing. Most of our immigrant population entered the United States before we engaged in the World War. The immigrants were largely in the adolescent and middle-aged periods of life, when the birth rate is high and the death rate relatively low. The fertility of the foreign-born women who came here before the war is now rapidly declining, and, with the reduction of immigration, there are relatively fewer younger women to take their places. With increasing age, death rates increase so that the balance of births and deaths among our foreign-born population is very different from what it was twenty years ago. Before the World War, the increase of our white population was due in no small measure to foreign immigrants and their immediate descendants. Formerly, the influx of this alien group tended to make the age composition of our white population relatively favorable for a high birth rate and a low death rate. But now, owing to the increasing age of the foreign elements and the restriction of new recruits from abroad, the birth rate of the foreign born has fallen below that of the native-born whites.

Another factor which makes the American white population abnormal in its age composition is the decline of the birth rate. This decline, while it is going on, tends to make a population pile up in the middle and older age groups. There soon come to be fewer children in proportion to persons of child-bearing age; hence we have the apparent paradox that a falling birth rate produces a population tending to have a high birth rate. If there are no changes either in mortality or in real fertility, the population will in time become stabilized, after which the rates of births and deaths will remain constant. If the birth rates and death rates of the several age groups of the population are known, it is possible to calculate what the natural increase of such a population will be when this stabilized condition has been reached. By making such a calculation, Dublin and Lotka have estimated that what they call the "true" birth rate of our white population in 1920 should be 20.9 instead of 23.4, and the death rate should be 15.43 instead of 12.41; hence the so-called "true" rate of natural increase should be only 5.5 per thousand instead of 11 per thousand. In other words, if people continue to die at all ages as fast as they did in 1920, and if women at different ages have the same number of children as they had at that time, our white population, when its abnormal age composition is outgrown, will be increasing at only half its present rate as indicated by the gross surplus of births over deaths. Undoubtedly our population will approach a stabilized condition, even though such a condition may be only approximately maintained. The death rate, as expressed in numbers dying per thousand in-

TABLE 2

CHANGING PROPORTION OF NEGRO FEMALES IN DIFFERENT AGE
GROUPS, FROM 1890 TO 1930

Age group	1890	1900	1910	1920	1930
0– 5	13.8	13.7	12.8	10.9	10.3
5– 9	14.5	13.5	12.7	12.1	11.4
10–14	13.5	12.2	11.7	11.8	10.4
0–14	41.8	39.4	37.2	34.8	32.1
15–44	45.1	49.9	49.3	50.6	52.0
Over 45	12.6	13.0	13.3	14.4	16.0

habitants, is bound to rise, even though deaths will probably become less frequent in every age group. For the same reason, the birth rate of the whites is bound to fall.

Now, what is the situation in respect to the Negro? Our colored population, as we have seen, has received relatively few additions through immigration. For several decades, it has been essentially a self-perpetuating group. The Negro birth rate has declined, but the recent marked reduction in infant mortality has tended to swell the age groups in the earlier years of life. However, notwithstanding the salvage of more infants and children, the proportion of Negroes under 5 years of age has steadily decreased during the past fifty years. In the same period, the proportion of Negro females in the child-bearing period (15–44 years) has steadily increased, as has also the proportion of Negro females in the older age groups. In a word, the Negroes, like the whites, are on the whole growing older. The general trend among Negro females is shown in table 2.

Compared with the white population, the Negroes are more concentrated about the middle ages of life. There are relatively fewer

Negroes in the period of childhood. There are relatively fewer, also, in the more advanced ages beyond 55. The proportion of children under 5 in 1930 (namely, 10.3) has come quite close to the proportion in the native white population (10.4). Previously, this proportion has run further below that of the whites. A little scrutiny of the statistics reveals that the chief reason for this change is, quite evidently, the falling birth rate of the foreign-born element of the population. If we compare the proportion of native white children under 5 of foreign-born or mixed parentage in 1920 and 1930, we find a remarkable drop from 13.3 per cent to 7.9 per cent. The children under 5 of native white parentage constituted 12.6 per cent of the population in 1920 and 11.3 per cent in 1930 as compared with corresponding percentages of 10.9 and 10.3 for the Negro children under 5. It is clearly the inclusion of the relatively infertile foreign-born whites with their anomalous age composition that has caused the proportion of native white children under 5 to approach so closely the proportion found in the Negroes. The difference, in the two races, has probably been exaggerated in all the census returns because of the larger omissions in the statistics of children of this age group in the Negro population.

From the data we have presented, it is evident that the age composition of our Negro population is becoming more favorable for a statistically high birth rate. A similar trend is shown also in our native white population, but the proportion of females in the child-bearing period has been higher among the Negroes in all censuses since 1890. This fact would tend to cause a higher birth rate, measured by the number of births per thousand inhabitants, in the Negro population, but a higher birth rate due to this cause does not necessarily mean a higher rate of reproduction. A measure of fertility which is in some respects more adequate is the number of live births per annum per thousand women of the child-bearing period (15–44 years). According to this measure, with precisely the same birth rate, one group might have a higher effective fertility than the other, provided that a greater proportion of the births occurred to females in the earlier years of the reproductive period. This is, in fact, what happens in the Negro population; normally, therefore, Negro generations succeed one another more rapidly than generations in the whites.

In the study of population changes, it is important to know what the actual rate of increase would be without regard to the disturbing elements of age composition, the proportions of the sexes, and other factors which are, from their nature, temporary in their effects. Two populations may have exactly the same excess of births over deaths, but if the one owes its rate of increase to an exceptionally favorable age and sex composition, and the other keeps up the same reproductive rate with an unfavorable age and sex composition, it is evident that, other things being equal, the latter will soon be increasing more rapidly than its rival. Until a few years ago, students of vital statistics paid almost no attention to stabilized rates of increase. In a volume entitled *The Balance of Births and Deaths,* the well-known statistician, Kuczynski, pointed out that, in most of the nations in northern and western Europe, although there are more births than deaths, the population would not increase were it not for the circumstance that its age composition is especially favorable for a high birth rate and a low death rate. The method of calculation employed was to ascertain from the birth rates and death rates in the several age groups how many female babies would be born for every thousand females starting at age 0, the assumption being made that the birth rates and death rates would remain constant in these several age groups. Since the sex ratio at birth is a very constant figure, there being about 105–6 males born to every 100 females, the total number of children and the general birth rate may be calculated from the data. In Germany, for example, although in 1925 there were many more births than deaths, 1,000 females at the prevailing rate of increase would produce only 937 females to replace them.

The situation in the United States is rapidly approaching that of northern and western Europe. In 1930 Dublin and Lotka made another estimate of what they called the "true" rate of natural increase of the white population of the Birth Registration States of 1920 for the years between 1920 and 1928. Their calculation had to be made on the basis of estimates of population which at best left a considerable margin of uncertainty, but, according to the evidence at hand, the true rate of natural increase sank from 5.2[1] in 1920 to 4.4 in 1925 and to 1.8 in 1928, the corrected birth rate be-

---

[1] According to a revised estimate.

ing 17.3 per thousand and the corrected death rate being 15.6. The authors state that, "Should the next year by any chance bring a further decline by .8 per thousand, we should actually have reached a birth rate of 18.6, practically the same figure that has been shown above to correspond to just that fertility which, with the existing age distribution, will only just suffice to keep the population at a standstill. Any further decline in fertility would, in the absence of immigration, mean ultimately a diminishing population, even though for a time this might not become apparent, owing to the residual effects of past higher fertility."

Now that the birth statistics for 1930 have appeared, it is possible to make estimates of the stabilized increase of our white and colored populations based on the enumerations of the latest (1930) census. In 1930 the Registration Area for Births had been enlarged until it included all of continental United States except Texas and South Dakota. Consequently, the stabilized rate of increase in the population of the Registration Area would approximate quite closely the rate for the entire country. In making an estimate of the stabilized rate of increase one needs to know the number of females in the various age groups of the child-bearing period, and the number of births and deaths per thousand females of all age groups. I have endeavored to calculate the stabilized rate of increase for the white population of the Registration Area according to the method employed by Kuczynski and by Dublin and Lotka, and have found that 100,000 white females at the fertility rate prevailing in 1930 would give rise to 112,949 daughters. Of course, not all these daughters would survive to maturity. In order to ascertain how many of these daughters would reach the age of their mothers, one has to multiply the number of female births per thousand females in each age group by a "survival factor" representing the number of survivors in the several age groups out of every thousand born. By so doing it is found that of every 112,949 daughters born to 100,000 mothers, only 99,943 live long enough to replace the preceding generation. In making this estimate I have based the calculation on the white female population as of July 1, 1930, and have distributed the persons of unknown age in proportion to the numbers in the several age groups.

The number of females surviving in the several age groups was

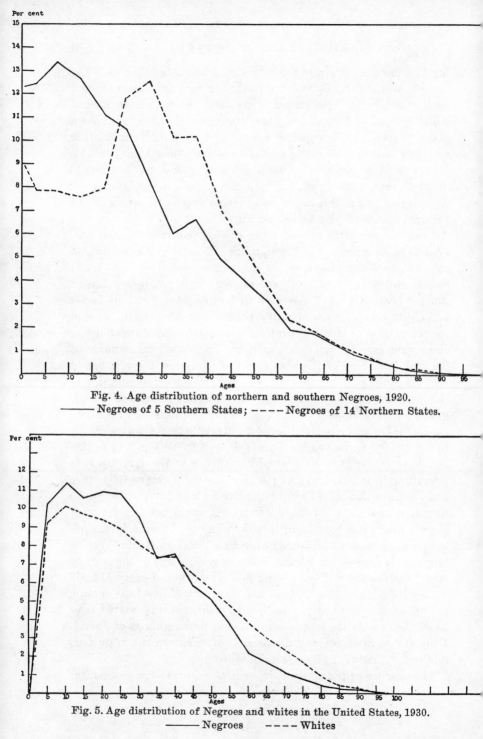

Fig. 4. Age distribution of northern and southern Negroes, 1920.
———— Negroes of 5 Southern States; ———— Negroes of 14 Northern States.

Fig. 5. Age distribution of Negroes and whites in the United States, 1930.
———— Negroes ———— Whites

estimated from the preliminary life table for 1929–1931 recently issued by the Bureau of the Census. If reasonable allowance is made for incomplete registration of births, the stabilized increase of the white population would be somewhat greater than our figures indicate. Not improbably the white population in 1930 was reproducing at a rate sufficient to insure its perpetuation in a stabilized age distribution. With the fall of the birth rate after 1930 it is very doubtful if the rate of reproduction is sufficient for continued perpetuation.

This conclusion, which was expressed in a recent paper,[2] has been confirmed by a study by Lotka,[3] who has calculated the stabilized growth rate of the population of the United States for a number of years preceding and following 1930. What he terms the net reproductive rate in the United States shows the following course: for the year 1920, 1,166; for 1925, 1,128; for 1928, 1,049; for 1930, 1,079; 1932, 997; 1933, 940; 1934, 980. "It appears," says Lotka, "that our population must have passed the deadline from the black into the red on the ledger of population balances about the time of the last census, 1930, or soon after."

The stabilized rate of increase of our Negro population in 1920 was investigated by Miss Parker and myself for two groups, the one consisting of the Negroes in fourteen states of the North, the other including the Negroes in five states of the South. The choice of these groups was determined by the fact that data on the Negro mortality of approximately these regions were available in the Abridged Life Tables for 1919–1920. In 1920 there were no life tables for the whole Negro population of the United States. The Abridged Life Tables for Negroes applied to certain selected groups, that is, in states with less than 4 per cent Negroes, states with more than 5 per cent Negroes, large cities, and the Original Registration States. The stabilized increase in the five selected Southern States was found to be 5.9 per thousand, a rate rather greater than that for northern white women at that time, but less than the stabilized increase of white women in the South. In the

[2] Holmes, S. J., "Passing a Turning Point in Population Growth," *Social Science.*, 11:259–261 (July, 1936).

[3] Lotka, A. J., "Modern Trends in the Birth Rate," *Ann. Am. Acad. Polit. Soc. Sci.*, 188:1–13 (1936).

North, however, in spite of the favorable age composition of the female Negro population, the stabilized rate of increase was far below what was needed to maintain the stock. In all probability these stabilized rates were too low, because, in working them out, the birth statistics upon which they were based were taken at their face value. Birth registration is seldom complete, and its adequacy varies greatly in different states and cities. It is always conceded to be much less complete for Negroes than for whites; consequently the stabilized rates for Negroes are too low in a greater degree than those for the white population.

Professor Whelpton has made an estimate of the stabilized increase of the Negroes in 1920 on the assumption that birth registration was 25 per cent incomplete. He obtained a rate of 13.0 per thousand for southern Negroes, and —4.8 per thousand for northern Negroes. Both of these rates are appreciably higher than those obtained by Miss Parker and myself for approximately the same areas. According to the estimates of Miss Parker and myself, the stabilized rate of Negro increase calculated on the basis of a 25 per cent incomplete birth registration would have been —5 per thousand for northern, and about 14 per thousand for southern Negroes, a result as close as could be expected to that obtained by Professor Whelpton for slightly different areas. Even if birth registration in Negroes fell short as much as 35 per cent, which is scarcely probable, the stabilized increase of northern Negroes in 1920 would still be insufficient to maintain the group.

The birth statistics for 1930 made no separate tabulation of the births of Negroes as distinct from other colored people for mothers in the several age groups. In order to get an idea of the stabilized increase of the Negroes, one may estimate the rate for the entire colored population or one may endeavor to estimate the rate for the Negroes alone after calculating the number of births in the various age groups that should be assigned to Negro females. I have made such an estimate according to the latter method for the Registration Area of 1930 and have found that, on the assumption of complete birth registration, 100,000 Negro females would produce 111,891 daughters at age 0. This number is clearly below what is necessary for maintenance in a stabilized population, as is shown by the fact that with the mortality rates of female Negroes in the years 1929–1931 only 89,061 of these daughters would live long enough to replace their mothers. If, however, we assume that there was a 10 per cent shortage in the registration of Negro births (it was probably somewhat greater than this), 100,000 females would produce 98,956 adult daughters, a number exceedingly close to the requirement for maintenance in a stabilized population. The inclusion of Texas and South Dakota, which were not in the registration area in 1930, would change but little the general rate. A similar estimate of the fertility rate of Negroes in fourteen of the Northern States shows that 100,000 females would produce only 96,673 daughters at age 0, thus showing a somewhat lower fertility rate than in 1920, when the same number would have produced 106,520 daughters.

An estimate of the fertility rate of the Negro population in the same five Southern States that we studied in 1920 shows that 100,000 colored females would produce 139,045 daughters. In 1920, 100,000 Negro females in these states produced 165,506 daughters; hence there has been a greater falling off in the fertility rates of the Negro females of these five states in the decade 1920–1930 than there has been among Negro females of the North. The registration of Negro births in these states appears to be relatively complete, being over 95 per cent in Maryland, Virginia, Kentucky, and South Carolina, and about 87 per cent in North Carolina (Whelpton). But even if no births were unregistered, the Negro population of these five states, with the death rates prevailing among Negroes in 1930, would be more than holding its own at a stabilized rate of increase, inasmuch as these 139,045 daughters would leave 108,886 survivors. Conditions in these states, however, may not be typical for the entire South. Between 1920 and 1930 the Negro population actually decreased in four of these states, Virginia, South Carolina, Kentucky, and Maryland, owing chiefly to extensive migrations to the North, and it might be conjectured that conditions which led to the emigration of so many Negroes might have checked the natural increase of those who remained. I have therefore experimented with another area, consisting of three Gulf States, Alabama, Mississippi, and Louisiana, in all of which the Negro population increased appreciably between 1920 and 1930. It turned out that in these states, although the Negro birth rate was fairly high, 100,000 females gave rise to only 124,335 daughters at age 0. According to

Whelpton's estimate, the registration of Negro births is much less complete in these states than in the five states previously mentioned, being somewhat less than 90 per cent in Alabama and Mississippi, and from 78 to 83 per cent in Louisiana. When allowance is made for incomplete birth registration, it is probable that the stabilized rate of increase of the Negro population of these three states is sufficient to maintain a slow growth with the birth and death rates of 1930.

The calculation of stabilized rates of increase for the Negro population in 1930 is fraught with several sources of error. In addition to the incompleteness of the registration of deaths, and especially of deaths in early infancy and childhood among rural Negroes, there is a good deal of inaccuracy in the reports of the ages of deceased individuals, thus falsifying our estimates of the average duration of life. There is also, as we have seen in Chapter II, "The Growth of the Negro Population," some inaccuracy in reporting the ages of the living. The tendency among Negroes over 20 years old to overstate their age would lead to a decrease of Negro females assigned to the early child-bearing ages and would affect age-specific birth rates and death rates, especially if reported ages on birth and death certificates erred in a different way from ages given to the census enumerator. And again, as I have pointed out, there is great uncertainty with respect to the completeness of birth registration among Negroes in the several states. Not improbably in extensive regions the registration of Negro births falls short of the true number by as much as 20 per cent, or even more. An investigation of the subject by Miss Foudray, in connection with the construction of life tables for Negroes for the years 1919–1921, led to the conclusion that the deficiency of birth registration was about 25 per cent for Negroes and about 9 per cent for whites. Since then, birth registration has become more nearly complete. Dr. Whelpton has attempted to estimate the deficiencies of birth registration in the several states, and he finds evidence of great variability in respect to both whites and Negroes. The state with the lowest record for birth registration is Oklahoma, which records less than 75 per cent among the whites and less than 40 per cent among the Negroes. That 10 per cent of Negro births escape record at the present time is a very conservative estimate.

Bearing in mind that Negro birth rates are too low, we may, however, be warranted in making the following statements:

1. In the Negro population of the Northern States the stabilized rate of increase is insufficient to perpetuate the stock.

2. In the United States as a whole the stabilized rate of increase is not far from zero for both Negroes and whites.

3. In large cities, both North and South, the stabilized rate for Negroes is insufficient for permanent maintenance.

4. In most states of the South the stabilized rate is sufficient to produce a slow increase of the Negro population.

According to a recent estimate by Whelpton, in which allowance was made for incompleteness of birth registration, the fertility rate of Negroes was 99 per cent of the rate required for permanent maintenance, and that of the whites was 103 per cent, in the period 1929–1931. Owing to the sources of error to which allusion has been made above, the differences in the rates of increase of the two races may be a few per cent greater or less than the figures indicate. The fall of the birth rate since 1930 has probably caused the stabilized rate of both races to sink a little below the maintenance level, and the birth rate has fallen more rapidly in the whites than in the Negroes.

These conclusions with respect to the present inadequate reproduction of both the white and the colored population of the United States are in essential agreement with those of several critical students of population trends, such as Dublin, Lotka, Thompson, Whelpton, Lorimer, and Osborn. The slight rise of the birth rate after 1933 probably does not represent more than a temporary interruption of the general decline, as is indicated by the figure for 1935. Probably the rates of increase of both whites and Negroes will continue to decline, although there will be an actual increase of both races for several years. When the population has passed its peak and begins to decrease in numbers, will the whites or the Negroes propagate at the more rapid rate?

Dr. Whelpton has made several forecasts of the future growth of different elements of the American population including the native born, the foreign born, the Negroes, and other colored inhabitants. The forecasts are based on a number of different assumptions concerning the future course of immigration, birth rates, and death rates. It is noteworthy that if population growth follows the "median series," both the native whites and the Negroes will increase in their relative proportion to the total, while the proportion of the foreign born will decrease up to 1980, the last date for which forecasts are made. Between 1930 and 1980, Negro females will increase by more than 49 per cent and white females will increase a little less than 36 per cent. Personally, I have little confidence in long-distance forecasts of population growth. Dr. Whelpton has industriously worked out a number of them, and one may select the one that seems, for whatever reason, the most probable.

CHAPTER IV

THE TREND OF NEGRO MORTALITY

IN THEIR STRUGGLE for numerical increase American Negroes have long been handicapped by a death rate much higher than that of their white competitors. Under slavery, when most of the Negroes were employed on the farms and plantations of the South, their mortality was relatively low. If we can credit the rather meager statistics compiled before the Civil War, the death rate in several parts of the South was lower among the Negroes than among the whites. During the recruiting of soldiers for the Civil War, the general testimony of the examining surgeons was that the Negro recruits were of good physique and comparatively free from disease; relatively fewer Negroes than whites were rejected as unfit for military service. Tuberculosis was less common among them than among white recruits, and venereal infections were seldom encountered. While the Civil War was in progress, conditions began to change. Both tuberculosis and venereal diseases rapidly spread and soon became very prevalent. At the same time mortality from nearly all causes was greatly increased. All this was a perfectly natural consequence of the abrupt change in the status of the Negro population. Ignorant, improvident, and without financial resources, suddenly released from a condition in which they had been cared for by their masters, the Negroes soon began to show signs of physical deterioration. During the scandalous period of reconstruction and the decade immediately following, the vital statistics of the Negro went from bad to worse. Tuberculosis, syphilis, malaria, pellagra, and hookworm conspired to sap their vitality and to make them more prone to succumb to many other affections. The infant death rate was appalling, every third or fourth child being swept away before the end of the first year of life.

Knowledge of the vital statistics of our colored population previous to 1900 is, unfortunately, very incomplete. For most of our information we have to rely upon the decennial reports of the United States Census and the records of a few states and cities which made separate tabulations of Negro births and deaths in this period. In the census of 1870 it is estimated that about 40 per cent of Negro deaths were not recorded. Doctor J. S. Billings, in his excellent analysis of the vital statistics of the census years 1880 and 1890, estimates that about 30 per cent of Negro deaths were not recorded for these later periods. The records of Baltimore, Savannah, New Orleans, Mobile, Richmond, Charleston, S. C., and a few other cities, together with the fragmentary data afforded by medical articles and hospital reports, indicate that the death rate of our colored

TABLE 3

MORTALITY OF NEGROES AND WHITES IN THE REGISTRATION AREA,
FROM 1890 TO 1930

	1890	1900	1910	1920	1930
Whites..........	20.2	17.3	14.6	12.6	10.8
Negroes.........	32.4	30.2	25.5	18.7	16.5

population continued to rise for nearly a quarter of a century after the Civil War. Apparently it reached its climax sometime in the eighties. The decline of mortality which followed this period was accompanied by an even greater decline of the birth rate so that the net increase of the Negro population began to slacken. It is a striking fact that the period since the Civil War which saw the most rapid increase of our Negro population was a period when most of the Negroes were wretchedly housed in one- or two-room cabins which frequently had nothing but a dirt floor and when mortality took its heaviest toll of adults and infants alike.

In 1890 the mortality rate per thousand of the Negro population of the Registration Area was 32.40, as compared with 20.22 for the whites. At this time the Registration Area included Massachusetts, New Hampshire, Vermont, Connecticut, New York, New Jersey, and Delaware—all Northern States. By 1900, when this area was enlarged by the addition of Maine, Michigan, and Indiana, the Negro death rate was 30.2 and that of the whites, 17.3. Between 1890 and 1900 the Registration States showed a reduction of Negro mortality from 29.5 to 26.2, and the Registration Cities a somewhat greater reduction from 33.68 to 28.4, but since the Registration Area did not include any of the Southern States one cannot be sure that these figures represent very closely the general course of Negro mortality. In the same decade (1890 to 1900), however, there was a decrease of Negro mortality in Baltimore, New Orleans, Richmond, Washington, D. C., and Charleston, S. C. From 1900 to 1910, the data from the Registration Area and from various cities outside this area indicate that the Negro death rate had in general declined. During this decade our statistics on Negro mortality not

TABLE 4

EXPECTATION OF LIFE FOR NEGROES IN THE ORIGINAL
REGISTRATION STATES, FROM 1900 TO 1902,
1909 TO 1911, AND 1919 TO 1920

Year	Male	Female
1900–02................	32.5	35.0
1909–11................	34.0	37.7
1919–20................	40.4	42.4

only improved because of more nearly complete registration, but they also increased in volume through the inclusion of more states having a large Negro population.

The course of mortality was not downward in all places. Mr. J. Cummings, in the volume on *Negro Population: 1790–1915,* issued by the United States Census, states that "In fifteen of the thirty-three northern and western cities, the Negro death rate was higher and in eighteen cities it was lower in 1910 than it was in 1900. In each of the thirty-four southern cities with the exception of two, the Negro death rate was lower in 1910 than in 1900. ... The average Negro death rate for the southern cities as a group declined from 33.6 in 1900 to 29.6 in 1910; and for the northern cities from 27.1 to 25.1."

After 1910 the Negro death rate declined at a more rapid pace, although the decline varied greatly in different localities. One of the best measures of this decline is supplied by the life tables for the Negro population of the Original Registration States. The expectation of life in three successive decades is given in table 4.

The increasing life span of the Negro from 1900 to 1910 came about mainly through the reduction of mortality in childhood and early adult life. In the Original Registration States the mortality of male Negroes aged 30 to 75 was higher in 1909–1911 than in 1900–1902. A somewhat similar phenomenon is shown in several cities. According to G. W. Baker, "In Atlanta, Baltimore, Louisville, Memphis, Mobile, San Antonio, Washington, Atlanta City, Boston, Camden, Chicago, Cincinnati, Indianapolis, Kansas City, Mo., and Newark, the Negro death rate in 1910 was higher than in 1900 at age period 25–44 or 45–64 or both." During this period much the same trend was shown in the white population both native and foreign born, although the trend of mortality was downward in the more advanced age groups during the decade following 1910.

The increase of mortality after middle age is a phenomenon not confined to the Negroes. At different times such an increase has characterized the population of various foreign countries as well as of the United States. One potent cause of this condition is doubtless the increasing urbanization of the population. But opposed to the devitalizing influence of cities is the improved hygiene and sanitation, which has its greatest influence upon the earlier ages of life. Gains have more recently been made in the life expectancy of the more advanced age groups, but they are relatively small in amount and they become increasingly small as we approach extreme old age. Even in the best of all possible environments it is hardly to be expected that most of us would ever become centenarians.

In interpreting the mortality statistics of the Negro it should be borne in mind that the Original Registration States were all in the North where the Negro population is chiefly urban. Life in cities affects the Negroes much more unfavorably than the whites. With the expansion of the Registration Area so that it came to include more states of the South, with a larger percentage of rural Negroes having a lower death rate, there would be a tendency toward a reduction of the general death rate among Negroes whether or not mortality had undergone an actual decrease in the several areas. When statistics cover an expanding area they have therefore to be interpreted with some reservations.

The same caution applies to the interpretation of statistics on expectation of life yielded by the life tables. The tables for 1900–1902 and 1909–1911 were based mainly on the urban Negroes of the North. In the tables for 1919–1920, Negro death rates were calculated for a number of different groups, namely, the Original Registration States, states with less than 4 per cent of Negroes, states (mainly southern) with more than 5 per cent of Negroes, and large cities. The later tables show that the expectation of life was greater in the South than in the North for most age groups, except young adult and adolescent females and some of the very advanced ages (over eighty). For all ages up to eighty the expectation of life in urban Negroes was less than among Negroes in general. If we compare the relative expectancy of life among Negroes of the Original Registration States in 1910 with that in the same region in 1920, we find that the life span has considerably increased by the latter date, and that the expectation of life has increased somewhat in nearly all except the very advanced age groups. Such a comparison may not afford an entirely accurate gauge of the trend of Negro mortality, however, because the Original Registration Area received a large influx of relatively healthy Negroes between 1910 and 1920. Moreover, 1920, like 1919, was a year of low mortality, partly, perhaps, because the influenza epidemic of 1918 swept away many ailing people, thus leaving a hardier stock of survivors. It seems certain, however, that Negro mortality was reduced in this decade, but, as in the previous decade, the greatest saving of life occurred in infancy and early childhood.

After 1920 the Negro death rate declined for a few years and then rose, in 1926, to its highest point. In 1930 Negro mortality in the Registration Area was 16.5. According to the estimates of Thompson and Whelpton, the Negro death rate of the Registration States of 1920 was higher in the second than in the first half of the decade from 1920 to 1930, the crude rate being 16.6 in 1920–1924, and 17.7 in 1925–1929. Most of the increased mortality occurred in ages 25 to 84. There was a marked decline in infant mortality and a less striking decline of mortality in childhood and in the teens. A part of the rise of the death rate in the latter part of the decade may have been owing to the fact that after a few years the selective effect of the influenza epidemic had begun to wear off. Another factor tending in the same direction is the ever increasing urbanization of the Negro population.

In addition to the data on Negro mortality available in official statistics, a great deal of valuable supplementary material has been accumulated by the Metropolitan Life Insurance Company. This large company insures over two and a half million Negroes. The greater number of its Negro policy holders are wage earners, drawn mostly from the cities in both the North and the South. The Metropolitan Company insures Negroes of all ages over one year, but most of its clientele consists of persons in the adult and middle ages of life. The policy holders of an insurance company are, of course, not typical of the general population, because many individuals who would be poor risks are not accepted. But the trend of mortality in a large insured group reflects rather closely that of the population in general. Between 1911 and 1927 the death rate of Negroes insured by the Metropolitan Company declined from 17.5 per thousand to 14.0, or about 20 per cent. According to Doctor L. I. Dublin, the statistician of this company, "This marked decline is due, for the most part, to improvements in the death rates from tuberculosis, pneumonia, malaria, typhoid fever, and pellagra, and, in a smaller degree, Bright's disease. A number of factors are clearly at work which are operating favorably on the life and health of our Negro population. Particularly noteworthy has been the great development of health activities in the South and Southwest. The general economic status of Negroes has been better, both during the war period and in the decade since. The betterment has been a broad one, affecting virtually all areas, with scarcely a state (in which there is a significant Negro population) failing to show a decided decline in the total death rate. While it is true that the mortality among Negroes is still high, reflecting marked deficiencies in the health provisions for them, we cannot but conclude that the public health movement is making a favorable impress upon our colored population."

Between 1911–12 and 1926 the expectation of life of the colored Metropolitan policy holders at 10 years of age was increased from 41.32 to 44.84, or 3.5 years (8.5 per cent) for males, and from 41.30 to 45.60, or 4.3 years (10.4 per cent) for females. The later statistical bulletins of the Metropolitan Company show a slight rise in Negro mortality over its lowest figures in 1927, the rates per thousand for 1930, 1931, and 1932 being 15.20, 15.38, and 14.72 respectively.

The greatest reduction in the mortality of insured Negroes between 1911–1913 and 1925–1927 was among children from 1 to 14 years of age, the gain being 38 per cent. There was also a gain of 28.8 per cent in ages 15 to 24. It is in the younger age groups that we find the greatest differences between the mortality rates of Negroes and of whites. "Colored infants of both sexes," says Dublin, "suffer from death rates approximately two-thirds above that of the whites. In early childhood the margin is even larger. From five years of age up to adolescence, the margin is 57 per cent excess for males and 72 per cent for females. The most pronounced differences, however, are found between 15 and 25 years, where the death rate for colored boys and young men runs nearly two and a half times that for the whites, and where the mortality among colored girls is more than two and three-quarters times as high as for young white women. From early adult life to middle age (25 to 44 years) the comparison remains extremely unfavorable to the colored; while between 45 and 64 years, the adverse margins for the colored are not so large as with all earlier age groups. The death rate for colored women is still 60 per cent above that for white women. In old age, that is 65 years and over, the excess mortality for colored males and females is much reduced, being only 11 and 18 per cent respectively."

Differences in mortality in early life are particularly significant in relation to the relative rates of increase of competing groups. With respect to the biological struggle, the deaths that occur after the reproductive period are relatively unimportant. Environmental factors affect the life expectancy of old people far less than that of younger persons. In fact, most of the increase in the average duration of human life has been due to the reduction of mortality in children and young adults. The mortality rates of Negroes and whites differ most conspicuously in the ages in which much progress can be made in saving human life. There is not the least doubt that under proper conditions of hygiene and medical service a very great reduction of Negro mortality is entirely feasible. The Negro is no weakling. Typically he is a pretty tough and husky animal. Despite their malaria, pellagra, syphilis, tuberculosis, and other prevalent infirmities, the Negroes who were examined during the World War were found to compare very favorably, in physique, with the average of the white draft. Between 1906 and 1910 the number of recruits per thousand rejected from the army was 136.2 among the white men and 104.8 among the colored. For the years 1911–1915 the proportions were 113.4 for white men and 110.1 for colored. Many more Negroes than whites were rejected for venereal diseases, but a smaller proportion of Negroes than of whites was found to have defects of the eyes, ears, or teeth.

The Negroes may be more prone than the whites to succumb to certain diseases, but there is little doubt that a large part of their excess mortality is a result of unfavorable environment rather than inherited constitution. This fact, however, does not justify us in regarding constitutional factors as of small importance in causing the inequalities in the death rates of the two races. Whether environment or racial heredity is the main cause of the differential mortality of whites and blacks is a question which has provoked no end of rather fruitless controversy. There is little to be gained by discussing it in general terms. We can make some headway only by considering the operation of particular causes of death. To this end the following chapter is presented.

CHAPTER V

THE SELECTIVE ACTION OF DISEASE

ALTHOUGH the general mortality of Negroes is much higher than that of whites, different diseases affect the two races in different ways. The advantages of more favorable surroundings are everywhere enjoyed by the whites. Consequently where we find that, in spite of this fact, certain diseases are much less fatal to the Negro, we have strong reason to believe that this advantage is due to a racial idiosyncrasy. There are several diseases of this sort, such as scarlet fever, measles, erysipelas, and diphtheria. There are certain other maladies to which the Negro is susceptible to a degree that cannot readily be attributed to unfavorable surroundings.

The subject of differential mortality is full of pitfalls. One source of confusion is the failure to distinguish between a true racial immunity to a disease and an immunity slowly built up through the direct reaction of persons exposed to infection. Much has been learned about the acquisition of immunity which was quite unknown three decades ago. Even when two races exhibit marked differences in their reactions to a given disease and when the environmental conditions of the races are virtually the same, it is not always safe to attribute these differences to racial heredity. A child brought up in the city, where it is frequently exposed to minimal inoculations by pathogenic organisms, may develop a greater power of resistance to several diseases than a child who has been shielded from all sources of infection. During the Great War it was found that city bred recruits were less affected by a number of epidemic diseases than the more sturdy recruits from rural areas. Small doses of pathogenic organisms, instead of causing disease, may confer a certain degree of immunity to larger doses of the same kind of organisms. In this way peoples often develop a partial immunity to the infections prevailing in a particular region; other peoples invading that region may suffer severely from its characteristic maladies. The fact that in certain parts of Africa it is almost impossible for Caucasians to live because of malaria which seems to have little effect upon the native Negroes, has long been cited as an illustration of a true racial difference in susceptibility to disease.

One is never safe in denying the existence of such susceptibilities, but even in this striking example the chief factor involved is the gradual building up of an immunity during the lifetime of the individual.

The development of immunity to tuberculosis through minimal infections is now a well-recognized phenomenon, and it is taken advantage of in protecting children from this disease. Indeed, an appreciable proportion of the persons in whom a racial idiosyncracy seems to be present are probably protected by individually acquired immunities. On the other hand, the important rôle of genetic factors in disease resistance, which has been demonstrated in different races of plants and animals, makes it very likely *a priori* that races so different as the Negro and the Caucasian may differ in their reactions to pathogenic agencies. Little is to be gained by discussing the problem in general terms. Different diseases present their peculiar problems and these will be discussed in the following twenty-seven sections on particular maladies.

SCARLET FEVER

The Negro race has long enjoyed a partial immunity to scarlet fever. Deaths from this cause under one year of age are not very numerous, but since 1914 there have been nearly four times as many among the white as among the colored in proportion to the number of infants of these races. In older age periods the racial differences become more pronounced. From 1919 to 1923 inclusive, there were in the Registration States 785 deaths of white children and 35 of colored children under 1 year from scarlet fever, giving a ratio of 23.43 white infants to 1 colored. In the same area and period there were 8,095 deaths of white children and 137 deaths of colored children under 5 years, giving a ratio of 69.09 whites to 1 colored. Both of these figures are several times the expected ratio for all deaths, which for these years would lie between 5 and 6.

In his valuable survey of the vital statistics of the census of 1890, Dr. J. S. Billings states that the death rate (per 100,000) for scarlet fever "was much higher among the whites (14.20) than it was among the colored (2.72)." In a similar survey of the vital statistics of the census of 1880, Dr. Billings remarks that scarlet fever "caused a much greater proportion of the deaths among the whites

(20.9) than among the colored (3.9)." For a group of twenty-eight cities in 1890 the death rate for whites was 17.81 and for the colored, 3.84. Deaths from scarlet fever were not given for infants under 1 year in the 1890 returns, but the data collected for thirty-one cities showed 240 deaths among whites and 3 among Negro infants, and in children under 5 there were 2,511 deaths among

TABLE 5

SCARLET FEVER: MORTALITY AMONG POLICY HOLDERS, WHITE AND COLORED, IN THE METROPOLITAN LIFE INSURANCE COMPANY, FROM 1911 TO 1916; RATES PER 100,000 PERSONS INSURED

Age groups	White		Colored	
	Males	Females	Males	Females
All ages over 1 year....	10.6	8.6	2.5	2.2
1– 4................	53.5	48.8	16.0	22.2
5– 9................	24.3	23.4	8.8	6.4
10–14................	5.8	7.5	5.1	2.5
15–19................	3.0	2.9	1.0	2.3
20–24................	1.2	2.2	....	.5
25 and over..........	.4	.6	.2	.3

whites and 31 among Negroes. The total deaths under 1 year in these same cities were in the ratio of 7.6 white to 1 colored, and under 5 years in the ratio of 8.45 white to 1 colored.

Statistics of the census of 1870 show 20,011 deaths from scarlet fever among whites and 289 among Negroes, giving a ratio of 69.24 to 1, as compared with the ratio of 6.27 for deaths from all causes. Before this we do not have comparative statistics for any extensive area. In 1870 deaths of whites from scarlet fever were more than ten times as prevalent as among blacks on the basis of the general death rates of the two races. A certain amount of allowance should be made, however, for the inaccuracies in the returns of the 1870 census for the Negro population.

In this connection we may cite the experience of the Metropolitan Life Insurance Company. The results are summarized in table 5, which gives the death rates of white and colored policy holders from 1911 to 1916 based on 4,638 deaths.

A comparison of the death rates of white and colored persons by years showed that the death rates of both sexes were much greater for whites than for colored persons in each of the six years covered by the returns. The subsequent experience of the same insurance company shows much the same relation between the death rates of its white and colored policy holders.

TABLE 6

SCARLET FEVER: PROPORTIONS OF DEATHS IN THE WHITE AND COLORED POPULATIONS AS COMPARED WITH ONE THOUSAND DEATHS FROM KNOWN CAUSES

Region	1880		1890	
	White	Colored	White	Colored
North Atlantic Coast Region..........	....	....	3.94	1.83
Middle Atlantic Coast Region.........	23.4	5.7	7.63	2.13
South Atlantic Coast Region..........	22.2	2.1	0.39	0.62
Gulf Coast Region....................	2.4	1.6	1.38	1.23
Interior Plateau.....................	24.1	6.2	9.19	1.18
South Central Appalachian............	11.6	5.7	3.15	1.99
Ohio River Belt......................	43.8	14.8	5.67	0.32
South Interior Plateau...............	2.0	0.8	1.91	0.42
South Mississippi River Belt..........	15.9	4.5	3.26	1.63
Southwest Central Region.............	9.8	3.4	2.25	1.48
Central Region, Plains, and Prairies...	23.7	5.3	9.30	1.63
Total..............................	20.9	3.9		

In studying the racial incidence of a disease, one must guard against sources of error due to the peculiarities of its geographical distribution. Scarlet fever tends to be less prevalent in warmer climates, but this circumstance does not account for its lower fatality in the Negro population. If we study the mortality from scarlet fever in individual states or cities, we find that the whites have everywhere the higher death rates from this disease. This is well shown in table 6, showing the distribution of deaths from this cause in 1880 and 1890.

Similar high rates for the whites are found in several cities. In Baltimore (1905 to 1919) there were 457 deaths among whites and 31 among Negroes, giving a fatality, according to Howard (1924), "nearly three times greater in the white than in the Negro race." Morbidity rates of Baltimore for 1921 show a rate per 100,000 of 164 for whites and 39 for Negroes, based on a total of 1,065 cases. The history of scarlet fever in Baltimore, according to Howard, shows that "During the last 20 and probably the last 40 years, the morbidity rates have increased as the mortality rates have de-

TABLE 7

SCARLET FEVER: ADMISSIONS TO HOSPITAL, DEATHS, DISCHARGES, AND DAYS LOST AMONG WHITE AND COLORED TROOPS IN THE UNITED STATES ARMY, FROM APRIL 1, 1917 TO DECEMBER 31, 1919

	White		Colored	
	Number	Rate per 100,000	Number	Rate per 100,000
Admissions to Hospital	10,933	3.05	97	.34
Deaths..............	338	.09	2	.01
Discharges..........	18	.01	0	0.0
Days Lost...........	472,967	.36	4,639	.04

clined; in other words, the capacity of scarlet fever to attack the population has increased as its lethal force has diminished. . . . a very remarkable change has occurred in the ratio of mortality among Negroes as compared with whites. In 1850 the mortality rate for the former was only about one-fourth less than that of the latter, while during the past 15 years, the mortality was nearly three times greater among the whites than among Negroes."

The data for 1850, however, comprise a total of 225 deaths for both races in a population in which the whites were more than five times as numerous as the blacks. A difference of only ten deaths in the colored population would make a very material difference in the mortality rates of the two races. Although scarlet fever, like many other epidemics, varies in virulence in different times and places, I cannot find any adequate evidence of a general change in the way in which it affects the colored population. There seems to be little to cause changes in the diagnosis of scarlet fever, because there has been little improvement in the method of distinguishing this disease from others with which it may be confused.

The experience of the United States Army during the World War bears out the preceding conclusions concerning the racial incidence of scarlet fever, as may be seen in table 7.

MEASLES

According to many accounts, measles acts with very different degrees of severity upon the various races of mankind. That certain races show an extreme susceptibility to measles is owing in large part to the fact that they have built up no immunity against this disease. True racial differences in susceptibility probably exist, but they are more difficult to demonstrate than has commonly been assumed. The complications of the problem will become apparent as we proceed.

For the first year of life the death rate from measles is relatively low, and of the deaths which occur by far the larger number fall within the last six months. A compilation of deaths from measles occurring in the Registration Area for Deaths from 1914 to 1923 shows that the death rate among Negro infants is only about two-thirds as high as would be expected on the basis of total deaths. The ratio of deaths (colored to white) is 1 to 10.94 instead of 1 to 7.47, the ratio of infants' deaths for all causes combined. The data are sufficiently inclusive and extend over a sufficient period of time to eliminate the influence of the great annual and regional differences which are so apt to betray one in interpreting the statistics of this disease.

Since 1920, death rates both crude and adjusted have been published in the United States Mortality Statistics for the Registration States of 1920 and these show that except in two years, 1923 and 1924, the whites suffered more from measles than the colored population. These rates are given in table 8.

One meets with a good deal of variation in the relations between the rates for the white and colored populations from year to year as well as marked fluctuations in the general death rate from this disease. The more or less periodic epidemics which sweep over large sections of the country may prevail now in the North and now in the South, or again in the West. Since the proportion of colored people varies enormously in different parts of the Registration Area we would naturally have a high death rate for the colored population when measles prevailed in the South, and a relatively low rate when it prevailed in the North or West. Inasmuch as measles seems to thrive in all climates, these variations would tend to cancel out, in data covering a series of years. In 1923 and 1924 there was not only a high death rate from measles in the Registration States, but the death rate for the colored population rose above that of the

TABLE 8

MEASLES: DEATH RATES, CRUDE AND ADJUSTED, IN THE REGISTRATION STATES
OF 1920, FROM 1920 TO 1927

	White		Colored	
	Adjusted	Crude	Adjusted	Crude
1920.................	9.9	9.3	4.3	4.1
1921.................	4.6	4.3	3.6	3.4
1922.................	5.0	4.7	3.2	3.0
1923.................	11.2	10.5	16.8	15.7
1924.................	7.7	7.2	16.2	15.1
1925.................	2.6	2.5	2.0	2.0
1926.................	9.3	8.7	6.4	6.2
1927.................	3.9	3.7	5.7	5.5

whites, whereas in the five preceding years the death rate for the whites exceeded that for the colored.

The clue to the exceptionally high rate for the colored population in 1923 and 1924 is found in the fact that the general measles rate increased very greatly in several of the Southern States. According to the volume on Mortality Statistics for 1923, "Comparing the rates for 1922 and 1923 for the 37 Registration States shown for both years, increases in 1923 are shown for 32 states, the largest increase appearing for Delaware (from 1.8 to 25.2), Rhode Island (from 0.8 to 21.8), North Carolina (from 0.9 to 21.9), and Virginia (from 1.5 to 22.3)." The fact that measles was especially severe in states of the South caused the Negro mortality from this disease to exceed that of the whites for the total area.

In comment on the measles rates for 1917 and 1916, in the report on Mortality Statistics (1917), the following statement is made: "Comparing the Registration States for 1917 and 1916, decreases are shown for 1917 by 11—Connecticut, Massachusetts, Michigan, Minnesota, New Jersey, New York, Ohio, Pennsylvania, Rhode Island, Virginia, and Wisconsin,—while 4—Kentucky, Maine, North Carolina, and South Carolina, show rates in 1917 more than five times those of 1916." In all the last-mentioned states except Maine, in which the Negro rate was based on less than five cases, the death rate of the white race exceeded that for the colored. A higher rate for whites is shown in some other Southern States, but not in all, for the same year.

It is one of the seeming paradoxes, such as are often found in vital statistics, that the addition of areas, in each of which the white death rate for a particular disease is greater than the Negro rate, may give for the region as a whole a death rate which is higher for Negroes than for whites. Failure to be on one's guard against this possibility may very easily lead to error in the interpretation of statistical data. This source of error is especially likely to betray one in the problem with which we are dealing. One of the best ways of avoiding the statistical pitfalls occasioned by the uneven geographical distribution of disease is to study the death rates in particular localities over a series of years. We have therefore compiled data on the course of mortality from measles during several years in a number of states (see Table VI, Appendix). The results show that in general the mortality rate of the Negroes is usually less than that of the whites.

There are, however, several exceptions in which the death rate among the colored exceeds that of the white population. These may sometimes result from chance fluctuations where the number of deaths was small, but the preponderance of Negro deaths in some states in 1923–1924 is probably due to other causes. For the year of greatest mortality from measles (1917), the rate for whites exceeded that for the colored in all states listed in the table, except Maryland, and in this state the measles rate was the lowest for all the recorded states.

However, even when we study the comparative death rates of the white and colored population in individual states we do not avoid all the errors due to differences in geographical distribution. Death rates from measles are usually higher in cities than in rural districts. The proportion of whites and Negroes is usually much different in cities from what it is in the country. In several of the Southern States with the largest colored populations, Negroes are predominantly rural in distribution. In the North and West they are largely concentrated in cities.

A study of the relative death rates of the races in cities affords a means of avoiding errors due to the cause just mentioned, but at the same time it introduces the chance of falling into others. One circumstance to be considered is the relative proportion of children to that of older persons in the two races, since the race with the largest proportion of children is apt, other things being equal, to have the higher death rate from measles. A large part of our data on the death rates of the white and colored populations of cities is confined to the last twelve or fifteen years. In this period, owing to circumstances connected with the Great War, a great stimulus was given to the urban migration of Negroes, and this migration has affected the Negro population of different cities in a very unequal manner. Estimates of the Negro population which have been made year by year are very apt to be quite different from the true number. I strongly suspect that this circumstance has contributed not a little to cause the variations in Negro death rates which the statistics of our cities exhibit. The same factor of recent migration would affect greatly the proportion of Negro children in different cities.

Formerly the opinion was frequently expressed that measles is more fatal to Negroes than whites. Dr. E. R. Corson in his extensive paper on "The Vital Equation of the Colored Race," after remarking that diphtheria and scarlet fever are less common among the colored people, states that "measles and whooping cough are both very much more fatal among them." This conclusion is supported by the data contained in the reports of the United States Census for 1870, 1880, and 1890. In 1870 there were reported 2,059 deaths from measles among the Negroes and 7,158 among the whites. This gives a death rate of 30 per thousand of total deaths for Negroes and 16.8 per thousand of total deaths for the white population. In 1880 the proportion of deaths from measles to 1,000 deaths from all causes was 12.12 for whites and 23.75 for Negroes. Although the measles rate was relatively high in the Southern States in 1880, we find that the rates in the several regions were higher for

Negroes than for whites. Taking the areas in which the rates for the two races are given, we have embodied the results in table 9.

With the exception of the last two areas, in which the excess of white deaths from measles is not great, the data show a rather striking preponderance of deaths in the colored population. It should be borne in mind that the returns of the deaths in the censuses of

TABLE 9

MEASLES: DEATH RATES PER THOUSAND DEATHS FROM ALL CAUSES IN THE WHITE AND COLORED POPULATIONS, IN THE YEAR 1880

	White	Colored
Middle Atlantic Coast Region..................	6.3	8.3
South Atlantic Coast Region...................	14.0	22.6
Gulf Coast Region............................	7.1	9.4
Interior Plateau.............................	6.5	18.3
South Central Appalachian Region..............	9.4	21.5
Ohio River Belt..............................	9.9	15.4
South Interior Plateau.......................	11.0	26.7
South Mississippi River Belt..................	4.4	7.7
Southwestern Central Belt.....................	16.7	14.4
Central Region Plains and Prairies............	11.0	10.4
Total.......................................	9.1	17.7

1870, 1880, and 1890 were very incomplete. The data have a certain value, however, for purposes of comparison, although it is probable that Negro deaths were reported less frequently than those of whites. Under the circumstances it is more accurate to use the proportion of deaths from a particular disease to total deaths, as is done in table 9, than it is to employ deaths per thousand of the population, which gives too low a rate of mortality. For the entire United States the proportion of deaths from measles to 1,000 total deaths in 1890 was 10.45 for whites and 14.87 for Negroes. The data from the Registration Area for that period show a death rate per 100,000 inhabitants of 13.23 for whites and 19.58 for the colored. At the next census (1900) the death rates from measles in the white and colored races were not so far apart. The rates in the Registration Area per 100,000 population were 13.1 for the whites and 15.02 for the colored. Death rates of infants under 1 year, however, were 150.0 per 100,000 population for the white and 219.6 for the colored.

Taken at their face value, the data here presented point to the conclusion that measles is coming to act with decreasing severity upon the colored population. But statistics, and especially vital statistics, cannot always be taken at their face value. There are in fact several sources of error which we should consider before we may justifiably have confidence in the conclusion just stated. There is the source of error already alluded to, arising from the uneven geographical distribution of the disease. So far as the later data on measles are concerned we have been able to make fairly adequate allowance for this factor. The less complete data for earlier decades do not permit us to do this so well, but the probabilities are that this disturbing factor does not account for the observed result.

There is the matter of the different age composition of the two races and the changes which the races have undergone in this respect in the past few decades. We should naturally expect a race with a large proportion of children under 5 years to have a high death rate from measles. But measles is a children's disease because most adults are already protected by having had it when young. Aside from this circumstance the disease bears little relation to age. Where two races are commingled, the one which has reduced its birth rate the more rapidly would have relatively fewer susceptible individuals and so would show a lower rate for the disease. In large sections of our country, but by no means in all, this is the condition that is presented. This is indicated in several of the Southern States by the fact that the proportion of children under 5 has decreased more rapidly in the Negroes than in the whites. In the North the proportion of children under 5 among the Negroes is very much less than it is in the South. It is a significant fact that when we consider only deaths under 1 year of age we usually find the same excess for whites as we find in more advanced age groups. The data for the age groups given for 1920, 1921, 1922, and 1923 show that the white excess is found (except in 1923) for each age group up to the adolescent period, when the numbers become too small to be significant. The same conclusion is borne out by the statistics of the Metropolitan Life Insurance Company. It is quite evident that differences in age composition can explain only a part of the racial incidence of the death rate from measles.

A factor of possibly considerable influence on the secular trend of mortality in the two races is changes in habits of reporting causes of death. In measles and other diseases affecting infancy and childhood, the original infection may afford the occasion for an attack of pneumonia or some other fatal malady, and the question may arise, whether the death should be recorded as due to the original disease or the secondary complication. In general, physicians report the final complication as a cause of death less frequently than formerly. Negroes are especially prone to succumb to the respiratory sequelae which commonly follow children's diseases. Consequently, changing customs of reporting deaths might not only make changes in the death rates for children's diseases, but also changes in the relative rates for the two races.

Another factor lies in the changing economic and educational status of the two races. With measles, especially, lack of intelligent care may cause disastrous results. Doubtless an improvement of the economic and educational status of Negroes would greatly reduce their death rate from measles. In many places at least, the lot of the Negro has been much improved, but it is still more unfavorable than that of the whites. That, in spite of his inferior status, the Negro should have the lower rate for measles is all the more evidence of his relative immunity to this disease. Whether his former conditions of life were so bad as to more than compensate for his natural immunity is questionable.

Lack of adequate care is probably one of the reasons why the measles rate varies so much in different national groups in the United States. In 1900 the measles death rate in children under 1 year was 279.2 per 100,000 for those of Italian parentage, 208.8 for those of Irish parentage, 119.1 for those of native parentage, and 219 for those of colored parentage. For reasons already discussed we should be careful in drawing conclusions from these data, but the facts indicate that status is a very important factor in the measles death rate. In the light of these facts we might be prone to explain the relatively high mortality from measles among the whites as due mainly to the presence of large numbers of immigrant stocks of inferior social and educational status. These stocks have gone in large numbers into the Registration Area. They are notoriously prolific, and their infant mortality from most causes is high. Their presence therefore naturally tends to swell the measles rate of the white population, but it should be borne in mind that a relatively high measles rate is also found among the whites in most of the Southern States, where the proportion of recent immigrants is much smaller than it is in states of the North.

TABLE 10

Measles: Admissions to Hospital, Deaths, Days Lost, and Discharges, in the United States Army, From April, 1917 to December 31, 1919

	White		Colored	
	Number	Rate per 1,000	Number	Rate per 1,000
Admissions...........	90,112	25.01	4,870	17.00
Deaths...............	2,228	.62	116	.40
Days Lost............	1,723,795	1.31	106,551	1.02
Discharges for Disability..........	142		7	

In order to have a basis for further comparison I have calculated the ratio of deaths from measles to total deaths in the white and colored populations of New York City from 1910 to 1923 inclusive. The ratio of deaths from all causes in Negroes and whites was 1 to 24.59, and the ratio of deaths from measles in Negroes and whites was 1 to 48.21, which indicates that the whites have almost twice as high a death rate from measles as would be expected from the general death rates of the two races. This can scarcely be attributed to unfavorable conditions of life, since the Negro population in New York is probably not so favorably situated as most of the whites.

Of special interest in this connection are the data on measles in white and colored soldiers during the World War. I have compiled the data on measles given in the volume on Medical and Casualty Statistics (15) of the United States Army and have embodied them in table 10. These data are especially significant because the effects of better care and previous immunization would doubtless favor lower morbidity and mortality rates from measles among the whites.

DIPHTHERIA

The relatively low death rate of Negroes from diphtheria has often been commented upon. For each of the ten Southern States reporting deaths of both whites and colored from diphtheria, the death rate, so far as reported, from 1914 to 1923, with the single exception of one year, 1921, in Maryland, has been higher for whites than for Negroes; and in this exceptional year the excess for the colored was slight (13.0 per 100,000 colored; 12.2 per 100,000 white). For the fifteen cities reporting Negro deaths there has been somewhat more irregularity, but despite exceptions in a few scattering years the higher death rates for the whites are very noticeable.

The census of 1880 gives the deaths from diphtheria in relation to 1,000 total deaths in several large areas in the United States as 39.80 for whites and 17.7 for the colored. For the same regions in 1890 the rates were 36.17 whites and 26.06 colored. In the returns for 1880 and 1890, deaths from croup were listed separately and it is significant that in both censuses the rates for whites were markedly higher than those of the colored population. Doubtless most of the deaths attributed to croup were caused by diphtheria. For the Registration Area for 1890 the death rate from diphtheria among the whites was over twice as great as that of the colored (100.35 per 100,000 as compared with 46.91). In the Registration Cities it was relatively still higher (118.15 whites: 47.21 colored). In the Registration Area of 1900, the death rates for white and colored, respectively, were 45.9 and 30.5. Among the native born whites we find still higher diphtheria rates, 130.1 in 1890, and 59.1 in 1900, a circumstance due to the relatively small number of children among the foreign born.

In his valuable paper entitled "A Statistical Study of Diphtheria," Dr. F. S. Crum (1916) states that "In thirty southern cities combined, during the years 1909–1913 the average annual death-rate of the white population from diphtheria and croup was 13.7 per 100,000 of the population against an average rate of only 8.1 for the Negro population." The statistics of the Metropolitan Life Insurance Company tell a similar story. In every year from 1911 to 1916, the rate for whites was over twice that for the colored among the wage-earning policy holders. The higher rate for the whites was found in all the age groups up to adolescence, when the number became too small to give significant ratios.

Although children and adults show a lower rate for diphtheria among Negroes than among whites, this relation is frequently reversed in infants under 1 year of age. From 1914 to 1923, inclusive, there have been 8,047 deaths among white infants and 1,128 among the colored. The ratio of deaths (white to colored, 7.13) is rather less than it is for all causes, 7.47, thus showing a higher percentage of deaths among the colored population. The data on the diphtheria death rates of the white and colored populations under 1 year show that for each of the years included in the infant mortality statistics for the Birth Registration Area since 1916, the rates for Negro infants have exceeded those for whites. The same is shown in the census data of previous decades. After the first year the racial incidence undergoes a striking change, the rates for the whites showing a marked increase. Table 11, taken from the United States Mortality Statistics, is particularly instructive on this point.

As table 11 shows, for every year from 1920 to 1927 the general death rate, both crude and adjusted, is markedly higher among the whites, and for every year the same is true for the several age groups. The excess of the white death rate shows itself even in the second year of life. The data on which the table is based include over 50,000 deaths, so the chances that the relations disclosed result from fortuitous variations are quite negligible. It seems, therefore, to be quite clearly established that the Negro death rate for diphtheria exceeds that of the whites in the first year and that after this period the rate for the whites is markedly in excess of that of the colored.

One might be tempted to suppose that the superior resistance of the Negro children after the first year is because a larger number of susceptibles have been killed off in infancy. I think, however, that the selective elimination of Negro infants can account for only a small part of the low Negro death rates from diphtheria in the later age groups. The reason for this opinion is that the death rate from diphtheria in infancy is too low to confer any great degree of protection upon the survivors. The number of children dying in the first year among the whites is much less than the number dying in any single year up to the fifth, but in the colored population

TABLE 11

DIPHTHERIA: DEATH RATES PER 100,000 POPULATION, WHITE AND COLORED, IN
THE REGISTRATION STATES OF 1920, FROM 1920 TO 1927

Age groups	1920		1921		1922		1923	
	White	Colored	White	Colored	White	Colored	White	Colored
All ages								
Crude............	16.0	8.6	18.5	10.2	15.2	10.2	12.7	8.0
Adjusted.........	16.9	8.7	19.6	10.4	16.2	10.5	13.5	8.4
Under 1 year........	50.1	72.6	49.3	87.4	51.6	69.6	41.0	85.3
1 to 4..............	93.9	40.9	104.0	46.4	90.0	55.0	74.0	41.1
Under 5 years.......	85.5	47.3	93.6	54.6	82.7	57.9	67.9	50.0
9 to 14.............	12.4	4.8	15.2	7.8	11.3	8.4	9.4	2.8
15 to 19.............	3.7	2.3	4.2	2.0	3.6	2.0	3.6	0.8
20 to 24.............	1.8	0.8	2.0	1.5	1.5	1.0	2.0	1.7
25 to 34.............	1.3	0.6	1.4	1.0	1.4	0.5	1.1	0.9

Age groups	1924		1925		1926		1927	
	White	Colored	White	Colored	White	Colored	White	Colored
All ages								
Crude............	9.8	6.9	8.0	6.8	7.6	6.2	7.8	6.8
Adjusted.........	10.5	7.3	8.5	·6.9	8.1	6.4	8.3	6.9
Under 1 year........	33.7	59.5	29.5	49.5	23.9	42.3	20.3	41.3
1 to 4..............	58.1	37.1	45.4	36.2	45.8	35.7	45.8	37.9
Under 5 years.......	53.5	41.5	42.4	38.9	41.6	37.0	40.9	38.6
9 to 14.............	7.3	2.8	6.1	3.3	4.9	3.7	5.7	5.5
15 to 19.............	2.5	1.4	1.8	0.9	1.5	1.1	1.4	1.5
20 to 24.............	1.3	1.4	1.2	1.0	0.9	0.6	1.1	0.8
25 to 34.............	1.0	1.5	0.8	0.6	0.8	1.0	0.7	0.7

deaths in the first year markedly exceed those of any subsequent
year of the first quinquennium. Nevertheless, the rate for the colored population does not preponderate over that for the whites in
the first year to a degree that would account for the excess mortality
of the whites in the later age groups. In the Registration States of
1920 in 1922, for example, I find that if we assume that Negro in-

fants died of diphtheria at the rate obtaining for white infants in that year, the deaths from this cause would have been 78 instead of 106. The twenty-eight excess deaths distributed among subsequent age groups would have very little influence in equalizing the death rates of the two races in the later age periods. It is quite evident, I think, that the extent to which natural selection may act in the first year is quite incapable of conferring upon the Negro the degree of protection which is so strikingly shown by his low death rate in later life. It is true that the difference in the death rates in the two races affords an illustration of natural selection. But the differential death rates act on the basis of an inherent difference between the two races which antedates the action of selection instead of being caused by its operation during infancy.

It is a noteworthy fact that the percentage of positive Schick tests for diphtheria is much the same in Negroes as in whites. Dr. L. T. Wright (1917) tested 210 persons all but three of whom were colored, and found that 86, or 40.95 per cent, gave a positive reaction while 124, or 59.05 per cent, reacted negatively. Doull and Fales (1923) found a "slight but not significantly lower carrier rate among the colored children than among the white children" in the schools of Baltimore. Doull and Bull in studying a ward in Baltimore found that of 8,433 whites, 4,741, or 56.2 per cent, gave a Schick positive test, and of the 561 colored, 311, or 55.4 per cent, gave the same reaction. In addition, Dr. Doull remarks, "we also studied the Schick test and the efficacy of toxin-antitoxin in several institutions for Negroes. The net results for all this work would seem to indicate that the Negro and the white are not widely different with respect to antitoxin immunity to diphtheria."

It is probable that the low mortality of the Negro from diphtheria depends mainly upon his ability to escape infection, since, when the disease is once contracted, it is at least as likely to prove fatal as it is in the whites. The ratio of deaths to cases in the District of Columbia (1908–1924) was 1 to 12.94 among the Negroes and 1 to 16.77 among the whites. Likewise in New Orleans (1910–1919) the ratio of deaths to cases was 1 to 6.49 in Negroes and 1 to 21 in whites, and further data are supplied by the statistics of Baltimore. (See Appendix, Table IX.) As a rule, the whites enjoy the advantage of greater promptness of diagnosis and treatment with antitoxin. How the ratio of deaths to cases would compare in the two races under similar environment and treatment we do not know. A close approach to this position is afforded by the experiences of the American Expeditionary Forces, 1917 to 1919. Although the admission rate for whites was much greater than for Negroes, the case fatality of the Negroes was the higher; but, as only five fatal cases of diphtheria occurred among the Negroes, we cannot place much reliance on the ratio of deaths to cases.

WHOOPING COUGH

In striking contrast to the three preceding diseases, whooping cough shows a higher death rate among the colored than among the white population. In the Registration Area for Births the rate in the first year of life is more than twice that of the whites for every year from 1916 to 1923 inclusive. A similar high excess of Negro deaths is shown in the four subsequent years of childhood, after which the death rate from this disease falls to a comparatively low level. In fact, more than 95 per cent of the deaths occur in children under 5 years of age. The excess of Negro mortality continues through several later years, although the number of deaths soon becomes so small as to make comparisons untrustworthy.

The same high rate for Negroes is shown in the earlier records of vital statistics. Dr. Crum (1915), in a paper on "A Statistical Study of Whooping-cough," states that "In Charleston, S. C., during the period 1822 to 1848, the average annual death-rate of the colored population was 650.5 per 100,000 against a death-rate of 305.8 for the white population." In five large southern cities cited by Crum, the Negro death rate averaged over three times that of the whites, and the experience of the Metropolitan Life Insurance Company with its wage-earning policy holders, 1911 to 1916 inclusive, showed a rate for the Negroes nearly double that of the whites. In the Metropolitan data children under 1 year were not included.

Howard states that in Baltimore whooping cough is "over five times as fatal for Negroes as for whites," and he presents evidence to show that the virulence of the disease has undergone fluctuations in the course of several years. As to morbidity, Howard finds that it "was much greater among the whites than among the Negroes." Crum showed that in Washington, 1908–1912, the attack rate was 23.6 per 10,000 among the whites, and 22.5 among the Negroes. With infants under 1 year the attack rate was nearly twice as high among the Negroes and was somewhat higher (177.3 :157.8) in years 1 to 4, but after the fifth year white children were attacked much more than the colored (10 to 19 years, whites 7.0, colored 4.8). Both Howard and Crum attribute the low morbidity rate of the Negro chiefly to incompleteness of reporting.

It is probable that the high mortality of colored children from whooping cough is occasioned by the associated pulmonary affections to which the Negroes are so susceptible. Out of 1,000 deaths from this disease in the mortality experience of the Prudential Life Insurance Company, 62.7 per cent presented some kind of pulmonary complication, for the most part pneumonia (Crum).

MALARIA

The natural immunity of the African Negro to malaria has been discussed in scores of books and papers, but the matter has now been shown to be less simple than it formerly appeared. There seems to be quite adequate statistical proof of the conclusion that in several parts of Africa the death rate of whites from malaria has been several times that of the adult native population. The records of the United States Mortality Statistics, however, show that the Negro death rate from malaria is several times that of the whites. In the Registration Area for 1921, for example, the death rate was 21.9 per 100,000 for the colored, and 1.9 for the white population. One obvious explanation of this circumstance is the fact that Negroes are abundant in some of the regions of the South which are the most severely infested with malaria. If, however, we attempt to avoid the fallacy of geographical distribution by comparing the malaria rates for the two races in individual states and cities, we find an almost uniformly higher rate for the colored population. This is clearly indicated in table 12 (p. 66), which shows that in individual states of the South the rate for the colored exceeds that for the whites both in rural districts and in cities.

The experience of the United States Army during the Great War yielded further data on racial susceptibility to malaria. Craig states that "The experience of our Army in this respect is similar to that

of other armies and demonstrates that there is no such thing as a
true racial immunity to malarial infections." One is scarcely justified, however, in citing the evidence as demonstrative. The white
and colored troops were differently situated in respect to exposure
to malaria both before and after their induction into the Army, so
that the results are inconclusive one way or the other. In the Civil

TABLE 12

MALARIA: DEATH RATE PER 100,000 POPULATION, WHITE AND COLORED,
IN CERTAIN SOUTHERN STATES, 1921

	Cities		Rural Districts		Total	
	White	Colored	White	Colored	White	Colored
Florida.............	3.5	25.4	23.7	36.7	18.6	33.9
Louisiana...........	4.4	17.6	28.2	30.8	20.5	28.0
Mississippi..........	17.5	66.6	37.2	63.0	35.4	63.2
North Carolina......	2.8	14.1	4.6	12.5	4.4	12.7
South Carolina.......	4.7	46.1	10.4	45.5	9.6	45.5
Tennessee...........	9.2	41.9	11.0	25.3	10.7	30.3

War the number of deaths per thousand in the armies of the North
was 17.4 for the whites and 30.1 for the colored.

The superior resistance of the natives in the malarial districts of
Africa has apparently been acquired mainly through early infection. Laveran (1898), Koch (1900), and later observers found that
most of the children in malarial districts harbored the plasmodia
of this disease. The adult population that had not been killed off
had probably developed a partial immunity, and this protected
them against the severe ravages of malaria which occur in unprotected races that come to live in the infested region. Even the American Negroes who went to Liberia showed a marked susceptibility
to malarial fevers. Whether, in addition to the protection which
the Negro has acquired in his native habitat, there is also a measure
of real racial immunity, we are not, I think, in a position to decide.

The malaria case mortality of the Negroes is greater than that of
the whites although not more so than it is for many other infectious
diseases, and it may be accounted for in the same way. Doctor F. L.
Hoffman (1918) has pointed out that in Mississippi, 1915–1916, the

morbidity rates for malaria were higher for the whites than for the colored. This held true for each of the twelve counties of the Yazoo Delta region of Mississippi in 1915–1916 and for each of the groups of counties for which data are cited, the differences in most instances being very marked. In the greater number of these counties, however, the death rate from malaria was higher among the blacks. During the Civil War the admission rates for malaria were markedly higher for the colored troops than for the whites, but the reasons may have been geographical.

ERYSIPELAS

All the available evidence indicates that the Negro enjoys a marked natural immunity to erysipelas. The disease is ubiquitous in its distribution and shows no especial preference for particular geo-

TABLE 13

ERYSIPELAS: DEATHS IN THE WHITE AND COLORED POPULATIONS IN THE
REGISTRATION STATES FOR 1920, FROM 1920 TO 1923

Age groups	White	Colored	Ratio, white to colored	Ratio of deaths from all causes, white to colored
All ages.............	9,405	396	23.75	7.78
Under 1.............	2,972	126	23.59	6.52
Under 5.............	3,367	143	23.67	6.51
10–14...............	82	11	7.45	5.75
14–19...............	153	11	13.91	3.87
25–29...............	223	13	17.16	4.25
45–49...............	417	21	19.86	5.91

graphical regions. In whatever period or place adequate data have been collected, they consistently show the same low mortality of the Negro race. Taking as a fair sample the deaths in the Registration States for 1920 from 1920 to 1923, we have, in table 13, totals for a selected series of age groups.

The fatalities for all age groups are much greater in the white population than in the colored population. Erysipelas is extraordinarily fatal in infancy and it also tends to spread in insanitary surroundings; we should therefore expect to find it much more prevalent among the colored race. Taking deaths under 1 year in the white and colored populations from 1914 to 1923 inclusive, we find a total of 7,498 whites and 248 colored, giving a ratio of 30.23 as compared with an expected ratio of 7.45 based on deaths from all causes. These data indicate that the proportion of deaths among the whites is relatively high in infancy and early childhood. It becomes reduced for a span of several years and is increased again in the more advanced age groups. There are few diseases in which a racial idiosyncrasy is more pronounced. One is naturally led to associate the Negro's immunity to erysipelas with his similar immunity to scarlet fever. The Negro's superior protection against both of these diseases may depend upon a higher resistance to strep-tococci, which are held to cause these maladies.

The relatively low Negro rate for erysipelas is shown in the earliest available statistics. In the census for 1870, 3,037 deaths among whites and 116 among Negroes were attributed to this cause. These give a ratio of 26.18 whites to 1 Negro as compared with an expected ratio based on deaths from all causes of 6.33 whites to 1 Negro.

TETANUS

Tetanus, like erysipelas, is commonly a wound infection, the umbilicus being a frequent channel for the entrance of both infections in early infancy. Both diseases might be expected to show a higher incidence among Negroes, owing to the insanitary conditions which so frequently surround the Negro infant. The high Negro rate for tetanus may be plausibly explained as resulting solely from these external factors. If so, this serves to point all the more strongly to the importance of the racial factor for erysipelas.

SYPHILIS

Statistics on mortality from syphilis are admittedly far short of representing the real damage done by this disease. Deaths ascribed to syphilis are not numerous as compared with deaths from other causes. But if Osler was correct in his estimate,—and perhaps there was no one better qualified to judge,—syphilis would take first rank among the fatal infections. All the available evidence indicates that this disease is much more prevalent among the Negroes than among the whites. According to some estimates over 50 per cent of the Negro population is infected with it, but such opinions are not based on adequate data. One of the best indices of its relative prevalence in the two races is supplied by the examination of soldiers in the Great War. The admission rates were 12.63 per thousand for whites and 64.99 for the colored. For the United States Army in Europe the rates were less (5.90 white; 16.66 colored), but for the United States Army in the United States there was not only a greater prevalence of this disease, but a higher proportion, among the colored troops (17.66 white; 111.09 colored). Deaths attributed to syphilis were nine times as numerous among the colored as among the white soldiers (.02 white; .18 colored, per 100,000).

Valuable additional data are to be found in the statistics of the wage earners insured in the Metropolitan Life Insurance Company (1911 to 1920). Rates of mortality from syphilis were, white males, 16.4 per 100,000; white females, 7.1; colored males, 46.1; colored females, 25.7. For both sexes combined the death rate among the colored was about three times that of the whites.

According to Royster, out of 1,000 children visiting a free clinic at Norfolk, Va., 15.47 per cent of the Negroes gave a positive Wassermann reaction and 7.4 per cent gave a positive reaction among the whites. Dr. W. R. R. Granger, a colored physician of Brooklyn, N. Y., after discussing a series of findings on the relative occurrence of syphilis in Negroes and whites, remarks: "Having become intensely interested in the subject because I felt that the figures usually given were much too high, I made a routine Wassermann on 1,040 consecutive colored patients seen by me in private practice. 15.6 per cent were undoubtedly positive for syphilis, 10.7 per cent were doubtful (I put the one plus in the latter group), and 74.6 per cent were negative. Several of those who were negative had been treated previously for a positive reaction. Only 53 of the 153 positive cases of syphilis took any treatment. Many stopped after one visit and a few completed a course. Only ten cases kept under observation until pronounced cured."

There have been many reports on the percentage of cases of syphilis in both the white and the colored races in hospitals and clinics. The literature on the subject is extensive and we shall confine ourselves to only a few typical studies. The percentages of positive reactions to serological tests among Negroes were 27.8 in the Flint

Goodrich Hospital, New Orleans; 28.0 in the Obstetrical Clinic of the Philadelphia General Hospital; 34.0 in the Grady Maternal Clinic in Atlanta; and 28.0 in the St. Louis Maternity Hospital. Keidel and Moore report 22.9 per cent of positive Wassermann reactions among the Negroes in the Johns Hopkins Hospital, and 7.6 per cent among the whites. According to Reinhard the rate for syphilis was nine times as high for the colored as for the whites in the records of the Baltimore clinics, but the increase in the cases treated is probably not indicative of an actual increase in the prevalence of the disease. Dr. Jason states that Wassermann tests carried out in 4,595 colored patients in five years in the Freedmen's Hospital in Washington, D. C., showed a positive reaction in 892, or 19.4 per cent of the cases. The highest percentage, 31.6, was found in the gynecological clinic. Of the unemployed single girls under twenty years of age who visited the clinic, the percentage of positive Wassermanns was 20.8 for those living with their parents, 28.57 for those living with other relatives, and 45.8 for those living with "friends."

Naturally the percentage of syphilitic cases would be greater among patients than in the general population; but several studies of unselected groups have given evidence that syphilis is widespread among apparently healthy Negroes. Wassermann surveys of the whole Negro population of a number of rural counties carried on by the United States Public Health Service have shown about 20 per cent of positive reactions. In an examination of 2,030 unselected infants of St. Louis, Jeans and Cooke found about 15 per cent of hereditary syphilis in the Negroes and 1.8 per cent among the poor whites. The studies of Carley and Wenger on 7,228 rural Negroes of Mississippi have revealed an appalling situation that is probably widespread in the Southern States. In this investigation the planters rounded up all their Negro help, and the complement fixation test was given to all persons over 9 years of age and to a number of younger children. In the whole group a positive reaction was given by 19.3 per cent of the males and 18.0 per cent of the females. The maximum number of infected persons of both sexes was found between ages 20 and 29. The distribution of infected cases by five-year age groups, from under 5 to over 50, is shown in table 14 (p. 71).

About the same number of persons of each sex were examined and showed about the same degree of infection. No clinical cases were included in this group. "All subjects examined were, to all intents and purposes, well." Happy, carefree, exhibiting little foresight and having a sex appetite which is described as "enormous," these rural Negroes naturally fall into loose sexual habits which inevitably result in a wide spread of syphilitic infection. The authors state that "Promiscuity before marriage and again soon after

TABLE 14

SYPHILIS: DISTRIBUTION OF CASES PER AGE GROUP

	Under 5	5–9	10–14	15–19	20–29	30–39	40–49	Over50
Negroes examined....	33	774	1,356	1,116	1,419	918	876	826
Positive Wassermanns	1	47	119	141	367	257	155	125

marriage is the rule," and that exceptions are rare. They also believe that syphilis is even more prevalent in rural Negroes than their results indicate. But whether or not this is true, there is strong justification for their conclusion that "from a public health and economic point of view, syphilis is probably the major public health problem among rural Mississippi Negroes today." Reporting on a survey of Macon County, Georgia, Gill states that 1,282 out of 3,603 Negroes who were given the Kahn test reacted positively. Of 511 cases of syphilis in Negro women, 161, or 36 per cent, had one or more miscarriages, or an average of 1.9 per woman. One woman had eleven, but many of the women had never been pregnant. Most of these women (over 970) had no knowledge of any primary lesion of the disease, although a positive history was reported by 49.3 per cent of the men.

According to Maxcy and Brumfield, about 9.8 per cent of the adult colored population of Albemarle County, Virginia, are infected with syphilis. Most of the other general surveys have given higher rates. The percentage for Glenn County, Georgia, was 26.1; for Tipton County, Tennessee, 25.5; and for Bolivar County, Mississippi, 23.9. A survey of Pitt County, North Carolina, including 11,931 persons tested, gave a lower percentage, namely, 12.5. These figures afford ample justification for the statement of Dr. Granger that "Syphilis is certainly the peer of diseases among Negroes."

Aside from the fact that syphilis is more frequently neglected and allowed to pursue an unchecked course among the Negroes than among the whites, there is no conclusive evidence that it is on the whole more severe upon the Negro race. Some medical writers remark upon the severity of syphilis among the Negroes and attribute it to a racial idiosyncrasy, and others express quite the reverse opinion. Keyes, for example, in a standard treatise, states that "Negroes, although utterly careless about treatment, are relatively immune to syphilis and rarely exhibit parasyphilitic lesions." There are, however, good indications that the two races react somewhat differently to this disease. Dr. Zimmermann (1921), who has made a comparative study of syphilis in Negroes and whites, states that the former manifest more severe osteoarthritic and cardiovascular symptoms, more polyadenitis and iritis, but less tabes and paresis than the whites. Thompson and Kingery (1919) find, in agreement with Hazen, that, although syphilis may express itself in characteristic ways in Negroes and whites, there is "no difference in the course of the disease in the two races," or in their response to treatment. Characteristic skin manifestations, however, have been described by a number of writers. Hazen says that "moist papules and condylomas" and annular lesions are much more common in Negroes than in whites. And Turner in a study of ten thousand syphilitics of both races also mentions characteristic differences in skin reactions, and states that gummata of the lymph nodes are about twice as frequent in Negroes as in whites. He also found that "general paresis was seven times as frequent in whites as in Negroes," and that "Tabes dorsalis . . . was much more common in white males than in white females or Negroes or either sex."

It has frequently been stated that manifestations of neurosyphilis are relatively rare in the Negro race. For a long time this was probably true, but there is now no doubt that general paresis and tabes dorsalis have increased in the Negro population since the Civil War. According to the experience of the Metropolitan Life Insurance Company from 1911 to 1916, the death rate from general paresis was greater for the colored than for the white policy holders. The Army data show a higher percentage of cases of tabes and general paresis in the World War in the Negro recruits. Further evidence of the prevalence of these maladies in the colored population is given by the investigations of R. H. Foster, who has made an extensive study of the statistics of hospitals receiving Negro patients. He finds a markedly higher percentage of cases of general paresis among both male and female Negroes than among the whites. The clientele of a hospital, however, represents a selected group which may not be typical of the general population. The data published in the annual volumes on Mortality Statistics afford much more extensive material, although it may not be entirely reliable in respect to the accuracy of diagnosis of the causes of death. In the Registration States, in the years from 1920 to 1932 inclusive, the percentage of total deaths caused by general paresis was 0.435 for the whites and 0.501 for the colored; for tabes, the percentages were 0.131 for the whites and 0.067 for the colored. Taking the percentages from a constant area, the Registration States of 1920, makes little difference. The percentages are: for general paresis, 0.451 white, and 0.544 colored; and for tabes, 0.136 white, and 0.073 colored.

The statistics for the Registration States show that the death rate from both tabes and general paresis has decreased considerably among the whites between 1920 and 1932. There have actually been fewer deaths from both these causes in the last few years than from 1920 to 1923 despite the increase of the population and the greater number of total deaths. This fact harmonizes with the frequently expressed conviction that syphilis is less common than it was a decade or two ago. There has been a decline also in the percentage of deaths attributed to both these maladies in the colored population, but the decline has not been so rapid as in the whites. Taking the data on the mortality from general paresis from 1920 to 1923, we find that for each of these years the percentage of deaths was greater for the whites than for the colored. But for each of the years from 1929 to 1932, the percentage of deaths from general paresis was higher in the colored than in the whites. This reversal is evidently to be attributed to the slower decline of mortality from general paresis in the colored population. The colored death rate from tabes has declined a little more rapidly but it continues to be a little more than half the rate for the whites.

Syphilis is undoubtedly the chief factor in the relatively high rate for stillbirths and abortions among the Negroes and an important factor in early infant mortality. According to the Mortality Statistics of the Registration Area, 1914 to 1923, infant deaths from syphilis have been more than three times as frequent among Negroes as among whites. Owing to its rôle in the causation of abortion and early infant mortality, to say nothing of its contributing greatly to the death rate in later years, syphilis is a powerful force in checking the natural increase of the Negro population. This condition is due to social rather than biological causes and it may be remedied in time. The success of the two races in grappling with the problem of syphilis will have much to do with the outcome of the biological struggle for supremacy.

There is evidence that the prevalence of syphilis among Negroes varies a good deal with social class. In the Wheatly Provident Hospital of Kansas City, Mo., patronized by the better class of Negroes, routine Wassermann tests on 1,648 patients gave 6.6 per cent of positive reactions as compared with 34 per cent in the Municipal Hospital of the same city. Of 701 students tested in Lincoln University, Kansas City, only 9 gave positive reactions, and only 5 per cent of positive reactions were found in the colored students of the Lincoln High School. These data afford ground for the conclusion that a widespread campaign of education may result in reducing this great scourge of our Negro population.

TUBERCULOSIS

Much has been written on tuberculosis in the Negro. The course of tuberculosis among Negroes before and after the Civil War has been treated at some length in the papers of Hoffman (1896) and Corson (1893), to which the reader is referred for fuller data. The native African tribes seem to have been relatively free from tuberculosis, but, like many other peoples who have not encountered this disease, they are particularly susceptible to its ravages when once it gains a foothold. This is certainly true of the natives of several parts of Africa today. And it was true of the African troops recruited during the Great War.

In the period of slavery the Negro death rate from tuberculosis was probably not high. There are very few statistical data on the subject and these relate mainly to cities, where tuberculosis was doubtless much more common than in rural communities. In Charleston, from 1822 to 1848, the Negro death rate was somewhat below that of the whites, although the white rate was very high. In Baltimore, we have the death rates for Negroes and whites for only one year before the Civil War, namely, 1850, when the mortality rates for pulmonary tuberculosis were calculated by Frick as 317 for the whites and 468 for the Negroes.

As opposed to these data on urban death rates, we have a somewhat better index of the prevalence of tuberculosis supplied by the recruiting statistics collected during the Civil War, 1861–1865. These data were based on the examination of 315,620 white and 25,828 colored recruits. Those rejected for tuberculosis amounted to 11.4 per thousand examined among the whites, and only 4.2 per thousand among the colored. Scrofula, however (which is due to tuberculosis), was a little more prevalent among the colored recruits (2.8 per thousand white recruits, 3.8 per thousand colored). Further evidence of the relative rarity of tuberculosis in Negroes before the Civil War is given by the testimony of several physicians with extensive experience among the colored population. Dr. Buckner, who examined over 1,600 recruits, remarked that "Tuberculosis is very rare among them; and contrary to the generally received opinion in the slave states, they are now, as far as my experience goes, no more subject to scrofulosis than other people." Corson states: "I have been assured by physicians who practiced among them before the war, and when their physical condition was so much better than it now is, that consumption was almost unknown. The finding of any tubercular lesions in the lungs at an autopsy was always a surprise."

Although the colored recruits for the Civil War had a relatively low rate for tuberculosis at the time of their enlistment, the disease spread rapidly among them and soon caused a death rate far in excess of that of the white soldiers. Among the white soldiers the average annual case rate for consumption (1861–1865) was 6.06 per thousand and the death rate 2.18 per thousand. Among the colored troops the corresponding rates were (1862–1865) 7.26 and 6.31. Death rates per thousand for respiratory diseases among white and colored troops were 7.40 and 32.35 respectively. These facts seem to indicate that the Negro was unusually susceptible to pulmonary diseases when once brought into intimate contact with them. Doubtless the living conditions of the Negro soldiers were not so favorable as those of the whites, as is indicated by their higher death rates for most other diseases, the mean annual death rate for the whites being 53.48 and that of the colored, 143.40. Dr. Hunt in his valuable report, *The Negro as a Soldier*, expresses the opinion that "While it must be admitted that temporary causes had much to do with the frequency of lung diseases among the Negroes, it will still be found that they are vastly more liable to this source of mortality than the whites. . . . It was found that when fairly enlisted, clothed and fed, and subjected to the same methods of life as the white soldier he still exhibited a far greater ratio of deaths from pulmonary disease." Corson states that, "to the physician treating the disease among the colored, its great fatality is but too apparent. I can hardly recall a case where I have stayed it and they died without the slightest response to treatment and in a very short time."

The proneness of the Negro to succumb quickly to tuberculosis has been frequently commented on. Unfortunately it has not been possible to obtain data on the tuberculosis death rate of Negroes and whites living under the same environmental conditions. Even in the army such differences cannot be entirely eliminated, since the factors of poor education and insanitary habits are always operative to a greater or less degree. The serious ravages of tuberculosis among the Negroes following the Civil War are to be attributed in large measure to the wretched housing and unwholesome environment in which so many of the Negroes were compelled to live. Crowded into small cabins, insufficiently clad and fed, and often affected with devitalizing maladies of malaria, syphilis, and pellagra, the Negroes were exposed to almost ideal conditions for the spread of pulmonary diseases. Their death rate from tuberculosis for the first three or four decades after emancipation came to be about three times as great as that of the whites. Data are not available for tracing the course of their tuberculosis death rate during this period in any large part of the United States, so we must rely upon the statistics of the few cities which kept fairly adequate records with respect to this disease.

Perhaps the most valuable records of the course of tuberculosis

in the two races are those supplied by Howard (1924) from the
vital statistics of Baltimore. In this city separate tabulations of
deaths in the two races have been kept from 1875 to the present
time. These official records have been modified by Howard by add-

TABLE 15

TUBERCULOSIS: DEATH RATES PER 100,000 POPULATION, WHITE AND COLORED,
OF BALTIMORE, MD., FROM 1876 TO 1920

PULMONARY TUBERCULOSIS

Years	White	Colored	Years	White	Colored
1876–80.........	299	633	1901–05.........	189	488
1881–85.........	279	667	1906–10.........	179	498
1886–90.........	239	552	1911–15.........	148	444
1891–95.........	199	485		129*	
1896–00.........	174	440	1916–20.........	150	406

ALL FORMS OF TUBERCULOSIS

Years	White	Colored	Years	White	Colored
1901–05.........	215	559	1911–15.........	173	529
1906–10.........	203	562		150*	
			1916–20.........	172	487

* Inclusive of a five-year average of pulmonary deaths in sanatoria.

ing to the deaths recorded for Baltimore those inhabitants who died
in sanatoria outside the city. As thus corrected the deaths of the
white and colored population of Baltimore are given in table 15.
A more extended table giving death rates of the white and colored
of both sexes year by year is given in Howard's report (p. 381), as
well as other tables for particular age groups of whites and colored,
male and female.

We do not have reliable data on death rates for large areas in
the United States previous to the census year of 1890. At this date
the death rate from consumption in the Registration Area was
546.1 per 100,000 for the colored population, and 230.0 for the
whites. In the Registration Area for 1900 it was 490.6 for the colored (or 485.4 for the Negroes), and 175.3 for the whites. By 1910

the death rate from tuberculosis (all forms) was 463 for the Negroes and 148 for the whites, but a part of the fall probably should be attributed to the inclusion of additional rural Negroes in the expanding Registration Area.

Because of the dangers in drawing conclusions from the statistical data afforded by a changing area, the trend of tuberculosis mortality is best followed in the populations of fixed areas. Since 1911 the United States Mortality Statistics have given the annual death rates of the white and colored populations of a number of states and cities. These data show that in most areas the death rate from tuberculosis has declined in both Negroes and whites.

All the preceding data clearly show a decline in the death rate from tuberculosis for both whites and blacks, but our knowledge of the early part of this decline is quite indefinite. The death rates of whites from this disease began to decline before the Civil War. The tuberculosis death rate of the colored population increased after the war and then declined, but when the highest death rate occurred is uncertain. The Baltimore statistics show that the death rate among Negroes increased from 1875 to 1883, when it reached its highest point. For the whites the highest rate after the Civil War (318) occurred in 1876, after which there was an irregular but slow decline. In general, the death curves of the two races take the same course, but the decline in the whites is more rapid until about 1900 when there is a rise for a few years followed by a decline after 1906; after 1909 the mortality began to decline in the blacks also. Up to the year of the great influenza epidemic (1918), the tuberculosis rate of the Negro had made little improvement in twenty-five years. During the decade between 1900 and 1910 its general course was rather upward than downward.

The trend of the tuberculosis death rate of the two races in the District of Columbia is similar to that in Baltimore. The highest rate (7.05) was for the period 1885–1889, after which there was a fall followed by a period of about fifteen years with relatively little change. This was succeeded by the more rapid decline that has characterized the tuberculosis death rate in most localities in the past few years. In most states the general decline since 1900 has been very uneven. Since 1918 or 1919 the rates are consistently relatively low, perhaps in part because the great influenza epi-

TABLE 16

Tuberculosis: Death Rates According to Age, per 100,000 Population, White and Colored, in the Registration States of 1920, From 1920 to 1923

Age groups	1920		1921		1922		1923	
	White	Colored	White	Colored	White	Colored	White	Colored
All ages								
Adjusted..	96.2	263.0	82.3	242.5	81.1	237.4	79.4	231.5
Crude....	99.5	263.5	85.3	243.2	84.1	238.2	82.4	232.2
Under 1 year	103.4	195.1	92.2	180.7	85.5	172.8	77.0	174.6
1–4........	40.6	92.1	32.3	86.4	31.4	89.7	31.2	99.4
Under 5 yrs.	52.7	112.7	43.8	105.3	41.7	106.3	39.8	114.4
5– 9.......	14.9	57.1	12.7	44.0	10.9	38.3	11.3	40.6
10–14.......	19.0	93.6	16.2	82.4	14.3	71.7	13.6	71.3
15–19.......	78.2	310.0	67.4	290.2	67.9	270.7	67.5	279.6
20–24.......	138.8	493.2	120.7	453.8	118.3	443.7	118.2	417.4
25–34.......	145.0	409.9	119.9	395.0	120.1	388.1	114.8	382.5
35–44.......	133.8	314.8	112.9	281.9	109.8	288.4	108.1	272.6
45–54.......	125.0	269.9	108.9	248.5	107.1	235.1	104.6	227.4
55–64.......	134.3	264.4	121.7	244.4	118.9	250.8	116.3	248.0
65–74.......	155.9	282.3	141.2	228.2	149.4	258.3	149.8	209.1
75..........	145.4	233.3	127.7	234.5	129.0	215.7	133.0	194.7

demic carried off many persons of weak constitution who would otherwise have died of tuberculosis somewhat later. In part it probably came about through the same causes, whatever they are, which occasioned the previous decline.

Significant differences in the age distribution of deaths from tuberculosis are shown by the white and colored races. Even in the first year of life the rate is higher among the colored, as is shown in table 16 and our data compiled in Table XXIV of the Appendix.

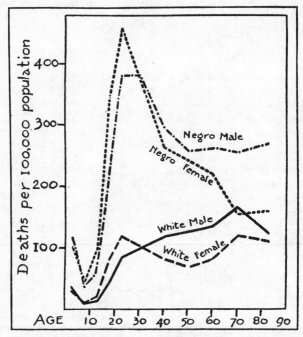

Fig. 6. Mortality from tuberculosis in whites and Negroes according to age in the Death Registration Area of 1920. After Sydenstricker.

The relatively lower Negro rates from tuberculous meningitis and abdominal tuberculosis (Table XXIV) should not be taken too seriously. The percentage of error in the diagnosis of tuberculous meningitis as shown by the investigation of the Census Bureau in 1911 was over 20 per cent; and it is probably higher for Negroes, especially in the first year of life. The data on abdominal tuberculosis are based on a relatively small number (147) of Negro deaths and include many cases which would probably be classified differently by different physicians.

The ratio of Negro to white deaths rises until the period of adolescence, when it reaches its maximum, but it continues to be relatively high even in old age. Among men of the ages of military service, the tuberculosis rate of the Negro is relatively high. The recruiting statistics gathered in the World War showed, in striking contrast to those of the Civil War, that the rate of admissions to sick report for tuberculosis of the lungs was more than two and one-half times as high among the Negroes as among the whites. "This," say Love and Davenport (1919), "is a little greater difference than the average of the past ten years, when the colored have about two times the admission rate of white troops. In tuberculosis of other organs the rate for the colored troops is twice that for the whites." In speaking of tuberculosis among adolescent Negroes insured by the Metropolitan Life Insurance Company, Dr. Dublin remarks: "The disease is a veritable scourge among young Negroes. At the ages between ten and fourteen years the tuberculosis death-rate among colored boys is eleven times as high as it is among white boys of the same ages. Colored girls of the same age period show a tuberculosis rate eight times greater than that of the white girls. Tuberculosis is preëminently a disease of young people but it is especially so among colored people. In fact, the great excess of tuberculosis mortality among Negroes is almost entirely limited to the early years of life. After age 35, there is not much difference in the effect of the disease in the two races. The disease runs a more rapid course among Negroes, perhaps, because the power of resistance to the disease is much lower among these people than among the whites. More than five years could be added to the life span of colored people if tuberculosis were brought under control."

In attempting to understand the reasons for the distinctive characteristics of the Negro death rate from tuberculosis, we must consider a number of factors. The greater prevalence of malaria among Negroes is of only minor importance. Of greater influence is the effect of syphilis, which is much more prevalent among Negroes than among whites. The degree to which tuberculosis is aggravated by this disease cannot be measured, but it is very considerable. Then there are the effects of ignorance, bad housing, overcrowding, improvidence, and other environmental factors about which so much has been written. Properly to evaluate the influence of these factors as compared with the effect of a hereditary diathesis is a difficult problem which still shows little prospect of a speedy solution. The extensive controversial literature on the subject has at least brought out the fact that the field is full of pitfalls and that it is dangerous to take statistical evidence at its face value.

It has been abundantly proved that tuberculosis runs in families, but this, as has so often been urged, may arise from infection instead of through heredity. Against the attempt of Pearson to meet this objection by showing that there is little correlation for tuberculosis between husband and wife, where chances for infection are abundant, it has been urged that tuberculosis is usually acquired in childhood when, in fact, the greater number of persons become infected. However, the contention has been made that if most people become infected early in life whether they come of tuberculous parents or not, and if children of tuberculous parents most frequently manifest the disease, the indication is that the deciding factor is to be sought in the genetic constitution of the individual. Although the proponent of the tuberculous diathesis may plausibly employ this argument in support of his position, we should not lose sight of the possible influence of repeated and mass infections which are now known to be of great importance in many infectious diseases. In several families studied by Pearl there was a larger number of tuberculous children in tuberculous families where there was close contact with the diseased individual, than in tuberculous families in which the contact was less close. There is abundant evidence that tuberculosis is common where opportunities for infection are plentiful. Several studies have shown that tuberculous infection, as revealed by the tuberculin test, is relatively rare in rural communities in both blacks and whites. In a study of 1,654 school children in a rural community in Minnesota, Slater finds that among children who had been exposed to tuberculosis 81 per cent gave a positive tuberculin reaction; of the children who were not exposed only 5.3 per cent gave a positive reaction, and for instances of doubtful exposure the percentage of positive reactions was 8.6. On the other hand, numerous tests have shown that most city dwellers become infected before they reach adult age.

Opie has expressed the opinion that a larger proportion of the colored population escape infection in childhood, and are therefore more prone to succumb to the disease in later life. This opinion, which was based upon a relatively small number of cases, has not, as a rule, been supported by recent studies. Hetherington and his coworkers, in a survey to determine the prevalence of tuberculosis in Philadelphia school children, found that the percentage of posi-

TABLE 17

POSITIVE REACTIONS FOR TUBERCULOSIS IN THE WHITE AND COLORED POPULA-
TIONS IN PHILADELPHIA AND IN RURAL AREAS OF THE SOUTH

Age groups	5-9		10-14		15-19	
	Number	Percentage	Number	Percentage	Number	Percentage
WHITES						
Philadelphia schools.	446	51.1	904	73.4	1019	82.5
Tennessee..........	478	36.8	510	60.8	126	67.4
Alabama...........	22	36.4	27	44.4	21	76.2
COLORED						
Philadelphia schools.	496	57.1	808	79.9	187	87.1
Tennessee..........	178	44.4	262	72.9	86	70.1
Alabama...........	995	30.9	1141	51.7	1219	69.1
Florida.............	415	28.9	394	51.5	205	80.9
South Carolina......	685	29.9	900	48.3	236	68.2

tive tuberculin reactions was much the same in whites and blacks, being 73.9 per cent and 72.9 per cent respectively. Jewish children showed about the same percentage as the others. Tuberculin tests made on 1,108 colored children in an overcrowded school showed that among 188 children aged 5–9 years, the percentage of positive reactions was 57; in 249 children aged 10–14, it was 87.1; and in children aged 15–17, it was 95.3.

In his studies on the prevalence of tuberculosis in rural communities of Tennessee, Alabama, Florida, and South Carolina, Aronson found that the rates for rural areas are lower than those for Philadelphia, although they are fairly high for both races. The table (17) shows that the percentage of children infected increases rapidly with age. In the colored population it reaches its maximum of 92.8 per cent in the forty-seventh year. Aronson's data also show that tuberculosis is, as a rule, quite as common in children of school age in Negroes as in whites. In the earlier period of infancy Asserson finds that out of 3,374 white infants tested in New York City, 386, or 11.3 per cent, reacted positively to tuberculin, and 69 out of 594, or 11.6 per cent, of colored infants, gave a positive reaction. Jewish children gave only a slightly higher percentage of positive reactions than the colored, namely, 12.7 per cent. Mortality was exceedingly high among infants exposed to active cases of tuberculosis in the family.

Similar results with respect to the racial distribution of tuberculous infection in children have been reported by Donnelly. Among 1,954 white and 400 Negro children who were skin tested for tuberculosis in 1932, there were 22 per cent of positive reactions in the whites and 24.7 per cent among the Negroes. In 1934, 2,348 white and 400 Negro children similarly tested gave 19.1 per cent of positive reactions in the whites and 20.1 per cent among the Negroes. The Negroes, who were mostly "pure blacks" from North Carolina, showed a higher percentage of strongly positive reactions than the white children showed. Donnelly concludes that the susceptibility of the adult Negro to tuberculosis cannot be attributed to lack of infection in childhood.

Apparently, differences in the tuberculosis mortality of different racial stocks depend not so much upon susceptibility to infection as upon the reaction to infection after it has been acquired. Even in early childhood, tuberculosis seems to behave in different ways in the white and the Negro races. According to Johnson and Myers, the initial infection with tuberculosis is rarely fatal, even in colored children. It is in their reaction to subsequent infection that the two races differ more conspicuously. In the Negro a second infection results in a different and frequently much more severe type of disease. The first infection, although seldom causing death, often results in allergy in the Negro child which makes it prone to succumb to a later infection with the same or similar kinds of bacilli. Dr. C. B. Gibson, who has made observations on the course of tuberculosis in white and Negro children in hospitals where they were both kept under similar conditions, found that primary infections usually made satisfactory progress. He reports, however : "Negro children with secondary or adult pulmonary tuberculosis of any greater extent than minimal almost invariably failed to recover" ; "No Negro child who ever had positive sputum recovered."

The several studies that have been made on the pathological manifestations of tuberculosis in white and colored races reveal a number of characteristic differences. It is true that almost any kind of tuberculous lesion may occur in both blacks and whites. The differences concern the relative prevalence of certain types of disease. In general, the Negro is more prone to tuberculosis of the so-called childhood type, which runs a relatively quick course, whereas in the whites it more frequently assumes the character of a slow, chronic infection. In a comparative study of 402 autopsies at the Henry Phipps Institution, Everett found that the "childhood type of tuberculosis occurred only twice in white adults, but in half of the 44 colored people who died of tuberculosis." Latent tubercular lesions were more common in the whites (197 whites, 109 blacks), and in only 12 whites and 17 blacks were there no tubercular lesions at all. The formation of fibrous tissue was more common in the whites, and lesions of the apex of the lung were much more common in the blacks, occurring in over half the Negroes with the childhood type of tuberculosis. "The anatomical characteristics of tuberculosis in the American Negro," says Dr. Everett, "differ widely from those of white people of the same community."

In contrast to the conclusions of Rogers, based on a study of 150 autopsies in whites and Negroes, that "pulmonary tuberculosis shows no essential difference in type or extent," Pinner and Kasper, in their study of 303 colored persons and 219 whites who died of tuberculosis, found "miliary tuberculosis in 37.3 per cent of the colored and 15.5 per cent of the whites, haematogenous metastases in 84.2 per cent of the colored and 40.0 per cent of the whites, and lymphatic metastases in 66.8 per cent of the colored and 10.8 per cent of the whites. The most characteristic peculiarities of tuberculosis in the adult Negro are

"1. Massive lymph node caseation.

"2. Massive exudative lesions which do not respect the normal anatomical boundaries of organs.

"3. A type of generalized tuberculosis without the formation of miliary tubercules, but with irregularly scattered nodular, exudative foci."

It is difficult to account satisfactorily for the characteristic pathological differences in the tubercular lesions of whites and blacks on the ground that Negroes are not so frequently tuberculinized as the whites, because the percentages of infected persons are not greatly different in the two races. Negroes are more apt to receive repeated infections in their homes and elsewhere, because their surroundings are less sanitary and tubercle bacilli are more frequently encountered. This fact may account for the greater prevalence of the disease among them, but not for its characteristic pathology.

TABLE 18

VITAL CAPACITY OF WHITE AND COLORED CHILDREN

Age groups	Mean vital capacity			
	Whites		Colored	
	Male	Female	Male	Female
6– 7	1,185	1,094	1,089	935
8– 9	1,511	1,367	1,167	1,212
10–11	1,840	1,690	1,597	1,450
12–13	2,271	2,142	1,931	1,750
14–15	2,839	2,257	2,351	1,968
16–17	3,690	2,365	3,050	2,115

One fact that makes it not improbable that the Negro is especially disposed to contract tuberculosis is that his lung capacity is relatively less than that of the white man. Smillie and Augustine have measured the "vital capacity" of a group of white and colored prisoners, and a large group of white (539) and colored (397) children. In the prisoners who were apparently free from tuberculosis, the lung capacity in the whites was markedly greater. In the children the relations are shown in table 18.

The children were normal rural children of Alabama living under similar environmental conditions and having about the same food. Smillie and Augustine remarked that "the Negroes, both males and females, in all age groups studied showed a consistently and markedly lower vital capacity than the whites. Measurements of sitting height explain this discrepancy in part, since the Negroes have a shorter trunk length than whites. Even when calculated on the basis of sitting height, however, the vital capacity of Negroes is more than 15 per cent lower that that of the whites."

Similar findings have been reported by Roberts and Crabtree from measurements of 1,564 white and 1,254 Negro children, the vital capacities of the Negro children being definitely lower than those of white children of the same age, body weight and standing height, lower than those found by Smillie and Augustine. "White girls exceed Negro girls by 7.2 per cent; and white boys exceed Negro boys by 12 per cent. With the same body weight white girls exceed by 10.2 per cent, and white boys by 14.9 per cent. With the same height white girls exceed by 6.8 per cent and white boys by 11.2 per cent."

The existence of racial idiosyncrasies in reactions to other diseases may be considered to create a certain presumption that similar idiosyncrasies occur in relation to tuberculosis. But with epidemic diseases especially, the occurrence of hereditary racial susceptibilities is not so easily established as it once seemed. We read of a relatively mild disease such as measles proving a fatal scourge among the Polynesians and we conclude that these natives do not enjoy the same immunity to this disease that the whites enjoy. But so competent an epidemiologist as Dr. V. C. Vaughan is not convinced that we would fare any better if we lived like the native Polynesians and were suddenly struck by a strange epidemic which left few well people to look after the sick. It is often difficult to separate the effects of social and genetic factors influencing mortality, and never more so than in respect to the colored population living in our midst. Many writers speak naïvely of the two races in a given area as being exposed to the same environment regardless of the fact that food, clothing, housing, and exposure to various epidemics may differ as greatly as the most wholesome residence on Fifth Avenue from the most crowded tenement in Harlem. The statistician may sometime measure and evaluate the chief environmental factors which contribute to the differential death rate. Frequently this task is thought to be much easier than it really is. In studying the influence of poverty on the death rate from tuberculosis, we might compare the relation of this death rate to wages. But finding, as we do, that the death rate from tuberculosis goes up as income goes down does not prove that the small income brought about the increase of tuberculosis. Both may result from ignorance and incompetence. We should bear in mind, also, that persons who are tuberculous, are unable to earn as much wages as those who are healthy.

Where improvement in conditions of life is promptly accompanied by a reduced death rate from a given malady the environmentalist has a plausible case. Few would deny that improved hygiene and sanitation have been factors in the reduction of the death rate from tuberculosis, although Pearson and his followers may be right in their contention that the race is becoming, for some reason, less susceptible to tubercular infection. Apparently, the Negroes are following the whites in developing a degree of immunity to this disease. The Negroes were unusually prone to fall victims to tuberculosis when the disease was first well introduced among them, as is indicated by their death rate and the rapid course of the malady when once contracted. Probably a large part of the decline in their death rate came because of a gradually acquired immunity, but it is very questionable whether this immunity can be ascribed to the operation of natural selection alone. Racial immunities to infectious diseases are probably built up chiefly by other methods, such as the gradual immunization of individuals through minimal infections, aided in many cases by the transmission of antibodies through the placenta. By the latter method young children may derive a temporary immunity to some of the common infections early in life, and if in the meantime they become inoculated with very small doses of infectious material, they may acquire a lasting protection. That children become gradually immunized to tuberculosis is indicated by the observations and experiments of Calmette on animals and human beings, and by a great deal of later experimental work. To build up an immunity by the method described would probably not require more than a few generations, and the colored race has certainly been exposed long enough to tuberculosis to profit by its contact with the disease. In fact, Dr. Bushnell (1920) thinks that the Negroes were "tuberculinized" almost as much as the whites at the time of the Civil War, but this seems hardly probable in the light of the general course of the tuberculosis death rate.

There have been few studies on the racial incidence of tuberculosis in which environmental factors have been equalized. Cunningham (1894) has found that Negro convicts living under the same conditions and especially selected on the basis of sound physique showed much higher disease rates for pneumonia and tuberculosis than the whites. They were also inferior to the whites in chest development. Carter (1926a) found in comparing 5,000 white and 1,700 colored patients living in sanatoria under the same conditions that the whites improved much more than the Negroes, and that the mulattoes improved more than the blacks. He also observed that light-colored mulattoes were more resistant to tuberculosis than the darker ones. These data on the mulattoes run counter to a widely prevalent opinion among physicians with respect to the general weakness and high tuberculosis rate of the mulattoes as compared with pure whites or Negroes. Grandy (1924) in studying 967 white and 822 colored children of Norfork, Va., found that the colored children are heavier for their height and have a better posture than the white children and show in general good physical development, but they have a high rate for tuberculosis "due to a racial lack of resistance." Their living conditions, as Grandy points out, are "certainly no worse than those of some of our foreign born Jewish citizens who apparently show the greatest resistance to tuberculosis."

As Dublin and Baker have shown in their study of the mortality of foreign race stocks in Pennsylvania and New York, there are great differences in the death rates from tuberculosis among peoples living in congested areas of cities, where the conditions are apparently the most favorable for the spread of tuberculous infection. The Jews, for example, show relatively little tuberculosis even in crowded urban districts.

In the light of such facts it is difficult to escape the conviction that hereditary racial factors play a prominent part in the differential death rate in this disease. This conviction does not rest upon rigidly demonstrative evidence, but it constitutes, I believe, the best judgment which can be made on the basis of the various facts available. It is made probable *a priori* by what is known of the influence of racial factors in animals and plants, and more specifically, as shown by the experiments of Wright and Lewis, by the differences in susceptibility of races of guinea pigs to tubercular infection. It is also strongly supported by the evidence afforded by tuberculosis in fraternal and identical twins. The problem has proved to be a peculiarly baffling one, but it can be definitely solved if data are collected on a sufficiently extensive scale with an ever watchful eye upon several matters which present alternative possibilities of interpretation.

THE RESPIRATORY INFECTIONS

Ever since emancipation, the colored population of the United States has suffered from a very high death rate from respiratory diseases. It is not possible to trace with any accuracy the course of the death rate from specific respiratory affections in either whites or Negroes, owing to changes in the categories of diagnosis and the lack of adequate records. According to the United States Census of 1890, the pneumonia death rate in the Registration Area was 182 per 100,000 for whites and 278.97 for the colored population. In 1900 the pneumonia death rate was 184.8 for all whites and 349.0 for the colored. The rates for the whites in both 1890 and 1900 were raised somewhat on account of the high mortality from pneumonia among the foreign born, which was 223.9 and 209.8 respectively for these years. The rate for the native born was 167 (1890) and 176 (1900). The rate for cities in the Registration Area for 1900 was 201.8 for whites and 263.1 for the colored; in the rural parts of the area the rates were respectively 135.3 and 176.7. In Baltimore the rates for all the pneumonias were over twice as high for the colored population as for the whites in every year between 1906 and 1924 with the exception of 1918, the year of the influenza epidemic. Deaths from pneumonia are notoriously more common in cities than in rural districts, and the fact that the pneumonia rate was higher in both races in 1900 than in 1890 may be attributable to the increasing urbanization of the population.

The lack of sufficiently complete data, the fact that the pneumonia death rate fluctuates so greatly owing to climatic changes, and the varying prevalence of other intercurrent diseases, like measles and influenza, which dispose people to contract pneumonia, make it difficult to ascertain whether this disease was actually increasing or decreasing previous to 1900. The data from Baltimore and other cities which kept records during this time do not show any consistent trend. Since 1900 the general death rate from pneu-

monia has gradually declined. Not only is this true for the Registration Area as a whole, but also for its various subdivisions. A part
of this decline may be spurious because, as stated in the volume
on Mortality Statistics for 1914, "the practice of writing merely
'Pneumonia' or 'Broncho-pneumonia' and of omitting the name of
the disease that was the primary cause was far more prevalent than
it is today." The influenza epidemic in 1918, with the slower rise
of the pneumonia rate in the two years preceding it, caused a striking interruption of the general decline of the curve of pneumonia
mortality. The pneumonia rate after 1918 has been very uneven,
owing in large measure to less severe epidemics of influenza, but in
general the rates after 1918 have shown a downward course. Taking for comparison the years 1910–1915 and 1920–1925, thus omitting the years of the great epidemic, we find a marked decrease in
the pneumonia death rate in the latter period. In the Registration
States of 1920 for the 5-year period, 1920–1924, the death rate for
all respiratory diseases was 120.85 for the whites and 199.05 for
the colored. Similar rates for respiratory diseases are shown by the
wage earners insured by the Metropolitan Life Insurance Company (1911–1916), namely, 124.38 for the whites and 190.53 for
the colored. The fact that the Metropolitan group consisted of wage
earners probably explains the smaller difference in the death rates
of the two races. From the data published from time to time by the
Metropolitan Life Insurance Company, one would conclude that
among white industrial policy holders there has been a noticeable
fall in the pneumonia death rate between the period 1911–1916
and the last quinquennium, among the whites, and an actual rise
among the colored. This is true for respiratory diseases as a whole
and for pneumonia, lobar and undefined.

The Negro seems peculiarly liable to succumb to lobar pneumonia
as contrasted with broncho-pneumonia. Although the death rate
from broncho-pneumonia has been greater among the Negroes than
among the whites, the ratio of deaths (white to colored) from this
cause in the Registration States of 1920 (1920–1924), namely 7.81,
was higher than it was for deaths from all causes, 7.607, whereas
for lobar pneumonia the corresponding ratio was 6.69. That the
ratio 3.01 for "pneumonia undefined" in the same period and area
shows a very high Negro mortality doubtless indicates less preci-

sion in specifying the causes of Negro deaths. That a large part of these deaths was caused by lobar pneumonia is made evident by an investigation of the accuracy of reports on the causes of deaths carried out by the Bureau of the Census in 1911. Further inquiry into reports of deaths certified as due to pneumonia not otherwise defined "resulted in a change of assignment in 416 out of 1,013 cases (41.1 per cent), and confirmed the diagnosis of lobar pneumonia in 518 cases (51.1 per cent), leaving only 79 deaths still undefined."

For some reason the racial distribution of deaths from pneumonia in the records from Baltimore compiled by Howard does not correspond closely with the preceding data. For the period 1906–1920, the death rates of whites and colored were 69 and 178 (ratio 1:2.57) respectively, and those for lobar pneumonia were 110 and 265 (ratio 1:2.40). Since broncho-pneumonia is predominantly a disease of childhood and lobar pneumonia is relatively more frequent among adults, differences in age composition of the two races in different localities would give rise to differences in the relative prevalence of the two affections. This, however, would hardly account for the distribution of the pneumonias in Baltimore, nor for the marked variations in the proportions of deaths due to these two causes in different cities. Aside from the uncertainties of diagnosis, which are many, there are also differences in the prevailing types of infection in different times and places. The preponderance of data indicates, however, that the Negro is relatively more susceptible than the white race to the lobar type of pneumonia both in infancy and in more advanced ages.

Instructive data on the prevalence of pneumonia in the two races are supplied by the records of white and colored recruits for the World War. "For 1917," according to Love and Davenport (1919), "the rate for lobar pneumonia was four and a half times, for broncho-pneumonia three times, as great for colored as for white men. In the ten year record the colored rate is 2.2 times the white rate for broncho-pneumonia. Given, then, troops under similar environment in the presence of conditions favoring pneumonia, there are relatively two or three times as many colored troops as white who show symptoms of the disease." During the World War the admission rate for broncho-pneumonia was a little more than twice as high for the colored as for the white soldiers, and for lobar pneumonia the admission rate was more than four times as high for the colored. The death rates for these diseases were respectively 1.80, whites, and 3.71, colored, for broncho-pneumonia, and respectively 1.96, whites, and 7.75, colored, for lobar pneumonia. Even among respiratory diseases lobar pneumonia stands out as a very prevalent and fatal disease in the colored soldiers as in the colored civil population. The statistics for respiratory diseases for the United States Army throughout the entire period of the war are given in table 19.

As may be seen from the table, the death rates for all forms of respiratory infections are higher in the colored troops, but they are very much higher for lobar pneumonia than for other forms of respiratory infections.

The Army data are of especial interest in relation to the problem of racial susceptibility to respiratory disease. Unquestionably an appreciable part of the high mortality among the colored civil population is to be attributed to unfavorable conditions of life. But in the World War, white and Negro recruits were given much the same medical examination when they entered the Army, and they all had to pass much the same tests of physical fitness. While in the Army they lived under more or less similar conditions; nevertheless the pneumonia rates among the colored were even higher relative to those of the whites than they are in the general population. Even in the Army, conditions may have been somewhat less favorable for the Negroes, but this fact surely cannot account for the enormous differences in the incidence of pneumonia, and especially lobar pneumonia, in the two races. These same differences are found both in the soldiers quartered in America and in those who were in Europe.

In dealing with the problem of racial susceptibility it may be instructive to allude briefly to the death rates from pneumonia among different elements of the white population. The foreign-born inhabitants show a distinctly higher pneumonia rate than the native born.

As shown in table 20 (p. 96), the mortality of the foreign born is intermediate between that of the native born and the colored. The use of adjusted instead of crude death rates reduces the rate

TABLE 19

RESPIRATORY DISEASES: ADMISSIONS TO HOSPITAL, DEATHS, NUMBERS, AND
RATES PER THOUSAND, IN THE UNITED STATES ARMY, FROM
APRIL 1, 1917 TO DECEMBER 31, 1919

	Total enlisted troops				
	Influenza	Bronchitis	Broncho-pneumonia	Lobar pneumonia	Total
Admissions					
Whites:					
Number..............	671,322	214,561	24,422	31,903	942,208
Rate.................	186.50	59.61	6.78	8.86	261.75
Colored:					
Number..............	59,448	20,045	4,825	11,482	95,800
Rate.................	207.46	69.95	16.84	40.07	334.32
Deaths					
Whites:					
Number..............	20,888	334	6,480	7,073	34,775
Rate.................	5.80	.09	1.80	1.96	9.75
Colored:					
Number..............	2,287	42	1,063	2,222	5,614
Rate.................	7.98	.15	3.71	7.75	19.59

UNITED STATES ARMY IN THE UNITED STATES

	Influenza	Bronchitis	Broncho-pneumonia	Lobar pneumonia	Total
Admissions					
Whites:					
Number..............	476,816	.....	13,297	21,886	660,400
Rate.................	242.62	.....	6.77	11.14	336.04
Colored:					
Number..............	38,863	.....	2,759	7,016	61,601
Rate.................	266.51	.....	18.92	48.10	422.41
Deaths					
Whites:					
Number..............	14,617	.....	3,429	4,330	22,400
Rate.................	7.44	.....	1.74	2.20	11.39
Colored:					
Number..............	1,567	.....	634	1,363	3,567
Rate.................	10.74	.....	4.35	9.35	24.46

TABLE 19—(*Continued*)

UNITED STATES ARMY IN EUROPE

| | Total enlisted troops | | | | |
	Influenza	Bronchitis	Broncho-pneumonia	Lobar pneumonia	Total
Admissions					
Whites:					
Number..............	176,240	.....	10,761	9,000	256,099
Rate................	119.92	.....	7.32	6.12	174.25
Colored:					
Number..............	18,619	.....	1,986	4,149	31,435
Rate................	152.10	.....	16.32	33.89	256.89
Deaths					
Whites:					
Number..............	5,753	.....	2,919	2,414	11,390
Rate................	3.91	.....	1.99	1.64	7.75
Colored:					
Number..............	628	.....	395	778	1,839
Rate................	5.15	.....	3.23	6.36	15.05

of people whose mothers were born abroad and raises the rate of the native American stock of native parentage, but the differences are nevertheless sufficiently striking. Among the foreign born there are striking differences among white immigrant groups. The Irish have an exceptionally high death rate from pneumonia, as they have also from tuberculosis. The pneumonia death rate among the Italians, also, is high, although their mortality from tuberculosis is less than that of most of the immigrant stocks. The marked differences in the pneumonia death rates of different groups in the white race have been adduced as an argument that the high rate among Negroes is due almost entirely to environment instead of racial heredity. The argument is based on the assumption that the differences in mortality among the whites are the result of environmental causes. If one compares the pneumonia rates obtaining in different countries with the rates occurring in the representatives of these countries in America, no very close correspondence will be found. This does not necessarily disprove the existence of racial diatheses

provided we admit that environmental factors are, as they are
known to be, of great importance also. At present we cannot be said
to have conclusive evidence either for or against the existence of
racial diatheses to pneumonia in subdivisions of the white race.

There are differences in the age incidence of pneumonia characteristic of the two races which are similar to those of tuberculosis.
In early life (1–4 years) the death rate from lobar pneumonia in

TABLE 20

Pneumonia: Mortality Among Native-Born and Foreign-Born Whites;
Rates per 100,000

Date	All whites	Native-born whites	Foreign-born whites	Colored
1890.....................	182.24	167	223.9	278.97
1900.....................	184.8	176	209.8	349.00

Negroes is over twice that of the whites. In ages 5–15 the racial differences in mortality are reduced, but in ages 15–25 the rate for the
colored population is over three times that of the whites. The trend
for the age groups is well shown in the data on the wage earners
insured by the Metropolitan Life Insurance Company. Racial differences in the age distribution of broncho-pneumonia as shown by
the data of this Company are also striking.

Mention should be made of the sex distribution of lobar pneumonia because for some age groups, especially in ages 25–55, according to the experience of the insurance company, the death
rate of males is about twice that of females. Both previous and subsequent to this period the preponderance of male deaths is much
less. The highest death rate for males as compared with females
corresponds roughly with the period of greatest difference in exposure of the two sexes. For broncho-pneumonia the sex differences
in mortality are very much less for nearly all age groups and frequently they are to the advantage of the males. The experience of
the Metropolitan Company with respect to sex differences of mortality from the two types of pneumonia in the years 1911–1916 may
be summarized as follows: Lobar pneumonia—white males, 82.6,
white females, 63.0; colored males, 141.5, colored females, 97.2;

broncho-pneumonia—white males, 29.6, white females, 29.2; colored males, 37.7, colored females, 33.7.

One very significant fact in connection with the possible influence of racial heredity upon mortality from pneumonia is that some data apparently indicate that the case fatality from this disease may be actually lower among the Negroes than among the whites. Should this prove to be true, pneumonia would stand in sharp contrast to tuberculosis, in which case fatality is very much higher in the colored race. If unfavorable environment and inadequate care were the main reasons for the fatal termination of cases of pneumonia, we should certainly expect that the Negroes would show a smaller percentage of recoveries than is shown by the whites. Dr. F. B. Kelly (1926), in describing a series of 6,500 cases of lobar pneumonia in the Cook County Hospital, Chicago, states that "From 1917–24 the case fatality was 39.2% for 3,749 white males and 34.7% for 818 white females, 30.6% for 1,876 colored males and 31.9% for 388 colored females. Every year the case fatality of the male Negroes has been 5 to 13 per cent below that of the male whites, with a difference of 8.8% for the entire 7½ years. The female Negro case fatality has been 4.6% less than that of white females in the same period. In two years, however, the difference favored the white females." The same writer states that "Chittard found a case fatality of 31.2% in 250 cases compared with 30.6% in the native born whites." In commenting on the relation of case fatality to age, Dr. Kelly states that "The case fatality for the two races was the same up to the '40 year and over' groups, above which the Negroes had the greater resistance."

It is somewhat dangerous to draw conclusions on the basis of human material which comes into a large city hospital, because it may be selected in different ways from among the two races. Dr. Kelly says that "it may be claimed that the recent migration northward has brought a larger percentage of the strong hardy members of the race with a naturally greater resistance than general. However, most of these newcomers are under 40 years of age, in which class the case fatality has been the same as in the white race."

In order possibly to secure more information on this subject than is available in the literature, I wrote to several physicians associated with large hospitals in the Southern States. Most of the replies failed to supply any conclusive data. Dr. J. H. Musser, how-ever, who kindly sent me some statistics from the Charity Hospital in New Orleans, reported that in 1926, out of 101 cases of lobar pneumonia among the Negroes, 33, or 32.7 per cent, died, and out of 65 cases among the whites, 30, or 46.2 per cent, died. In 1929 the case mortality was slightly higher in the Negroes. Dr. Musser states that, although the Negroes are especially prone to contract pneu-monia, "we have never considered that after the Negro has devel-oped pneumonia he is more likely to die than the white man."

Further data have been kindly supplied me by Dr. J. Ritter, from the case fatality records of whites and blacks in Miami, Fla., for the years 1927 to 1933 inclusive. In these years there were 202 cases of lobar pneumonia and 105 deaths, or a case mortality of 52.0 per cent among the whites, and 170 cases with 98 deaths, or a case mortality of 52.9 per cent among the blacks. With broncho-pneumonia the case mortality of the blacks was lower, but rela-tively higher as compared with that of the whites, being 42.55 per cent (188 cases), and that of the whites, 30.13 per cent (385 cases).

A much greater body of material collected under more nearly comparable conditions is supplied by the experience of the United States Army. Howard and Love, in summarizing the data on mor-tality from pneumonia in 1918, give the following description: "For the white troops the death rate for these two pneumonias was 4.89, and for the colored, 15.81. The total number of pneumonia cases among the white troops in the United States and Europe, counting the cases complicating measles and influenza, was 94,505, with 28,969 deaths. Among the colored troops, enlisted men, there were 19,319 cases with 4,720 deaths. The incidence rate for the white troops was 44.11 and for the colored, 115.28. The death rate for the white was 13.52, and for the colored, 28.17. The case mor-tality for primary and secondary pneumonia for the whites was 30.6 per cent, and for the colored, 24.4 per cent; for primary pneu-monia for the whites it was 26.4, and for the colored, 21.6 per cent. It is apparent, then, that the colored race has an incidence rate nearly three times as high as that for the white, a death rate nearly twice as high, but a case mortality rate about 20 per cent lower for all pneumonia, both primary and secondary." The case fatality rates for the whole period of the war are shown in table 21 (p. 99).

One explanation of the relatively low case mortality of the Negroes in the Army may be that pneumonia is more apt to attack Negroes at an early and therefore more vigorous age. If for corresponding age periods the Negroes should exhibit a lower case mortality than the whites we should have the rather unusual com-

TABLE 21

RESPIRATORY DISEASES: PERCENTAGE OF DEATHS TO CASES IN THE UNITED STATES ARMY, FROM APRIL 1, 1917 TO DECEMBER 31, 1919

	Influenza		Broncho-pneumonia		Lobar pneumonia	
	White	Colored	White	Colored	White	Colored
United States Army in United States......	3.1	4.0	25.8	23.0	19.8	19.4
United States Army in Europe..........	3.3	3.4	27.1	19.9	26.8	18.8
Total, United States Army.............	3.1	3.8	26.5	22.0	22.2	19.3

bination of greater proneness to contract a disease with a greater power of resisting it when once contracted.

Dr. S. D. Collins, in reporting the result of a survey of respiratory diseases in six large cities having a considerable number of colored inhabitants, states that, "As regards the proportion of respiratory cases that were fatal, the indications are that, in the six cities combined, 2.7 times as many cases were fatal among colored as among white patients, the ratio varying in the different cities from 1.9 in Boston to 4.2 in Baltimore. Mention has already been made of the possibility that the minor respiratory cases were less completely reported to the canvassers by the colored families than by the white, and, if such was the case, a part or all of this large excess in the indicated case fatality would be due to the incompleteness of respiratory cases. However, the indications are that pneumonia, which was presumably well reported by both races, was also considerably more fatal to colored than to white patients. Considering the six cities combined, the estimated pneumonia fatality of colored patients is indicated as 51 per cent in excess of the fatality of white patients. In every one of these cities the colored pneumonia fatality is in excess of that of the whites, the relative excess ranging from 4 per cent in Kansas City to 68 per cent in Baltimore. In New Orleans, where, like Baltimore, the number of surveyed Negroes was large, the excess was only 12 per cent."

These data were collected during the influenza epidemic of 1928–29, and whether or not because of this fact the case-fatality rates for pneumonia are typical of usual conditions, is uncertain. The white and colored cases surveyed were mostly in homes, where they are subject to the varying environmental conditions that commonly surround the two races. In the general population one might obtain fatality rates quite different from those found in patients under the more nearly uniform environment of a hospital or the Army. In this survey the incidence of pneumonia was found to be much the same in the two races ; "the mortality rate for the colored population was 56 per cent higher than for the white population of the same cities." What the relative mortality of whites and Negroes would be under comparable conditions in respect to age and environment is still uncertain.

That certain groups of Negroes should have a relatively low case fatality from pneumonia is all the more remarkable because Negroes in general suffer more than the whites from malaria, tuberculosis, syphilis, and other devitalizing afflictions which would naturally tend to reduce their power of recovery. Dr. Reitzel (1928), in studying the rôle of syphilis in the mortality from pneumonia in a hospital at Galveston, Tex., remarks that "Among the 146 colored patients of this series (all cases of lobar pneumonia) 50 had either positive Wassermanns or post mortem evidence of syphilis, and in this group the fatality was 28 per cent. There were 57 who had negative Wassermanns with a fatality of 10.5 per cent. Among the 39 cases in which the Wassermanns were not reported, the fatality was 25.6 per cent." The author remarks upon the delayed resolution of pneumonia in syphilitic patients and quotes the experience of other physicians to the same effect. In connection with what has been said concerning case fatality in the two races, it may be mentioned that in the same hospital the case fatality of 143 whites for lobar pneumonia was 19.5 per cent, and that of the 146 colored was 21.6 per cent.

The Negro death rate from bronchitis is much higher than that of the whites, but in infancy the ratio of Negro to white deaths is less than that of deaths from all causes. For the whole period of the Great War the admission rates for white and colored soldiers, in United States Army hospitals were 59.61 and 69.95 respectively, and the death rates .09 and .15 respectively, per thousand.

INFLUENZA

Owing to the intimate association of influenza with various kinds of pneumonia it is practically impossible to obtain data on deaths from influenza free from complications with these other infections. Undoubtedly the higher influenza death rate in the general colored population is attributable in large measure to unfavorable conditions combined with a greater susceptibility to pneumonia. During the Great War the difference in the death rates of white and colored troops from influenza was not nearly so great as it was for pneumonia, being 9.78 for the colored and 5.80 for the whites. There is quite satisfactory evidence that the Negro is not attacked so readily as the white man, but that when once attacked his chances for recovery are not so good.

The data on morbidity from different camps in the Great War are somewhat conflicting, but for this fact there are several reasons. Soldiers who had been seasoned by several weeks' service were not so liable to contract influenza as were new recruits. As Howard and Love observe, troops from the rural districts, especially in the South, were more susceptible to influenza and pneumonia than those from the Northern and Eastern States. Opie *et al.* (1919) found that at Camp Pike the Negroes who had been in camp for six weeks or more and who had afforded no previous cases of the infection developed influenza in only 7.6 per cent of cases, and that, in a new group in which influenza had appeared, there were 43.6 per cent of cases. Opie *et al.* attribute differences in influenza mortality to environmental factors instead of race; nevertheless the attack rate of the "old" white soldiers was about double that of the seasoned Negroes. For Camp Pike as a whole the rates were 246 per thousand for whites and 133 per thousand for Negroes.

Although in a few camps the Negroes were reported to have been attacked more frequently than the whites, in others the Negroes had the lower rate. Howard and Love found that in 1918 the influenza rate for white troops of the South was 247.11 and for the colored, 154.58. However, for the whole war period, April 1, 1917–December 31, 1919, there were 671,322 admissions for whites, or 186.50 per thousand and 59,448 or 207.46 per thousand for the colored. For the same period the admission rate for white soldiers was higher than it was for the colored in the Army quartered in the United States, for nearly every month, and for the Army in Europe the admission rate was higher for the colored troops for every month except October, 1918, when the epidemic was at its height.

In surveys of the incidence of influenza among the civil population carried out by the United States Public Health Service soon after the epidemic of 1918, the attack rate was found to be higher in the whites. According to Frost (1920) : "In the seven localities with considerable colored population, the incidence rates among the colored were uniformly lower than among the white, the differences persisting after adjustment of the rates to a uniform basis of sex and age distribution. . . . This relatively low incidence in the colored race is contrary to what would have been expected *a priori* in view of the fact that the death rate from pneumonia and influenza is normally higher in the colored than in the white, and that the colored population live generally under conditions presumably more favorable to the spread of contact infections." When comparison was made between the case fatalities in these same localities, the colored population was usually found to have the higher rate. In the United States Army's experience, 20,888 deaths were attributed to influenza among the whites and 2,287 among the colored, giving a percentage (deaths to cases) of 3.1 for the whites and 3.8 for the colored.

In a study of the racial mortality from influenza in the twelve million industrial policy holders of the Metropolitan Life Insurance Company, Frankel and Dublin (1919) find that in the first three months of the epidemic, when the great outburst occurred, the death rate was 1,844 per 100,000 for white males and 1,522 for colored males, 1,723 for white females, and 1,504 for colored females. "After the severest period of the epidemic had passed, the colored group showed higher rates than the whites, and the amount of excess approximated what had prevailed in normal times, as the distance from the explosive period of the epidemic increased."

Craig and Dublin (1919) in their survey of the Metropolitan's experience for 1918 state that "While the colored race in 1918 suffered higher mortality than the white, the absolute amount of excess among the Negroes was very much less. Thus, while the maximum excess among white lives at the age period 25–29 years was 11.4 deaths per 1,000, that for the colored for the same age period was only 5.7 deaths per 1,000." During October, November, and December, 1918, the death rate from lobar pneumonia, broncho-pneumonia, and influenza combined was higher in the white industrial policy holders; "this in spite of the fact that the colored race ordinarily has much higher death rates from pneumonia than the whites." Up to age 15 the colored population had the higher rates from pneumonia and influenza, but for each quinquennium after age 15 the rate was less, the differences being most marked in the age group 20–40.

The United States Mortality Statistics show that for the whole Registration Area the Negro death rate from influenza in 1918 was somewhat higher than that of the whites, but that the difference was very much less than in previous and subsequent years. In Virginia, and in several cities with a large colored population (Indianapolis, Kansas City, Washington, D. C., Memphis, Nashville, Louisville, Norfolk, and Richmond), the death rate from influenza was lower in Negroes than in whites.

Normally, influenza affects most severely the very young (1–4 years) and those past the middle period of life, but in the months when the epidemic was most severe there was a third peak in the curve of mortality between ages 20 and 40. This peak was not so high relatively in the Negroes as in the whites, and as the epidemic continued it gradually disappeared until in the later period it was not seen at all. Apparently both the age incidence and the race incidence of the disease changed as time went on. Whether this was owing to changes in the persons attacked, changes in the causative organism, differences in the relative prevalence of the several other kinds of bacteria associated with the disease, or in part to the influence of climate, is uncertain. Certainly influenza during the period of its greatest severity in the latter part of 1918 behaved in several ways differently from the disease which usually goes under this name.

When we bear in mind that the Negro is peculiarly apt to contract respiratory diseases, the data from the distribution of deaths in the latter part of 1918, together with what we know of the morbidity of the two races from this disease, indicate that Negroes are less liable than the whites to become infected with the type of influenza which prevailed during the last great epidemic. This statement is not intended to apply to previous great waves sweeping over large populations, nor to what is commonly diagnosed as influenza in ordinary times.

The case mortality, to judge by the Army's experience, both in the United States and in Europe, is a little higher for the Negroes than for the whites, but this is probably owing to the Negro's susceptibility to pneumonia. Possibly the Negro may be less prone to contract influenza for the same reason that he is relatively free from colds and affections of the nose and sinuses, but we do not know whether influenza makes its first inroads in the nose, throat, or respiratory tract.

According to Dr. Collins' study of the influenza epidemic of 1928–29, "The case rate for influenzal conditions for colored persons was 41 per cent less than for whites in the same cities. The lower colored rate was consistently true in the various cities. How much if any of the difference was due to poorer reporting to the canvasser on the part of the colored families cannot be determined."

DISEASES OF THE NOSE AND THROAT

According to the Army Medical Statistics, Negroes are less affected by laryngitis, tonsillitis, and pharyngitis than are the whites. The admission rates per thousand, 1917 to 1919, were as follows:

	Whites	Negroes
Laryngitis	4.54	2.40
Tonsillitis, acute	43.97	31.25
Tonsillitis, chronic	6.00	2.14
Pharyngitis	12.87	9.02

In these affections it is not the ectoderm which is chiefly involved, but the parts attacked are very often affected by inflammation which spreads to them from the ectodermic lining of the vocal cavity and nose.

Our tentative conclusion in respect to the relation of the ectoderm to infection naturally leads one to expect a relatively low prevalence of nasal infections in the Negro race. The United States Mortality Statistics show a somewhat higher death rate from diseases of the nasal cavity among the Negroes than among the whites. Many deaths attributed to "diseases of the nose" are doubtless due to syphilis, which plays havoc with the nasal cartilages and bones and finally involves the brain. Most other nasal troubles are rarely fatal, so that mortality statistics tell us little in respect to the natural resistance of the nasal membranes to infection. Statistics of the relative prevalence of the common nasal infections in whites and Negroes are not so extensive as could be desired, but so far as they go they indicate that the Negroes are less afflicted than the whites. This is the testimony of Dr. Scheppergrell (1895), who has studied an extensive series from both races. Rhinitis, sinusitis, and most other diseases of the nose and adnexa showed a much lower incidence among Negroes than among white troops in the World War.

CANCER

The real influence of racial heredity upon the prevalence of cancer and other malignant tumors is difficult to ascertain on account of the fact that food habits, to say nothing of other environmental factors, have been found to exert a potent influence in the causation of these abnormal growths. Quite aside from the lower average age of primitive peoples and the fact that cancer is more apt to go unrecognized among them, many racial groups are remarkably free from cancer. There is also considerable evidence that when peoples suffering little from cancer come to adopt the food habits of modern civilized mankind their mortality from cancer increases. It will not be necessary to discuss the varied incidence of cancer, since the subject has been thoroughly treated in Dr. F. L. Hoffman's treatise on *The Mortality from Cancer Throughout the World,* and in his later brochure on *Cancer in Native Races.*

What is known of the relation between habits of life and the prevalence of cancer naturally disposes one to attribute the rather striking differences in the cancer mortality of whites and Negroes to causes other than race. Statistics on cancer are likely to be misinterpreted for a number of reasons. Since cancer is predominantly a disease of middle and later life, the age composition of a population has a marked influence upon its prevalence. As the Negro population has fewer persons in the higher age groups, we should expect to find among them a lower cancer mortality than in the whites. Moreover, cancer statistics are notoriously influenced greatly by the adequacy of diagnosis of the causes of death. Here again the statistics would tend to show a higher cancer mortality among the better circumstanced whites. Other things being equal, urban rates for cancer exceed those of rural districts, and possibly climate may be, in part, a factor in the higher cancer rates in the Northern than in the Southern States.

In studying the problem of the increase of cancer, as well as the relation of cancer to race, it is necessary to confine the investigation to a constant area. If, for instance, one were to compare the cancer mortality in the Registration Area of 1910 with that of the Registration Area in 1920, it would be found that the mortality rate for the colored population fell from 52.3 per 100,000 to 48.7. If one were to conclude from these figures that cancer had been decreasing in the colored population, he would be sadly misled. The reason for the decrease is the fact that during the decade 1910–1920 several states were added to the Registration Area which had a large Negro population with a low cancer death rate. If we consider the cancer mortality in individual states we find that in most of them there has been a marked increase.

In order to obtain a large amount of data for comparisons and at the same time avoid the source of error I have indicated, I have summarized the statistics on cancer for the Registration States of 1920 for the years 1920 to 1929 inclusive (see Appendix A, Tables XIII *et seq.*), and I have calculated the cancer death rates of the colored and the whites for different age groups and for several types of cancer. In this large area there has been a general increase of cancer in both the white and the colored populations. That this increase is not due to changes in age composition is shown by the circumstance that it occurs in nearly all five-year age groups in which the numbers are large enough to give reliable rates. The increase in cancer mortality is particularly marked in colored males over 45 years of age. In general, the cancer death rate has increased in the decade 1920–1930 more rapidly in the colored than in the white population. Perhaps one reason for this is the fact that a larger proportion of the colored population is coming to be exposed to the influences of urban life.

All students of cancer statistics recognize that progress in ascertaining the real causes of death leads to an increase in deaths ascribed to cancer. But if we attempt to explain the lower cancer mortality of the colored population as owing to inadequate diagnosis, we encounter a curious difficulty, namely, that racial differences in respect to cancer are relatively slight in the younger age groups, and even that cancer rates show a tendency to be actually higher in the colored population, whereas, as age advances beyond the middle period of life, cancer rates become relatively higher in the whites. This is true not only for total cancer, but also for cancers of the several organ systems. Even in skin cancer, in which the racial differences are enormous in the older age groups, the rates for the colored in the early age groups, especially in females, tend to exceed those for the whites. The theory that the low cancer death rate of the colored population is owing to faulty diagnosis involves the assumption that better diagnoses are made with the young colored population than with the whites, and that diagnosis is progressively less adequate for the colored people as they become older. This, on the face of it, seems an absurd position. The two races appear to have a different cycle of susceptibility to cancer, even as they have to tuberculosis.

The calculation of age specific death rates for the several types of cancer shows that the bodily distribution of cancer presents consistent and often striking differences in the white and colored races (Appendix A, Tables XIV–XXI). For most organs cancers are more frequent in the whites, except in the younger ages. Cancer of the female generative organs, however, is more prevalent in Negroes than in whites in every age group, but more especially in younger women. This predominance in the early age groups is sufficiently great to outweigh the relatively low Negro rate for other kinds of cancer and to make the total cancer mortality of females in the child-bearing period higher in the colored than in the white population. A large proportion of uterine cancers are traumatic in origin. They are notoriously rare in women who have not borne children. Less adequate care after childbirth, resulting in the neg-

lect of lacerations and other injuries, would naturally tend to cause
more uterine cancer among Negro women. Among Negroes it is
probable that a smaller proportion of uterine cancers are recognized in their early stages and remedied by surgery.

The statistics on cancer of the breast show that whites are more
apt to be affected than the Negroes. It is hardly probable that this
is because of more frequent failures to recognize cancer of the
breast in the colored population. There may, however, be causes
other than race which might account for the difference, because
among colored women the mammary glands probably function more
nearly in a normal manner than among white women. It is a curious
fact that spinsters are more apt to suffer from cancer of the breast,
and are much less apt to have cancer of the uterus, than women
who have had children. There seems to be something connected with
the nonfunctioning of the mammary glands which disposes them to
become cancerous. The racial differences in the incidence of breast
cancer, however, are much greater in the advanced age groups
when the functioning of the mammary glands is past, and least in
the period of active lactation. The situation is the reverse of what
occurs in respect to cancers of the female generative organs, which
in the period of child-bearing are about twice as prevalent in colored females as in white females, whereas after age 70 they are
only about 25 per cent more common. It seems not improbable
that the low rate for cancer of the breast among colored women
comes from the greater resistance of the Negro ectoderm to various
infections and injuries, but the evidence on this point is not conclusive. In the male, cancers of the breast are too rare to afford any
statistically significant comparisons.

The most striking difference in the cancer mortality of the two
races is found for cancer of the skin. In this type of cancer the
difference cannot be explained as a matter of diagnosis. The number of deaths attributable to cancer of the skin is so small that
the rates for the several age groups become unreliable; nevertheless a glance at Table XX (Appendix) will show a marked tendency
for the rates of the whites to be higher, especially in the advanced
ages. The data from the Metropolitan Life Insurance Company and
those derived from the United States Army in the World War cor-
roborate this conclusion. It seems to be quite evident that the rarity

of skin cancer in the Negro is a true racial trait, like his relative freedom from cutaneous diseases in general.

Whether the relatively low mortality of the Negro from cancer of the buccal cavity is attributable to racial heredity, is more uncertain. Among males the whites show a greater rate for buccal cancer in nearly all age groups, but in the females the racial differences are slight. The total number of cases is small, but the data are sufficient to show two things: the higher rate in white males and the much lower rate for females in both races. Inasmuch as a good deal of the cancer of the buccal cavity is probably a result of smoking, which is doubtless even now more prevalent in the male sex, it may be possible to explain the greater frequency of buccal cancer in white males as the result of habits rather than race.

NEPHRITIS, ACUTE AND CHRONIC

The death rate from nephritis is uniformly higher among the colored population. This statement is true for deaths under 1 year as it is also for the various higher age groups. The death rates of the white and colored populations for the Registration States of 1920 are shown in Table XXII (Appendix).

The experience of the Metropolitan Life Insurance Company parallels these statistics from the Registration States except that the death rates for insured workers are higher than those for the general population. The excess of the death rate in the colored workers is found for "each of the sexes and for every age." The mortality, from chronic nephritis, of males is appreciably greater than that of females. During the last two decades the mortality rate has been rising in the colored policy holders of both sexes, and has been slowly declining in the whites. The excess of Negro mortality is especially noticeable in the first year of life. In the period from 1914 to 1923 there were in the Registration Area 4,646 deaths among white infants and 683 among the colored, giving a ratio of 6.80 whites to 1 colored as compared with an expected ratio of 7.47 (white to colored) based on deaths from all causes, thus showing that Negro deaths from nephritis exceeded the expected number in the first year of life. The death rate from nephritis shows a good deal of fluctuation from year to year. The disease ranks among the more important causes of the high mortality of American Negroes.

DIABETES MELLITUS

The Negro death rate from diabetes has usually been considerably lower than that of the whites, but recent data show that mortality from diabetes has increased among the Negroes until it often exceeds that of the white population (see table 22).

TABLE 22

Diabetes: Mortality Rates per 100,000 Population, in the Registration States of 1920, From 1920 to 1927

	1920	1921	1922	1923	1924	1925	1926	1927
White:								
Crude............	16.9	17.6	19.7	19.0	17.4	17.9	19.3	18.7
Adjusted.........	15.9	16.5	18.3	17.5	16.0	16.8	18.1	17.6
Colored:								
Crude............	8.0	8.3	9.5	10.2	11.2	11.5	11.0	13.4
Adjusted.........	9.6	9.8	11.3	12.1	13.2	13.9	12.7	16.3

The excess of deaths among whites was shown in all the age groups from infancy to old age, but it tends to become relatively greater in the advanced periods of life. This is shown also by the statistics of insured wage earners of the Metropolitan Life Insurance Company for the years 1911 to 1916 inclusive. In both races and both sexes there is a relatively sudden increase in the death rate from diabetes between age groups 35 to 44, and 45 to 54 years, after which the rate rises rapidly to old age. In the earlier years of life male deaths tend to preponderate over female deaths, but after age 45 the rate for females suddenly exceeds that of the males and continues relatively high through the remaining years of life in both the white and colored populations. This same tendency is shown for both races in the differently situated wage-earning population insured by the Metropolitan Life Insurance Company.

As is well known, food habits have much to do with the prevalence of this disease, and they may explain most of the differences in the mortality of the two races from this cause. Despite the striking results obtained by the use of insulin, the general death rate from diabetes has been on the increase in the last three decades. In the recent experience of the Metropolitan Life Insurance Company "the death rate from diabetes among insured Negroes ... has actually exceeded that of the whites." Dr. Leopold reports that in 1930 the death rate per 100,000 from diabetes in Baltimore was 28.02 for the whites and 30.01 for the Negroes. He remarks that "Diabetes in Negroes is not different in any way from the disease as found among white people." A similar conclusion based on a study (published in 1928) of one hundred consecutive cases among Negroes has been drawn by Dr. Bowcock, who finds that reactions to insulin are virtually the same in both races.

DISEASES OF THE DIGESTIVE SYSTEM

For diseases of the digestive system, the colored population compares quite favorably with the whites. The colored population does not fill its quota of deaths from appendicitis, hernia, diseases of the liver, ulcer of the stomach and duodenum, and diseases of the pancreas. On the other hand, it has exceeded its quota for diseases of the stomach (cancer and ulcer excepted), peritonitis (without specified cause)—owing perhaps to faulty diagnosis, and diseases due to intestinal parasites other than hookworm. By far the largest single category of deaths is "diarrhea and enteritis." Most of these deaths occur in the first year of life and they are set apart as a separate category in mortality statistics of the United States. The number of young children dying of these complaints fluctuates exceedingly according to seasons and geographical environment. Maryland in the past few years has shown the highest rate for these diseases and about the highest excess of deaths among the colored population.

The reduction in the death rate from diarrhea and enteritis constitutes an important factor in the general decline of infant mortality which has occurred in the last two decades (Table XXIII, Appendix). Relatively, the death rate in cities has fallen in both races more rapidly than it has in the rural districts. Death rates from diarrhea and enteritis are higher among the Negroes than among the whites for all age periods. The statistics of the Metropolitan Life Insurance Company for insured laborers (mainly an urban population) agree substantially with those from the Registration States.

The Negro death rate from "dysentery" in the Registration Area is relatively much higher than that for whites, but this is mainly owing to the circumstance that a large proportion of such deaths is reported from the South, where the rate for both races is much higher than in the North. Dysentery is a very unsatisfactory category of diagnosis, since it includes infections of both the amoebic and the bacillary type, as well as many cases more properly attributable to diarrhea and enteritis, tuberculosis, and various other diseases affecting the digestive tract.

DISEASES OF THE HEART

In recent mortality statistics diseases of the heart cause by far the largest number of deaths attributed to any single type of disease. Formerly they were outnumbered by deaths from tuberculosis, but since 1912 deaths from heart disease have become the more numerous, and, because the death rate from heart disease has been increasing while the death rate from tuberculosis has been decreasing, the present disparity has become very marked.

A part of the statistical increase in deaths from heart disease as shown by figures from the Registration Area is spurious. Because the population is coming to be composed of a larger proportion of persons in the higher age groups, in which heart disease is more prevalent, the crude death rate would naturally tend to rise. Recently physicians have become much better equipped to diagnose heart disease than they were twenty years ago. Changes in the classification of causes of death have also occasioned the assignment to heart disease of a number of maladies that were previously not so classed. Dropsy, for example, has largely disappeared as a reported cause of death, and the dropsy cases have gone in part to swell the mortality attributed to diseases of the heart. Howard's instructive table of deaths from cardiac and renal diseases in Baltimore shows a gradual increase of the rates from heart disease from the absurdly low figures in the first half of the nineteenth century (it was not recognized at all before 1824) to 1918, when it reached its highest point.

Another factor in the statistical increase in mortality from heart disease is the fact that the Registration Area as it has been enlarged has come to include more and more states having a large Negro population, among whom heart disease is especially prevalent. The marked excess of Negro mortality is shown in all states and cities in which adequate records have been compiled. In general it exceeds that of the whites by about 50 per cent. It is markedly higher in cities than in rural districts for both the colored and white populations, but the excess of heart disease in the colored is greater relatively than it is in the whites. In other words, urban life tends to affect the colored population more unfavorably than the whites so far as affections of the heart are concerned.

Lower rates for the whites are shown in all age periods up to the advanced age groups (75 and over), when the scale turns in favor of the colored population. Syphilitic infection is also an important factor in the high Negro death rate from cardiac affections. Dublin, in reviewing a large series of data, states that "It is especially among the colored patients that syphilitic heart disease is prominent; in this group it accounts for about a third of the cases." Whether other factors favor the development of heart and circulatory disorders more, on the whole, in the Negroes than in the whites, is uncertain. In a summary of the extensive experience of the Metropolitan Life Insurance Company from 1911 to 1930, Dr. Dublin discusses the higher rate of colored policy holders not only for heart disease but also for the related disorders of arteriosclerosis, cerebral hemorrhage, and chronic nephritis. Among the colored clientele of both sexes the mortality from organic diseases of the heart has been distinctly on the increase since the decline following the influenza epidemic of 1918. It has risen less rapidly in white males since 1921, and has remained nearly the same in white females. Deaths from arteriosclerosis are more common in colored males from ages 35 to 64, after which the mortality of white males is the greater. Colored females have rates higher than those of white females in all ages.

Mortality from cerebral hemorrhage among insured wage earners in the colored is higher than in the whites in almost all age groups. Cerebral hemorrhage, although classed among nervous diseases, is commonly the result of arterial disease and is closely associated with cardiac and renal disorders. Statistically it has shown a marked increased in colored males, a fact paralleled by the increase of organic heart disease and chronic nephritis.

The excess of heart disease among the Negroes is all the more significant because the age composition of the two races would favor a much higher mortality from this cause among the whites. When adjusted instead of crude rates are compared, it is found that adjusted rates are higher than crude rates among the Negroes, and that the differences in the mortality of the two races are greater for adjusted than for crude rates.

In a physical examination of 1,000 Negro factory workers in Cincinnati, Allen found cardiovascular impairment in 55.6 per cent of the persons examined. Relatively heavy work and in addition syphilitic infection were held to constitute important factors in causing cardiac impairments. Davidson and Thoroughman find a high percentage of positive Wassermanns (25.3) in Negro heart cases, and they conclude that "syphilitic heart disease causes the greatest amount of disability next to the arteriosclerotic group." In a comparative study of cardiovascular syphilis in whites and Negroes, Cason finds that syphilitic heart disease is especially common in Negroes, but he believes that the larger amount of heavy work done by the Negroes may account for this fact. He agrees with Allen that a combination of heavy work and syphilitic infection is very apt to result in cardiac disorders.

Hedley has investigated 450 fatal cases of heart disease occurring in the Washington (D.C.) Hospital in 1932. Of these 108 were in members of the colored race. Rheumatic heart disease was more common in the whites, but, according to the author, "Hypertension is especially fatal in the colored race, more so among females than among males. . . . Syphilis of the aorta and heart is a very common cause of death among colored males but not so common among colored females. . . . Heart disease results in death considerably earlier in the colored race than in the white. This is due in part to the greater prevalence of cardiovascular syphilis, and to the greater frequency of arterial hypertension and to the more rapid progression of degenerative diseases."

DISEASES OF THE SKIN

As a rule diseases of the skin are less fatal to Negroes than to whites. The death rate from diseases of the skin and cellular tissues in the Registration States for 1920 (1920–1924 inclusive) was 4.30 per

100,000 for the colored and 3.63 for the white population, but the somewhat higher rate for the colored population is due largely to the inclusion of deaths from gangrene, which is not properly a skin disease. The colored population contributes a little more than its expected quota of deaths from gangrene, but much less than its expected quota of deaths from furunculosis. This is shown in the experience of the Metropolitan Life Insurance Company as well as in the Mortality Statistics of the Registration Area. Since fatal cases of furunculosis are often caused by a streptococcus invasion, the immunity of the Negro may be partly owing to the same factors that reduce his death rate from erysipelas and scarlet fever. "Acute abscess" and "other diseases of the skin and cellular tissues" show racial differences in mortality which are much less marked. Dr. R. H. Fox, in a paper on the skin diseases of the Negro based on 2,200 cases, remarks upon the relative rarity of furuncle, psoriasis, and dermatitis in Negroes, especially those with darker skins.

Facts of interest on the distribution of diseases of the skin in the two races were brought out in the examination of recruits for the World War. Love and Davenport state that "acute abscesses and inflammation of the connective tissue of the skin are about one-third as common in colored as white soldiers; boils are one-fourth as common; dermatitis from traumatisms are one-third as common, and venomous bites and stings have much less effect. As is well known, the reaction of the skin to cuts differs in the two races. Colored persons tend to form keloid tumors, or skin ridges along the scar." For the period of the World War the admission rates with respect to the more common skin diseases in the white and colored troops were as shown in table 23 (p. 116).

In a paper on "Syphilis and Skin Diseases in the American Negro," Dr. Hazen remarks upon the relative rarity of tineas, dermatangeosis, and other cutaneous affections in Negroes, but states that dermatitis is very common among them, as is confirmed by the testimony of Dr. Fox. The relative rarity of the itch among Negroes despite conditions which would naturally favor its spread supports Dr. Ritter's conclusion that "there is something resistant to the entrance of the itch-mite in the colored derma."

In general the Negro skin seems to be a more efficient organ than the skin of the whites. The important direct and indirect rôles played by the skin in the maintenance of vitality and resistance to disease are very imperfectly known. Some of the functional peculiarities of the Negro skin are obviously associated with the presence of pigment. The skin of the Negro is less readily penetrated by ultraviolet rays, and this circumstance affords a greater degree of protection against the injurious influence of tropical light. Ow-

TABLE 23

Skin Diseases: Admission to Hospital of White and Colored Troops in the United States Army, From April 1, 1917 to December 31, 1919; Rates per Thousand

	White	Colored		White	Colored
Carbuncle........	.59	.13	Herpes...........	.80	1.03
Furuncle..........	5.44	1.59	Scabies...........	8.29	2.37
Abscess...........	4.17	3.15	Psoriasis.........	.40	.09
Cellulitis.........	3.46	1.62	Impetigo.........	.71	.21
Defects of nails...	2.21	.64	Other diseases....	5.03	4.17
Eczema...........	1.06	.50			

ing to its pigment, the skin of the Negro radiates heat more rapidly than the skin of the whites. Whether the greater resistance of the Negro skin to infection is due in some way to the presence of pigment is uncertain. The skin of the Negro is thicker than that of the white man and its connective tissue elements show characteristic reactions to abnormal conditions.

THE FIBROID DIATHESES

Many writers have referred to the proclivity of the Negro to develop abnormal fibroid growths. Undoubtedly the proneness of the skin of Negroes to form keloid tumors and ridges depends upon a true racial idiosyncracy. The fibrous connective tissue of the derma, which is unusually thick in the Negro, seems to be especially responsive to traumatic stimuli. Whether a similar racial tendency to develop fibroid growths is present in other parts of the body, is not so certain. There is no question, however, that uterine fibromas and rectal strictures are relatively much more common in Negroes than in whites, whether as a result of a racial diathesis or of some other cause.

In a large series of cases of rectal disease, about 10 per cent of which occurred in Negroes, Dr. Rosser finds that, although rectal diseases in general are not especially prevalent in the colored population, stricture of the rectum occurred in 19 Negroes and 17 whites, or about 11 times as frequently as would be expected in the former race. "In a group of twenty cases that I have previously recorded," says Dr. Rosser, "it was noted that strictures in the race are accompanied by all manner of fibrous tissue overgrowths illustrating the fibroplastic diathesis." Dr. R. Matas states that "stricture of the rectum other than cancer, largely sequel to tuberculous or syphilitic infection, is notably in excess in the Negro (+68 per cent). Condyloma and papilloma, both of which are frequently of syphilitic origin, are also more common in Negroes."

Dr. E. G. Martin, of Detroit, states: "I have had the experience of operating on a large number of Negroes and have found the most virulent types of strictures. I have never seen anything comparable among the whites—long tubular strictures that are thick and are particularly inoperable without excision of the whole area. . . . It is a remarkable fact that I rarely find the strictures mentioned in the Negro male. As to syphilis, in nearly all cases of stricture in Negroes there is a positive Wassermann reaction. Of course, we see many cases of syphilis among the whites, but we rarely find the bad strictures among the whites." As to racial idiosyncracy, Dr. Martin remarks that stricture commonly follows some form of ulceration, and that "it is the greater frequency with which the colored population harbors the prime cause of the ulceration (the tubercle bacillus and the spirochete) that accounts for the greater frequency of the stricture in the Negro. While I am not prepared to deny that the histologic proof that such fibroid reaction in the Negro is peculiar and racial by excess of connective tissue proliferation, I cannot convince myself from personal observation that there is any real difference in the histology of a rectal stricture as seen in the two races."

Dr. C. F. Martin in describing a study of rectal stricture states that "It is rather curious to note that 167 of our cases, or 81.6 per cent, occurred in the Negro race, and all these were female. No stricture has been noted in the male in our service for two years." An intensive study of a series of Negro female cases convinced Dr.

Martin that the rectal strictures were a consequence of an infection with lymphopathia venerea, to which we have elsewhere referred. A positive Frei test was obtained in 20 out of the 25 cases studied, " a far greater number of patients than we found to have syphilis, gonorrhea or tuberculosis. It is just possible that this is a type of infection peculiar to the Negro race just as granuloma inguinale is rarely found in white persons." "Inflammatory stricture of the rectum," Dr. Martin concludes, "primarily is due to a specific infection classed variously as lymphopathia granuloma inguinale, climatic bubo, or, more appropriately, lymphopathia venereum. It is a disease peculiar to the Negro, possibly because of some racial susceptibility."

Dr. H. T. Hayes believes that strictures commonly follow some form of rectal ulceration and are more frequent in the female, especially among Negroes, but he holds that "gonorrhea is the infection most often responsible. The low percentage in the male is accounted for by the rarity of infections in the rectum. The Negro male has a higher percentage of urethral strictures, and he has a gonorrheal urethritis more frequently. There are strictures resulting from various other infections. . . . There is a high percentage of positive Wassermann tests in stricture, but that does not prove them to be syphilitic."

When we consider the relation of uterine fibroids to race we find that Negroes are affected very much more frequently than whites by the maladies of which fibroid growths are a secondary complication. Alsobrook, who reported on 1,000 cases of uterine fibroids in the Negro race, found salpingitis in 99.1 per cent. Miller finds that from one-third to one-half of all colored women over 50 years of age present fibroid growths. In the Charity Hospital of New Orleans, out of "299 cases of fibroids 89.9 per cent were in the Negro women, although the total gynecological admissions were only slightly greater in the Negro than in the whites."

In 125 cases of fibroid growths in Negro women, Witherspoon and Butler reported that "pelvic inflammatory disease, in the nature of salpingitis, or oöphoritis, pelvic abscesses, pus pockets, adhesions, etc., was observed in every instance. In addition the ovaries exhibited follicle cyst formation in 12 cases, or 96.8 per cent." In white women there is a strong association between uterine fibroid growths and the formation of ovarian follicle cysts. The authors conclude that "uterine fibroid development in the white and colored woman has the same source, namely, prolonged estrin stimulation, resulting from ovarian follicle cyst formation, but that the Negro presents a greater frequency of occurrence of fibroids because chronic pelvic infection, resulting in ovarian damage and dysfunction, is more common in her than in the white woman, and this abnormal ovarian secretion, the stimulation of which remains permanent, is prolonged sufficiently to be the igniting factor in the development of fibromyomata."

Moensch also attributes the greater prevalence of fibroids in Negroes to "the greater frequency of pelvic congestion and over activity of the ovarian hormone." Apparently uterine fibroids, like some other malignant growths in the American Negroes, are mainly a disease of civilization. Surmount and Sava in their extensive experience with the natives of Africa found only five cases of uterine fibroids, and three of these were associated with ovarian follicle cysts. A number of physicians have concluded that the proneness of Negro women to develop fibroids is a result of the notorious prevalence of gonorrheal infections in the colored population. Whether the walls of the uterus and rectum are more likely to respond to abnormal stimuli by the hypertrophy of fibroid tissue in the Negro than in the white is therefore open to doubt.

Dr. G. H. Day attributes the greater prevalence of urethral stricture in Negro males to the fibroid diatheses, "a keloid tendency in the urethra," but it does not appear evident that this may not be explained by the greater prevalence of gonorrheal infection.

LYMPHOPATHIA VENEREA, A "FOURTH VENEREAL DISEASE"

Several articles have recently appeared dealing with a malady which seems to be much more prevalent in Negroes than in whites. Dr. Grindon points out that lymphopathia venerea is the nineteenth name which has been proposed for this disease, but this fact did not deter him from suggesting two more. According to Sulzberger and Wise, the disease should be distinguished from lymphogranuloma inguinale, with which it has been confused. It commonly starts as a small sore on the penis appearing from six to thirty days after intercourse. Subsequently the inguinal lymph glands enlarge, and later other parts of the lymphatic system become involved. Dr. C. F. Martin states that the disease "is chronic, incurable, and tends toward a fatal termination." In females its beginnings are usually unnoticed, but it leads to pathological conditions of the reproductive organs, and especially to stricture of the rectum. All the Negro cases that were examined by Dr. Martin were females, and "all had perirectal deposits of inflammatory tissue with marked contraction of the lumen of the bowel." Apparently the disease is caused by a filterable virus.

In a study of 47 cases of lymphopathia venerea from the clinics of the Pennsylvania Hospital, by Veer, Cormia, and Ullery, it was found that 40 of the cases were afforded by the colored patrons although the latter constituted only 37 per cent of the patients treated. The disease appears to attack the two sexes in different ways. Of the 26 cases in which the inguinal glands were involved 22 were males and 4 were females, and 22 of these were colored and 4 were white. All the 21 cases of rectal stricture observed were in females, 18 of whom were colored women.

HOOKWORM DISEASE

A number of writers have remarked upon the relative freedom of Negroes from infection by hookworm. According to Dr. A. C. Chandler: "As a matter of fact the Negroes have markedly lighter infestations and also suffer less ill effects from a given degree of infestation than do the whites. According to Smillie and Augustine (1925), in one of the most heavily infested counties of Alabama less than 9 per cent of the rural Negro children of school age harbored more than 100 hookworms, and less than 1 per cent more than 500, whereas of the white rural school children in the same county more than 56 per cent harbored more than 100 worms, and more than 14 per cent harbored more than 500. In six different counties in different parts of Alabama, less than 4 per cent of the Negroes harbored more than 100 worms, and only 0.4 per cent, more than 500, whereas of the white children 33⅓ per cent harbored more than 100 worms, and 7.4 per cent harbored more than 500. Knowlton (1919), examining soldiers from Florida and the Carolinas, obtained an average of 155.3 worms in whites and only 38.3 in Negroes." Clinical cases in southern Negroes are rare.

Even heavy infestations fail to cause the anemia which is a common symptom of hookworm in whites, and apparently have little effect on general vitality. Cort and his coworkers found a remarkable degree of resistance to hookworm infection among the Indian-Negro mixtures in the Panama region, although the Indian race is apparently much less resistant than the Negro. Probably one factor in the low infestation of Negroes by hookworm is the thickness of the skin, which impedes the entrance of the larvae.

Further references on this topic may be found in the *Bibliography of Hookworm Disease* (Publication No. 11), issued by the Rockefeller Foundation, New York City.

RICKETS

Deaths diagnosed as caused by rickets are relatively few in number. Nevertheless this not uncommon disease probably indirectly results in many deaths in infancy and childhood. Almost all the deaths occur under 5 years of age, and appreciably more than half of them occur in the first year. Adding the deaths in the Registration States for 1920, from 1920 to 1923, gives 1,408 deaths among the whites and 500 among the colored. Taking those falling within the first year, we find 924 whites and 284 colored. The death rates per 100,000 population are .428 for the whites and 1.59 for the colored, a rate more than three times as high for the latter group.

Whether or not there is a racial diathesis to rickets cannot be decided. Syphilis, tuberculosis, and unfavorable conditions of life may, so far as we know, entirely account for the relatively high death rate from this disease in the colored population. Dr. G. N. Acker (1894), who has paid especial attention to the early symptoms of rickets which ordinarily escape record, makes the rather broad statement that "Negroes are almost without exception rachitic. This predisposition to rickets in the colored race would seem to be an acquired one, for it is stated that the native African seldom, if ever, shows any evidence of this disease." F. T. Mitchell, who has examined 500 colored and 500 white children from Memphis, Tenn., finds evidence of rickets in 87.6 per cent of the colored and in 49.8 per cent of the white children. Marked signs of rickets occurred in 11.2 per cent of the white children and 34.6 per cent of the colored.

DISEASES OF THE NERVOUS SYSTEM AND SENSE ORGANS

On the whole Negroes suffer somewhat more from nervous diseases than the whites. The Negro death rate is especially high for epilepsy, general paresis, and dementia praecox, and other psychoses. It is relatively low for tabes dorsalis and softening of the brain. Diseases of the nervous system also show a somewhat higher rate for Negro infants than for those of the whites. This is chiefly because convulsions have been included under nervous diseases and convulsions are much more prevalent among Negro than among white infants. Obviously "convulsions" is a very unsatisfactory category under which to classify real causes of death. The true cause of convulsions may not lie in the nervous system at all, since a number of disorders of the most diverse origin may terminate in convulsive seizures. More accurate specifications of the causes of death based on the primary source rather than the terminal symptoms of the reported death would materially reduce this category of diagnosis. Doubtless, therefore, a part of the high Negro mortality from convulsions is to be attributed to less precision in recording the cause of Negro deaths. Another factor is the prevalence of rickets, which predisposes infants to convulsive seizures. The relatively high preponderance of Negro deaths from epilepsy may be traceable in large measure to the greater prevalence of syphilis. The data on insanity show, if we can believe them, that insanity has increased among the colored population since the period of slavery. I do not quote the figures, because they are obviously unreliable. Hoffman, discussing the data on mental disorders among the Negroes before and following the Civil War, came to the same conclusion. When one considers the increase of alcoholism, tuberculosis, and syphilis, and the general physical deterioration of the Negro physique that followed emancipation, this increase of insanity seems quite inevitable.

The Negroes, however, are not represented in asylums in numbers comparable to their proportion to the general population. According to the statistics compiled by H. H. Laughlin, the Negro fills little more than half his quota of the asylum inmates of the United States. The Census Bulletin 119, entitled *The Insane and Feeble Minded in Institutions* (1910), shows that Negroes are relatively less represented in asylums than the whites. These facts signify very little with respect to the relative prevalence of insanity in the two races. It is often stated that there is less neurasthenia among Negroes than among whites, and that there were fewer cases among Negroes who were recruited for the World War. A number of writers (Pollock, McCord, and Bond) have pointed out that the rate for first admissions to asylums is higher for Negroes than for whites for several states of the North and West, but is lower in the South. How far this is owing to the factors of urban life, age composition, and facilities available for receiving Negroes is open to question. Probably the prevalence of syphilitic infection may predispose Negroes to other forms of insanity besides general paresis. For several reasons it is difficult to get really comparable statistics on the relative frequency of insanity in Negroes and in whites. Insanity has probably increased among Negroes since the period of emancipation, in part as a result of their increasing urbanization, but further than this it is unsafe to make surmises.

Negroes apparently suffer less than the whites from diseases of the ear. Otitis media, otitis externa, mastoiditis, and defective hearing were much less common in Negro than in white recruits in the Great War. Dr. Scheppergrell (1895) on the basis of data covering more than 40,000 cases states that "In chronic suppurative and non-suppurative inflammations of the middle ear, the ratio of the Negro is also small, being 16 and 26 respectively to 100 cases in the whites." Possibly the Negro's advantages in these respects may be due in part to his relative freedom from scarlet fever, diphtheria, measles, and affections of the nose and throat, which sometimes lead to infections of the ears as a secondary complication. They may also be in part owing to certain peculiarities in the structure of the Negro ear, as pointed out by Murrell (1887).

Negroes suffer very little from imperfections of the eye. Ocular defects were found to be less common in Negroes than in whites both in the Civil War and the Great War. Dr. S. M. Burnett, on the basis of a study of 1,514 colored and 811 white cases, finds that refractive anomalies are relatively infrequent among Negroes. However, iritis is about as common as in the whites, possibly as a result of syphilis. With respect to partial immunity to trachoma among Negroes, the doctors disagree.

PUERPERAL CAUSES

The death rate of the Negroes from causes connected with child-birth averages higher than that of the whites. Even the death rate of foreign-born white mothers of every nationality is exceeded by the rate for the colored population. Deaths from puerperal causes

TABLE 24

PUERPERAL CAUSES: DEATHS PER 100,000 LIVE BIRTHS IN CITIES AND
RURAL DISTRICTS OF THE REGISTRATION AREA

Registration area	1918	1919	1920	1921	1922	1923	1924	1925
Cities:								
White..............	9.3	7.6	8.2	7.4	7.0	71.	7.0	7.0
Colored..........	16.7	13.9	15.1	13.1	12.4	12.3	12.9	12.4
Rural districts:								
White..............	8.4	6.3	6.9	5.4	5.5	5.3	5.1	5.0
Colored..........	12.5	11.8	11.7	9.7	9.8	10.2	11.1	11.1

Registration area	1926	1927	1928	1929	1930	1931	1932	
Cities:								
White..............	7.1	7.0	7.2	7.3	6.9	7.1	6.9	
Colored..........	12.1	13.4	13.9	13.5	13.4	13.1	12.6	
Rural districts:								
White..............	5.2	4.9	5.4	5.3	5.2	5.0	4.8	
Colored..........	9.7	10.1	11.2	11.2	10.7	9.6	8.5	

are uniformly much higher for both colored and white persons in the cities than in the rural districts.

One large factor in such deaths is puerperal septicemia, which still shows an inexcusably high frequency. After the fall of the death rate from this disease following the discovery of its cause and the employment of precautions against the infection of mothers during delivery, this scourge has lingered on with relatively little abatement for many years. For females in the child-bearing period it still ranks, next to tuberculosis, among the chief causes of death. The rate for the colored population is nearly double that for the white (see table 25).

The age period of greatest mortality among the whites is 25–29, and among the colored, 20–24.

Among other puerperal causes of death, which as a group take an even higher toll than puerperal septicemia, the main cause is puerperal albuminuria and this likewise is more common in the colored population. For most of the other fatalities associated with pregnancy, the death rate among the colored population is also

TABLE 25

PUERPERAL SEPTICEMIA: DEATHS PER 100,000 POPULATION, WHITE AND COL-ORED, IN THE REGISTRATION STATES OF 1920, FROM 1920 TO 1927

	1920	1921	1922	1923	1924	1925	1926	1927
White:								
Crude..........	12.4	12.8	10.5	11.5	10.5	9.9	9.7	9.4
Adjusted........	12.4	12.9	10.5	11.8	10.6	9.9	9.7	9.4
Colored:								
Crude..........	23.0	23.3	20.7	20.9	22.5	22.5	17.8	21.9
Adjusted........	21.6	21.8	19.5	19.6	21.0	21.1	16.9	20.6

relatively high. Several causes conspire to bring about this result. Illegitimacy, syphilis, lack of adequate prenatal care and of asepsis during delivery naturally enhance the Negro death rate from most of the puerperal causes. If we can accept the statements in respect to the relative ease of child-bearing on the part of Negro mothers, whatever racial factors may be involved in the death rate from puerperal causes would probably be in favor of the Negro. The relatively high death rate of colored females is doubtless to be attributed mainly to environmental causes.

MALFORMATIONS

In the light of Dr. Mall's studies upon the causes of malformations, one would naturally suppose that the prevalence of tuberculosis and syphilis in the colored population would give rise to a relatively high proportion of anomalies leading to fatal results. I am inclined to set little store by the statistical data in this connection. It is probable that malformations would be designated as a cause of death much less frequently in Negro infants. Enumeration of the deaths in the Registration States for 1920 in 1920–1923 shows that the Negroes fall far short of supplying their quota, the ratio of deaths among white and colored being 19.48 to 1 instead of 7.78 to 1. The ratio of deaths under 5, when most deaths occur, is 19.60 to 1. Malformations of the heart show a slightly higher ratio for the whites, namely, 21.10 to 1 for all ages, and 20.0 to 1 for ages under 5. The tabulation of a larger series of deaths under 1 year in the Registration Area, 1914–1923, gives 109,047 deaths among white infants and 4,675 among colored, or a ratio of 23.41 white to 1 colored. The expected ratio based on all deaths is 7.47 to 1. In the same years and area, the ratio for congenital malformations of the heart, based on 66,806 deaths among the whites and 2,759 among the colored, is 24.21 white to 1 colored. The ratio for hydrocephalus based on 7,722 white and 478 colored is 16.15 to 1, and for other congenital malformations based on 34,519 white and 1,428 colored is 24.17 to 1. The data indicate that malformations result in death much more frequently in the white than in the colored population, but one may be justifiably skeptical about drawing this conclusion, in spite of the numerous cases which seem to support it.

CONGENITAL DEBILITY, ATROPHY, AND MARASMUS

The death rate from the several maladies grouped under this heading is very much higher in the colored than in the white population. No doubt numerous deaths for which syphilis is the primary cause are classed under this rubric. Infants predisposed to rickets, as so many are among the Negroes, often die of disorders of this class. Deaths from prematurity are more common in colored than in white infants, but the ratio of deaths from this cause is less than the ratio from all causes combined.

INJURIES AT BIRTH

Injuries at birth are relatively rare among Negroes notwithstanding the relative infrequency of skilled obstetricians in attendance. Theoretically one might attribute this to the absence of obstetrical meddling with the normal process of delivery, but I am inclined to take a more generous view and to ascribe the result, at least in part, to the greater ease with which the Negro mother gives birth to children. Doctor DeSaussure, who has made numerous observations on the delivery of Negro infants, says that "labor in the Negro is a simple act" and usually occasions little disturbance in the mother. The ease with which child-bearing occurs among primitive races has frequently been referred to, but it has probably been often exaggerated. In commenting on this matter, Professor J. W. Williams remarks (*Obstetrics,* pp. 169–170) : "It is generally believed that the comparatively difficult labors of the women of the upper classes are due to the enervating influences of civilization and luxury, while the easy labors of Negroes are considered as manifestations of a closer approach to Nature. Such conclusions are not justified by my experience, as the physical degeneration of colored women living in large cities is proven by the fact that in them the incidence of contracted pelvis is four or five times greater than in white women. Were this not counterbalanced by the lesser weight of the black children, and particularly by the smaller size and greater compressibility of their heads, labor would be a disastrous function, and would comparatively soon lead to a solution of the race problem. If the Negro children were as large and had as hard heads as in the upper classes, I should be obliged to perform cesarean section several times more frequently than I actually do."

On the basis of a large number (6,918) of cases Dr. C. J. Miller finds fewer abnormal deliveries in Negro women, and fewer vaginal tears, than among white women, the reason being the smaller size and smaller head of the Negro infants.

STILLBIRTHS AND ABORTIONS

The high percentage of stillbirths and abortions among Negroes is well known. Not only is this fact attested by several writers who have treated the subject specifically ; it is also indicated by the rather extensive data on stillbirths and abortions published by the United States Census. Data have now been published for the United States Registration Area for Births for thirteen years, 1918, 1922–1933, and they include a total of 792,227 cases among whites and 189,097 among the Negroes. The ratio of abortions and stillbirths per thousand births was about twice as high for the Negroes as for the whites.

Among urban Negroes especially, the practice of abortion appears to be increasingly common. In commenting on the Negroes of South Carolina, DeSaussure (1895) remarks that "abortions criminal and noncriminal are very common," and in agreement with many other writers on this subject he attributes a large proportion of stillbirths among Negroes to syphilis.

TABLE 26

DEATH RATES FROM VIOLENCE PER 100,000 POPULATION,
WHITE AND COLORED, FOR 1924

Age groups	White	Colored
All ages:		
Crude..................	80.8	132.6
Adjusted..............	76.5	133.1
Age groups under 1 year....	104.0	256.4
1– 4.....................	73.5	135.9
Under 5 years.............	79.2	160.0
10–14....................	37.3	49.8
15–19....................	60.7	109.7
20–24....................	69.9	171.7
25–34....................	62.8	175.8
35–44....................	76.8	145.8
45–54....................	85.9	126.0

EXTERNAL CAUSES

The death rate of the colored population from external causes is relatively high. Our colored people, however, show little proclivity to commit suicide, and their fatalities from automobile accidents (a not uncommon cause of death) are not so numerous relatively as those of the better circumstanced whites. The rate from miscellaneous sources of accidental deaths is higher for the colored population, and the rates for violent deaths are particularly high, as may be seen in the table of deaths for 1924 (table 26).

The most outstanding cause of deaths from violence is homicide. For several years the homicide rate in the Registration Area has been between five and eight times as high for the colored as for the white population. In 1928 it was 5.3 per 100,000 for the whites and 40.1 per 100,000 for the colored, and if the statistics included only males the rate for the colored population would be relatively still higher. Speaking of the wage earners insured in the Metropolitan Life Insurance Company, Dr. Dublin states that "from 15–35 years of age, Negro males have a rate approximately ten times that of white males. At these ages homicide ranks third as a cause of death, being exceeded only by . . . tuberculosis and the acute respiratory diseases. The experience of this company from 1911 to 1916 gave the following homicide rates per 100,000 persons: Male white, 5.4; male colored, 52.2; female white, 1.9; female colored, 14.1."

For the past decade the homicide rate has shown no improvement. Hoffman in his discussion of the Homicide Problem has shown that in a group of twenty-eight cities the homicide rate increased from 5.1 per 100,000 in 1900 to 10.3, the highest rate, in 1924. If these high rates continue and preserve their present distribution in respect to race, homicide will be a not unimportant factor in the relative increase of the two races.

CONCLUSION

It is evident that Negroes react quite differently from the whites to several kinds of disease. The differences would be still greater, no doubt, were it not for the extensive infusion of white blood into the Negro race. In spite of the numerous assertions which have been made concerning the physical weakness of mulattoes, I can find no valid grounds for concluding that they are constitutionally inferior to either the whites or the pure blacks. So far as our meager evidence goes, mulattoes seem to be intermediate in their reactions to disease as they are in the color of their skin.

In dealing with statistics on Negro mortality, one is continually haunted by doubts concerning the degree of reliability of the data. Studies of the causes of deaths revealed by autopsies as compared with the causes stated on death certificates have shown that physicians are far from infallible in their statements concerning why people die. That the data we have been compelled to employ contain many errors goes without saying, and they exhibit internal evidence of being less reliable for the mortality of Negroes than for that of whites. Nevertheless, the statistics on the mortality of the two races show a remarkable degree of consistency from year to year. To a certain degree this may be a consistency in error which future knowledge may afford the means of correcting.

Upon casual inspection it would seem that the Negro's immunities to disease are distributed without much rhyme or reason. The Negro is peculiarly immune to diseases of the skin and to certain infections such as scarlet fever, diphtheria, measles, erysipelas, chicken pox, and affections of the nose and sinuses, but he seems remarkably prone to contract infections of the respiratory tract. There is no adequate evidence that he has any less capacity to resist disease in general than the whites. The mortality of the Negro is so greatly affected by his unfavorable environment and habits of life that, for most diseases, it is quite impossible to detect any influence of hereditary racial factors, which may nevertheless be present.

In a previous paper (1928) I have made the suggestion that most of the Negro's immunities to disease may be interpreted as due to the superior resistance of his ectoderm. The pigment of his skin affords a direct protection against the injurious effects of light; in other respects, however, it seems probable that pigment is more of an index of a physiological power of resistance than a means of defense *per se*.

The interesting suggestion has recently been made that the pigment of the Negro's skin prevents him from gaining the full benefit of ultraviolet radiation, and hence predisposes him to rickets and tuberculosis. The greater thickness of the Negro ectoderm not improbably makes it better able to resist invasion by microörganisms. Since the nose, sinuses, and a part of the mouth cavity are lined with ectoderm which has been invaginated during embryonic development, the Negro may be somewhat better able to resist initial infection by those diseases which make their first inroads in the nasal or oral cavities. It is probable that the organisms which infect a person with scarlet fever, diphtheria, measles, and common colds begin their active proliferation in the mucous membranes of the nose and throat. The germs of pneumonia, however, may lie in the oral cavity and do no damage until they gain access to the respiratory tract. Whooping cough, like the typical respiratory diseases, may also be primarily an entodermic infection. Concerning the first inroads of the primary offenders in influenza, we are quite uncertain. It seems probable that the Negro is less apt than the white man to contract this disease. His greater mortality is owing to his susceptibility to pneumonia. Certain immunities of the Negro do not fall under the interpretation just given, but for most of them it offers a plausible explanation.

In considering the effects of differential mortality on the biological struggle between whites and blacks, it is important to recognize that disease may act as a selective agent in more than one way. If natural selection produces any change in the genetic composition of a people, it must act on the basis of hereditary differences. But the hereditary characteristics involved may have no direct connection with the differential mortality caused by a particular selective agent. Disease takes a much greater toll from the Negroes, quite regardless of any inherited susceptibilities which they may possess. The disadvantages which the Negroes suffer from disease somewhat more than outweigh the advantages they owe to their higher birth rate. There is no convincing evidence that their greater fertility results from their inherently greater reproductive capacity. Like their higher mortality, it is probably mainly the effect of their social and economic environment. Under conditions in which several diseases were completely eliminated, such as tuberculosis, pneumonia, venereal infections, and the other infections which are indirectly the causes of many of the disorders of the cardio-vascular-renal group, it might happen that the relative net increase of the two races would be quite different from what it now is. These diseases discriminate against the black man, but they do this because the black man lives in a social and economic environment largely dominated by the whites.

In the chain of effects connecting skin color with a relatively early demise there may intervene such factors as race prejudice, economic exploitation, poor educational advantages, and a multitude of other influences characteristic of modern American life. In one sense the color, kinky hair, flat nose, and other anthropological characters which cause Negroes to be recognized as such and treated accordingly may be said to be the indirect causes of their higher mortality, although these characters may have no conceivable physical connection with any cause of death. As matters actually work out in our present social régime, natural selection in the form of differential mortality from many diseases is operating on the basis of recognizable Negro features of structure.

Selective elimination may, of course, depend upon peculiarities having a fairly direct connection with survival or extinction. For most diseases, however, as we have pointed out in previous pages, it is very difficult to ascertain the extent to which differential mortality is a physiological consequence of differences in hereditary constitution. But however this may be, there is no doubt that natural selection works strongly against the Negro because of his inherited anthropological characters. It might not do so in a social order in which the status of the Negro was the same as that of the white man. Race prejudice, however, promises to be a potent selective agent in the interracial struggle for a long time to come. It helps to determine status, and status is an important aid to survival.

CHAPTER VI

INFANT MORTALITY

NEGRO INFANT MORTALITY has always been notoriously high, although it has been greatly reduced in the last two decades. Our knowledge of the infant mortality rates of Negroes for several years after the Civil War is very meager. Among the few cities of the South which made separate tabulations of the deaths of Negro infants, it was not uncommon to find that from one-fourth to one-half of the Negro babies died before the end of their first year of life. As late as 1890 a number of cities reported that for every thousand Negroes born, more than five hundred died the first year. After this date the records of these cities show a general though quite irregular decline in the infant mortality rates of their Negro populations. The data on infant mortality in the United States collected by the census are very imperfect. The establishment of the Registration Area for Deaths resulted in improved records of infant mortality, but such statistics, covering a wide area, were of little value before 1900. At this time the data on infant mortality for the Registration Area were as follows:

| | Total | Cities | Registration States | | Cities in other states |
			Urban	Rural	
White	143.4	154.2	162.4	107.5	145.6
Colored	297.0	307.0	318.9	190.3	303.3

Since the term "colored" includes other races besides the Negro, the rates for the Negroes would be slightly different from those given for the colored population. Infant mortality rates in terms of the number of births for the Negroes alone cannot be given because of the lack of birth records. These rates may be given, however, per thousand of the population under 1 year of age. For the census years 1900 and 1910, mortality rates for the two races were as follows: 1900, whites, 159.4, Negroes, 344.5; 1910, whites, 129.7, Negroes, 261.9. Since all census returns omit an appreciable number of children under 1 year of age, these death rates are doubtless too high for both Negroes and whites. In 1920, for instance, children recorded as being between 1 and 2 years of age outnumber those less than 1 year old, notwithstanding the fact that many children died in their first year. A better measure of true rates of infant mortality may be obtained from the life tables of 1901, 1901–1910, 1909–1911, and 1920, in which an effort is made to estimate the number of infants dying out of every thousand born.

TABLE 27

DEATH RATES PER THOUSAND BORN AMONG NEGROES AND WHITES ACCORDING TO LIFE TABLES, FROM 1901 TO 1920

	1901		1901–1910		1909–1911		1919–1920	
	Male	Female	Male	Female	Male	Female	Male	Female
Whites.....	133.45	110.61	127.38	105.51	123.26	102.26	92.43	73.61
Negroes....	253.26	214.75	241.41	206.24	219.35	185.07	144.95	120.35

Since these rates cover the same area, the Original Registration States, and are arrived at by employing methods which make allowances for the usual defects of the original data, they probably give us the best index of the trend of infant mortality in the Northern States for the period covered.

After 1916, deaths of Negroes as distinguished from other colored infants have been published by the United States Government in annual volumes on Birth, Stillbirth, and Infant Mortality Statistics for the Registration Area for Births. The deaths of white and Negro infants per thousand births are shown in table 28.

Part of the declining infant mortality shown in the table results from the expansion of the Registration Area. Originally the Registration Area for Births consisted mainly of Northern States. As states from the South were added, large numbers of rural Negroes were included in the area, and since the infant mortality of Negroes was much lower in southern rural districts than in northern cities, where most of the northern Negroes were concentrated, the total infant mortality rate would naturally be reduced. For this reason one will obtain a more accurate picture of the decline of infant mortality among the Negroes by studying the records of individual states and cities. We have therefore compiled Table XXIV (Appendix) showing the changes in infant mortality rates in a representative series of states and cities, both North and South.

In 1917 the infant mortality rate among Negroes was higher in the North than in the South, but owing to its more rapid decline in the North it has recently come to be about the same as in the Southern States. Whatever influence a northern climate may exert upon

TABLE 28

DEATHS OF WHITE AND NEGRO INFANTS PER THOUSAND BIRTHS, 1916–1933

	1916	1917	1918	1919	1920	1921	1922	1923	1924
White.......	99.0	90.6	97.4	83.0	82.1	72.5	73.2	73.5	66.8
Negro.......	184.3	142.5	162.5	134.3	135.6	110.7	111.7	111.9	114.1

	1925	1926	1927	1928	1929	1930	1931	1932	1933
White.......	68.3	70.0	60.6	66.0	62.2	59.6	56.7	53.3	52.8
Negro.......	112.4	112.1	109.9	105.9	101.5	99.5	92.7	84.1	85.4

the mortality of Negro infants is apt to be masked by the fact that most northern Negroes are in cities and most southern Negroes are still found in rural areas. In the black belt of the South pickaninnies may thrive in a cabin with a dirt floor, but it would be a quite different matter in northern Minnesota. Rural life seems to be especially unfavorable to northern Negroes both in the first year of life and in older age periods. But bad as the effects of an urban environment are upon the health of Negro infants, the influence of rural conditions in the North is apparently even worse. Comparing the rural with the urban death rates of colored infants from 1917 to 1927 in a group of six Northern States in which the colored population is mainly Negro, we find that for every year except 1920 the rural death rate is markedly in excess of the urban death rate. A similar comparison for the Southern States of Kentucky, North Carolina, and Virginia, discovers precisely the reverse relation. For every year from 1917 to 1927, urban rates in these states are greatly in excess of the rural rates. This very decided difference between the North and South is an important factor in the relative growth of the Negro population in these areas of the United States. In the

TABLE 29

INFANT MORTALITY PER THOUSAND BIRTHS FROM ALL CAUSES AMONG WHITE AND COLORED POPULATIONS IN URBAN AND RURAL AREAS OF A GROUP OF NORTHERN AND SOUTHERN STATES, FROM 1917 TO 1927

| Year | Northern (Indiana, Michigan, New York, Ohio, Pennsylvania, Maryland) | | | | | | Southern (Kentucky, North Carolina, Virginia) | | | | | |
| | White | | | Colored | | | White | | | Colored | | |
	Total	Urban*	Rural†	Total	Urban	Rural	Total	Urban	Rural	Total	Urban	Rural
1917	95.3	98.1	91.2	184.5	181.5	190.2	82.5	91.8	81.3	136.3	221.6	123.3
1918	103.0	105.0	100.2	198.2	191.8	211.8	85.8	108.7	82.7	144.7	238.3	131.1
1919	88.5	89.2	87.6	153.3	148.8	164.2	76.0	86.6	74.5	116.7	170.8	107.4
1920	87.5	90.3	83.0	163.7	165.0	160.1	71.0	77.7	69.8	113.6	178.8	100.6
1921	77.8	77.5	78.2	135.3	127.9	156.3	63.9	71.0	62.7	99.2	140.4	91.1
1922	77.0	79.2	73.8	132.6	126.9	149.6	66.5	73.6	65.2	105.4	144.6	97.7
1923	77.0	75.1	80.0	143.0	136.1	166.0	68.8	74.5	67.8	112.9	170.0	100.1
1924	69.7	70.6	68.3	125.9	123.8	133.8	65.4	68.9	64.7	108.6	156.1	97.9
1925	71.2	70.6	72.3	131.3	124.7	157.4	67.1	76.9	65.0	108.5	149.0	98.8
1926	73.6	73.0	74.6	134.3	131.3	146.0	71.3	80.5	69.3	110.9	161.4	98.7
1927	62.0	61.2	63.1	112.0	108.9	125.0	61.9	68.1	60.5	108.0	151.7	97.2

(* Urban—cities of 10,000 or over)   († Rural—the remainder of the state)

rural South the Negro birth rate is high and the infant death rate is relatively low. As a result, the net fertility of the rural South has been able to compensate for the deadly effect of cities upon their ever increasing numbers of Negro inhabitants.

The general trend of infant mortality among Negroes has been downward in urban and rural areas both North and South, but at

TABLE 30

INFANT MORTALITY PER THOUSAND POPULATION UNDER ONE YEAR AMONG
WHITE AND COLORED IN URBAN AND RURAL MARYLAND, 1906–1920

Year	White		Colored	
	Urban	Rural	Urban	Rural
1906.............	240.9	85.6	579.6	127.6
1907.............	233.4	88.8	570.6	143.2
1908.............	197.5	93.6	505.4	146.8
1909.............	193.3	96.8	453.2	161.9
1910.............	174.0	98.4	427.1	168.8
1911.............	152.3	97.6	373.7	170.6
1912.............	158.2	94.1	320.1	165.3
1913.............	146.6	114.0	331.1	223.6
1914.............	135.7	104.2	296.4	211.1
1915.............	108.9	113.8	243.7	229.4
1916.............	112.6	116.5	280.1	241.8
1917.............	110.9	119.2	254.7	248.2
1918.............	142.8	140.9	258.0	256.1
1919.............	104.8	100.2	197.1	208.3
1920.............	114.1	96.5	239.6	201.8

greatly different rates. In the North, infant mortality rates have fallen more rapidly in the city than in the country; in the three Southern States we have mentioned the decrease has been much the same in both city and country.

Comparing the trends of infant mortality in whites and blacks, we find that although the rates for the blacks are everywhere the higher, the general decline has taken place at much the same rate in the two races. Urban life is much more fatal to Negro than to white infants. Among the northern whites, urban and rural infant mortality rates are not greatly different, and in the last few years the urban rates have actually fallen below the rural. In the South the rural infant mortality rates among the whites are somewhat lower in the country than in the cities, but the differences do not compare in degree with those for the colored population.

It is a noteworthy fact that the infant death rates of the Negroes are conspicuously lower in the northern than in the southern cities.

TABLE 31

DEATHS PER THOUSAND BIRTHS IN WHITE AND COLORED POPULATIONS OF URBAN AND RURAL MARYLAND, FROM 1916 TO 1934

Year	White		Colored	
	Urban	Rural	Urban	Rural
1916	103	98	220	203
1917	103	99	194	205
1918	135	113	212	· 217
1919	90	96	143	173
1920	94	85	168	162
1921	80	82	125	165
1922	85	77	135	157
1923	77	84	139	170
1924	76	75	124	133
1925	73	81	124	169
1926	73	76	128	147
1927	71	64	126	144
1928	72	60	122	135
1929	63	77	108	132
1930	60	68	98	148
1931	66	65	112	154
1932	56	59	94	129
1933	56	53	91	120
1934	61	57	89	129

This is owing in part to the fact that more is done to promote infant welfare among Negroes in the northern cities, but it is, I suspect, due also to the fact that northern Negroes as a class are better educated, and enjoy a somewhat better economic status than that of the average urban Negro of the South. Whatever the advantages of a warmer climate may be, they are more than counterbalanced by the other advantages enjoyed by the Negroes in northern cities. Some interesting aspects of the trend of infant mortality among

Negroes are shown by Maryland, a state more or less intermediate between the North and the South (see table 30). The earlier data on infant mortality are expressed in terms of the number of infant deaths per thousand of the population under 1 year of age. They show a very high infant mortality among urban Negroes, and also that the mortality was much reduced by 1919 and 1920. The rural rates shown in table 30 for the years preceding 1914 should not be taken seriously, because death registration was very imperfect in the rural parts of Maryland. The establishment of the Registration Area for Births in 1915 made it possible to express infant mortality rates in terms of the number of deaths under 1 year per thousand births. These rates are so expressed in table 31, which indicates the trend in infant mortality from 1916 to 1934.

Urban and rural rates for the colored population of Maryland do not differ nearly so much as they do in other states of the South, and the differences are not consistently in favor of either urban or rural areas, although in later years the city rates have been the lower. Neither are there consistent differences for the whites.

In rural communities the mortality of colored infants is commonly over 50 per cent higher in the North than in the South. The natural explanation of this difference is to attribute it to climate. If this is true, it does not follow that the high colored death rate in the rural districts of the North is the result of hereditary racial factors; it may be caused by the inferior economic status of the colored population. This conclusion receives some support from the fact that infant mortality in several countries of Europe is considerably higher than for our own colored inhabitants. It is a well-known fact that infant mortality is enormously higher in families with a very small income than it is among the well to do. Where adverse conditions of climate are contended with, a people compelled to live in poverty is at a very great disadvantage. If white infants were subjected to the conditions that prevail in the homes of Negroes in the rural North, it is doubtful if there would be much disparity in the infant death rates of the two races. Possibly the white infants are less prone to die of respiratory affections. White children, as is shown by several series of measurements, have a higher "vital index," or lung capacity, than Negro children of corresponding ages, but we still do not know how far the reduced lung capacity of Negro children predisposes them to fall victims to respiratory diseases.

It is only for a relatively short period that we have had extensive data on the mortality of Negro infants from various specific causes. The annual volumes of Mortality Statistics contain records of the number of colored infants dying from different diseases in the first year of life, and since the Negroes constitute a very high percentage of the colored population of the Registration Area, the data afford a fairly accurate picture of Negro infant mortality. Since 1916 infant deaths have been recorded in the volumes on Birth Statistics for Negroes as distinguished from other colored elements of the population. These statistics cover deaths from several diseases for subdivisions of the first year of life. With the expansion of the Birth Registration Area until it now includes most of the states of the Union, the statistics on infant mortality are coming to be on a fairly satisfactory basis.

I have summarized in Table XXV (Appendix) the data on infant mortality in white and colored infants in the Registration Area from 1914 to 1923 inclusive, and have given the respective ratios of deaths in white and colored infants. Under the head of "colored" are included infants of all colored races, but, since only a small percentage of these are of Indian or Mongolian parentage, the data are fairly representative of the mortality of Negroes. In the absence of data for the computation of infant mortality rates, I have computed the ratios of deaths (white to colored) for various causes as a means of comparing the relative mortality of the two races. The ratio of deaths (white to colored) from all causes in the entire period (1914 to 1923) is 7.474 to 1. This is a convenient number to keep in mind when comparing the relative mortality of the races from particular diseases, but it should not be used except in relation to the data for this area and period. An inspection of the ratios in the right-hand column of Table XXV will reveal at once whether the death rate for a given disease is higher or lower than the expected rate based on all causes of deaths. A number higher than 7.47 indicates that, for the particular disease, the infant mortality rate for the whites is relatively higher.

Table XXVI (Appendix) gives the death rates of whites and Negroes from particular causes for individual years since 1916. In these data, which are compiled from the statistics on infant mortality published in the Birth Statistics, the deaths of Negroes are kept separate from those of other colored people. The rates are based on the proportion of infants dying under 1 year of age to one thousand of the population. Table XXVI makes possible a rough comparison of the death rates of Negro and white infants from different diseases.

It is apparent from both tables that the death rates of white and Negro infants from different causes vary widely. The Negro death rate is relatively low for measles, scarlet fever, erysipelas, malformations, diseases of the skin, and injuries at birth. It is relatively high for general diseases, typhoid, malaria, whooping cough, tuberculosis, syphilis, convulsions, lobar pneumonia, and external causes. The very high rate for "unspecified or unknown causes" as compared with that for white infants is simply an index of the greater proportion of inadequate diagnoses.

Chapter VII

THE NEGRO BIRTH RATE

UNTIL A FEW YEARS AGO knowledge of the Negro birth rate in this country was quite imperfect. That the Negroes were very prolific during the period of slavery and the first few decades after emancipation was a matter of common observation, and their high fertility was further attested by the relatively large proportion of young children as compared with adults in the Negro population. Table 32, which gives the percentages of the white and Negro populations under 1, 5, and 10 years of age, shows that there must have been relatively many more births among the Negroes than among the whites, especially since the infant and child death rate was much higher among the Negroes. If we measure fertility by the proportion of Negroes under 5 years of age to 1,000 women of child-bearing age (15–44 years), much the same relations are disclosed. All our data indicate that, although there has been a gradual decrease in the proportion of children in both whites and Negroes, this decrease has been the more rapid in the Negroes. The census of 1920 showed that the percentage of children under 5 years of age was precisely the same, namely, 10.9, for both races, although it was exceeded by the record (12.7) for the native whites. At this period the proportion of Negro children per thousand women of child-bearing age fell below that of the whites for the first time. By 1930 the percentage of Negro children under 5 years of age had sunk to 10.3, and for the native whites to 10.4.

One is not justified in attributing all the decrease in the proportion of children to the decline in the birth rate. A part of it represents the reduction of the death rate among persons of adolescent and middle age, which would naturally reduce the proportion of children per thousand of the general population. The death rate among the whites has fallen steadily during the past century, but, in the Negroes, for some time after the Civil War the death rate actually rose. As we have already pointed out, the period when Negro mortality was highest was a period of rapid natural increase. Nevertheless, during this time the proportion of Negro children decreased, as it has done in the subsequent period when the Negro death rate was falling. Unquestionably, however, the chief factor in the decreasing proportion of children in both races is the fall of the birth rate.

When the censuses for 1880 and 1890 were taken, attempts were made to gain some rough idea of the Negro birth rate. No data on births were collected, but the birth rate was estimated from the

TABLE 32

PERCENTAGES OF NATIVE WHITE AND NEGRO POPULATIONS OF THE UNITED STATES UNDER ONE YEAR, UNDER FIVE YEARS, AND UNDER TEN YEARS OF AGE, FROM 1880 TO 1930

Age group	1880		1890		1900	
	Native white	Negro	Native white	Negro	Native white	Negro
Under 1.............	3.3	....	3.0	2.8	3.0	2.8
Under 5.............	15.6	....	14.2	14.1	14.0	13.9
Under 10............	30.0	32.5	27.8	28.8	27.3	27.6

Age group	1910		1920		1930	
	Native white	Negro	Native white	Negro	Native white	Negro
Under 1.............	2.8	2.6	2.5	2.2	2.0	2.0
Under 5.............	13.5	12.9	12.7	10.9	10.4	10.3
Under 10............	25.5	25.6	23.0	24.5	21.7	21.8

number of children less than 1 year of age, plus the number less than one year old who were reported as having died within the year. In 1880 the percentage of children under 1 year of age in the whole United States was 3.39 for the colored, 3.29 for the native-born whites, and a quite negligible percentage for the foreign born whites. The birth rate estimated in this way was admittedly too low. But, according to Dr. J. S. Billings' report on the vital statistics of the 1880 census, "In the ten grand groups in which the distinction of color was made, the birth rate for the whites was 32.0 and for the colored, 38.6 per 1000 of the aggregate population, or for the whites 127.1 and for the colored, 163.8 per 1000 of women between the ages 15 and 49. . . . In these ten grand groups, out of each 1000 infants born, the number which died under three months of age was for the whites 66.7, and for the colored 71.4. The difference between the white and colored birth rate and the infant death

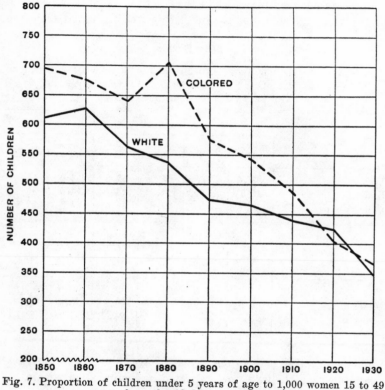

Fig. 7. Proportion of children under 5 years of age to 1,000 women 15 to 49 years of age classified by race: 1850–1930.

rate is less in the rural districts than in the cities. Taking 23 counties in the South containing cities or large towns, and having an aggregate population of 588,129 whites and 586,038 colored, we find that the birth rates per 1000 of the living population were, for the whites, 28.71, and for the colored, 35.08; and the proportion of those born and dying within the Census year per 1000 births was, for the whites, 100.01, and for the colored, 140.06." In fifty-one mostly rural counties of the South the birth rate was 34.31 for the whites, and 39.46 for the colored, and the infant mortality (per thousand born) was 62.61 for the whites, and 91.0 for the colored.

In 1890 the birth rate was estimated as it had been estimated in 1880. The percentage of the population under 1 year was 2.96 for the native whites, and 2.8 for the Negroes. For the total number of whites it was 2.48, the low percentage for the latter being the result of the inclusion of foreign-born whites, among whom there

TABLE 33

PROPORTION OF CHILDREN UNDER ONE YEAR PER THOUSAND WOMEN, 1890

	All ages	All women 15–50 years	Married women, 15–50 years
Whites.....................	54.11	104.20	205.63
Colored...................	58.78	120.73	237.80

was only a very small number of children under 1 year of age. Births in relation to women, whether one includes women of all ages or only those in the child-bearing periods, were more frequent in the colored population, as is indicated by table 33.

In the Registration Area, which at that time was mainly confined to a few of the Northern States and cities, the birth rate was higher in white than in colored women, as is indicated by table 34 (p. 146). In the rural parts of the Registration States, however, this relation was reversed.

Life in the North was not conducive to a high Negro birth rate. Births were less frequent than deaths, although in the South, in spite of the high infant mortality, the surplus of births over deaths was high. Hoffman quotes statistics from Alabama to the effect that from 1888 to 1893 there were 55,319 births and 26,834 deaths in the colored population, making a ratio of 2.06 births to 1 death. At the same time, the whites of Alabama were reproducing even more rapidly, with a ratio of 2.96 births to 1 death.

In 1900 the percentage of the Negro population less than 1 year of age was given as 2.8. The census of 1910 gave 252,386 children under 1 year of age out of a Negro population of 9,827,763, or 2.6 per cent of the total, as compared with 2.4 for the whites in general, 2.8 for native whites of native parentage, and 3.1 for native whites of foreign parentage. When we consider the infant mortality rate prevailing in 1910 (261.9 colored, and 129.7 white in the Registration Area), it is reasonable to conclude that the birth rate of the Negroes must have considerably exceeded that of the native-born whites, although it was less than it was in 1900.

The first systematic collection of birth statistics on a large scale began with the establishment of the Registration Area for Births

TABLE 34

PROPORTION OF CHILDREN UNDER ONE YEAR PER THOUSAND WOMEN
IN THE REGISTRATION AREA, 1890

	All ages	All women, 15–50 years	Married women, 15–50 years
Whites.....................	48.18	85.79	184.12
Colored...................	47.47	78.45	174.61

in 1915. The few states in the original Area (the New England States, New York, Pennsylvania, Michigan, Minnesota, and the District of Columbia) were all in the North and contained few Negroes. New states were rapidly added to the Area, and by 1920 several Southern States were included. The first few annual reports on Birth Statistics published by the Bureau of the Census indicated that the birth rate of the Negro population was lower than that of the whites. As more states from the South were added, the general birth rate for the colored was materially increased, and ever since 1919, when South Carolina, California, and Oregon were added to the Area, it has exceeded that of the white population. The birth rates for the whole Registration Area are shown in table 35.

Data covering the whole of an expanding area in which birth rates vary greatly in the states which are added do not give a fair comparison of the relative fertility of whites and Negroes. For such a comparison it is better to consider the birth rates of single states. Accordingly, I have compiled Table XXVIII (Appendix) showing the birth rates in various states, and I have also given in table 39 the birth rates of the white and colored populations in the rural and urban areas within each state. The rates for individual states given in the volumes on Birth Statistics apply to the colored population, which includes not only Negroes, but also a small percentage of other races, especially Indians and Orientals. In general, no great error is made by considering "colored" as virtually

TABLE 35

BIRTH RATES, WHITE AND COLORED POPULATIONS IN THE REGISTRATION AREA
FOR BIRTHS, FROM 1915 TO 1933

	1915	1916	1917	1918	1919	1920	1921	1922	1923	1924
Total:										
White.........	25.0	25.1	24.7	24.6	22.1	23.5	24.0	22.2	22.1	22.2
Colored.......	20.6	20.4	24.4	24.5	25.2	27.0	27.9	26.0	26.3	27.4
Urban:										
White.........	25.9	25 9	25.7	25.4	22.8	23.8	23.9	22.1	22.2	22.5
Colored.......	21.7	22.7	19.7	19.8	21.9	24.0	25.4	23.7	25.2	27.6
Rural:										
White.........	23.6	23.4	23.8	23.8	21.5	23.1	24.2	22.4	22.0	21.9
Colored.......	16.5	23.0	27.7	28.0	27.1	28.9	29.2	27.3	26.9	27.2

	1925	1926	1927	1928	1929	1930	1931	1932	1933	
Total:										
White.........	21.1	20.7	20.6	19.5	18.6	18.7	17.6	17.0	16.1	
Colored.......	26.7	24.9	23.6	22.2	21.3	20.7	21.2	21.3	20.0	
Urban:										
White.........	21.7	21.0	20.8	20.0	19.3	19.1	17.4	16.5	15.4	
Colored.......	27.0	24.0	23.4	21.6	20.6	19.2	19.3	19.1	17.9	
Rural:										
White.........	20.5	19.7	19.9	19.1	18.0	18.3	17.8	17.5	16.8	
Colored.......	26.5	25.5	23.8	22.5	21.7	21.7	22.4	22.7	21.3	

synonymous with Negro, especially when we are dealing with rates. In the census of 1920 the total number of Indians and members of other colored races amounted to 426,574, as compared with 10,463,131 Negroes, so that other colored peoples constituted but 3.29 per cent of the entire colored population. When we are dealing with limited areas, however, it becomes quite unjustifiable to assume that statements regarding the colored population are true for the Negroes. In some of the Northern States there are more Indians than Negroes, and in several others the percentage of Indians or other colored peoples as compared with Negroes is very high (New Hampshire, Vermont, Wisconsin, Utah, Minnesota, Nebraska, California). In California, the Japanese and Chinese constitute a fairly large proportion of the colored population and their birth rate, owing largely to their favorable age composition, is much higher than that of the Negroes; consequently, the general birth rate of the colored population would differ significantly from the Negro birth rate. In most states of the South the proportion of other colored races is so small as to be virtually negligible with respect to rates of births and deaths. The presence of Indians, who are mainly rural, in the several states of the North and West creates a marked discrepancy between the birth rate of the Negroes and that of the colored population in general. But so far as cities are concerned, rates which apply to the colored population are usually determined almost exclusively by the Negroes.

As has been stated repeatedly in the annual reports on Birth Statistics, it is not improbable that "registration of births is not as complete among colored as among white persons, and therefore, rates for the former class are too low." In the study of completeness of birth registration, undertaken to afford a basis for the life tables of 1919–1920, it was concluded that birth registration was incomplete to about 25 per cent among Negroes and about 9 per cent among whites. It is hardly likely that incompleteness of birth registration among the Negroes is so great as this at the present time. Another source of incorrectness in birth rates lies in the migration of Negroes from one region to another, thus falsifying the estimates of population in intercensal years. This migration has been especially extensive in the Negro race, and hence both birth rates and death rates are apt to be more inaccurate for the Negroes than for the whites. Populations upon which rates are based, are estimated to increase at a regular annual rate, but the occurrence of the Great War with a consequent dislocation of the Negro population has caused the Negroes in the North to increase very much more rapidly in some years than in others. If, for example, a small city in the North should receive an addition of ten thousand Negroes in the war period, that city would probably show a marked rise in the birth rate and death rate of its Negro population. The birth rates and death rates in regions which lose Negroes would also show anomalous changes. Population estimates made several years after a census are particularly likely to give misleading results. When, after ten years, another census affords a means of checking the previous estimate, the population during the intercensal years can be reckoned with a much greater degree of accuracy. After a census is taken, previous estimates of population are often revised. The result of such revision has been to show that birth rates of northern Negroes based on estimates of Negro populations made previous to the census enumerations of 1920 and 1930 were in several states much too high. The actual counts showed that many more Negroes were living in these states than had been assumed in the previous estimates. Hence the number of births per thousand Negro inhabitants was estimated to be too large. In 1927 the birth rate of the colored population in the state of New York, for example, was given as 33.1, and the white rate as 19.6. In 1920 the birth rates for the two races were 23.1 and 22.5, respectively; and the birth rates in 1930, 20.6 for colored and 17.0 for white. Clearly, the high birth rate of 33.1 for the colored population in 1927, and the still higher rate of 33.15 in 1925, were based on underestimates of the colored inhabitants in that state. Estimates of the relative birth rates in urban and rural areas are especially apt to be misleading in intercensal years because of the great variations in the volume of urban migration in different states.

The confidence which the general public is accustomed to place in official statistics on birth rates and death rates is very often misplaced, especially when one is concerned with data on Negroes in intercensal years. The birth statistics showed that the Negro birth rate had been rather strikingly increasing in several Northern States after 1920, but in the light of the 1930 census it is evident that much of this increase was not real. It is not improbable that the first great rush of Negroes into the North during the Great War tended to check the birth rate. But the trying time in which migrants were adapting themselves to a new environment was followed by a period of better adjustment, which might be expected to enhance the birth rate. In the *Negro Survey of Pennsylvania*, issued by the Department of Welfare, it is stated, in describing conditions prevailing in 1925, that "for the Negro (and this statement holds true for the general population of Pennsylvania) there is no class which can accurately be described as poverty-stricken. From the outbreak of the World War there has been such a material increase in wages that no group has been living so far below the subsistence level that it corresponds to the old 'submerged tenth' of fifteen years ago, or the more recent 'other half' concerning which

TABLE 36

PERCENTAGE OF MALES TO ONE HUNDRED FEMALES IN THE NEGRO POPULATION OF THE NORTHERN STATES, FROM 1910 TO 1930

	1910	1920	1930
New England States............	77.8	103.2	99.7
Middle Atlantic States.........	94.9	100.7	97.9
East North Central States.....	108.3	113.0	104.5
West North Central States.....	107.8	106.7	102.0

Jacob Riis used to write. Then, there are here and there dependent Negro families who have been compelled to seek relief from charitable agencies, but this has been because of one or another form of personal disability or seasonal unemployment." In general, conditions were without doubt more favorable to a high birth rate among northern Negroes in the relatively prosperous years following the war than they were at the height of the mass migration.

One factor in the low birth rate of northern Negroes in 1920 and the years immediately preceding and following this date is the fact that the early migrants of the war period were predominantly males. Later, with the growing migration of females also, the proportions of the sexes in the North became more nearly equal. This fact is clearly shown in table 36, which gives the percentage of males to 100 females in the geographic divisions of the North. It is evident that the sex ratio of the Negroes in 1910 and 1930 were more favorable for a rapid natural increase than in 1920.

Although a good deal of the rise of the Negro birth rate that is shown by the birth statistics after 1920 is spurious, it is not improbable that an actual rise occurred for a number of years following the first great inrush into the North. The general decline of the birth rate of northern Negroes has not been great; it has been much less, as a rule, than that of the whites. A part of this decline, it is probable, is attributable to the financial depression, which has tended to lower the birth rates of both races. But the fact that the causes which operate to reduce the birth rates of all peoples have not had a greater effect upon the northern Negro indicates that these causes were counteracted by factors incidental to a more settled life which tended to enhance the birth rate.

Unfortunately, we cannot place implicit reliance upon estimates of birth rates in intercensal years. We may, however, obtain some light on this question, as well as on the trend of the Negro birth rate in general, from the data on family size published by the Bureau of the Census since 1917. These data were compiled from statements given on birth certificates in answer to questions on the number of children born to mothers who had a child within the year. Inquiry was also made with respect to the number of children now living in the family and the ordinal position of the child born within the year. In table 37 I have compiled the data for the Registration Area for Births on the number of children already born and living, as well as the number within the year, to mothers grouped in the following classes : total white, native white, foreign-born white, colored, and Negro. It may be seen that, for every year from 1917 to the latest report, the number of children born to colored mothers appreciably exceeds the number born to all white mothers, and exceeds still more the number produced by mothers who were native born. Foreign-born mothers who bore a child within the year have had somewhat more children than women of color. After restrictions on immigration were imposed, foreign-born mothers have produced a relatively smaller proportion of children born in this country. Moreover, as the mothers who came here before the restriction of immigration will produce fewer and fewer children owing to their increasing age, we may expect this proportion to become still smaller in the future. Negro mothers lose a larger number of their children than do mothers of either foreign or native parentage (and especially than the latter), yet the number of their surviving children exceeds the number of surviving children of total white and native white mothers, although it is frequently exceeded by the number of surviving children of the foreign born.

TABLE 37

AVERAGE NUMBER OF CHILDREN BORN, BORN AND LIVING, AND PERCENTAGE
DYING, TO MOTHERS OF DIFFERENT CLASSES IN THE
REGISTRATION AREA FOR BIRTHS*

	1917		1918		1919		1920		1921		1922	
	Born	Living	Born	Living	Born	Living	Born	Living	Born	Living	Born	Living
Total White......	3.3	2.9	3.3	2.9	3.4	3.6	3.3	2.9	3.3	2.9	3.2	2.9
Native White.....	3.1	2.8	3.1	2.7	3.2	2.8	3.0	2.7	3.0	2.7	3.0	2.7
Foreign White....	3.8	3.2	3.9	3.3	4.0	3.4	4.0	3.4	4.0	3.4	3.9	3.4
Colored..........	3.8	3.2	3.8	3.2	3.8	3.2	3.6	3.1	3.7	3.1	3.8	3.2
Negro............	0	0	0	0	0	0	0	0	0	0	3.8	3.2
Percentage dying:												
Colored........	16.5		16.3		16.5		15.6		15.7		14.9	
Negro..........	16.5		16.4		16.9		15.9		16.0		15.2	

	1923		1924		1925		1926		1927		1928	
	Born	Living	Born	Living	Born	Living	Born	Living	Born	Living	Born	Living
Total White......	3.3	2.9	3.2	2.9	3.2	2.9	3.2	2.9	3.2	2.9	3.2	2.9
Native White.....	3.0	2.8	3.0	2.7	3.0	2.7	3.0	2.7	3.0	2.7	3.0	2.7
Foreign White....	4.0	2.4	2.9	3.4	3.9	3.4	2.9	3.4	3.9	3.4	3.9	3.4
Colored..........	3.7	3.2	3.7	3.2	3.6	3.1	3.7	3.2	3.7	3.2	3.7	3.2
Negro............	3.8	3.2	3.7	3.2	3.7	3.2	3.7	3.2	3.7	3.2	3.7	3.2
Percentage dying:												
Colored........	14.3		13.7		13.8		13.5		13.2		12.5	
Negro..........	14.6		13.9		14.1		13.6		13.3		12.5	

	1929		1930		1931		1932		1933			
	Born	Living	Born	Living	Born	Living	Born	Living	Born	Living		
Total White......	3.1	2.8	3.1	2.8	3.0	2.8	3.0	2.8	3.0	2.8		
Native White.....	3.0	2.8	3.0	2.8	3.0	2.8	3.0	2.8	3.0	2.8		
Foreign White....	3.8	3.3	3.7	3.3	3.6	3.2	3.6	3.2	3.7	3.3		
Colored..........	3.7	3.2	3.7	3.3	3.7	3.2	3.7	3.3	3.7	3.3		
Negro............	3.7	3.3	3.6	3.2	3.6	3.2	3.6	3.2	3.6	3.2		
Percentage dying:												
Colored........	12.2		12.1		12.3		11.4		11.4			
Negro..........	12.1		11.8		11.7		10.9		10.8			

* Exclusive of a few states. For exceptions see reports in Birth Statistics for the several years.

Data on the number of living children per mother are given for the total colored and the Negro population in the volumes on Birth Statistics from 1917 to 1923. After 1923, the data were no longer published, but since the percentage of living children in relation to the total number born is given for each class, I have calculated the number of living children for the remaining years and embodied the results in the table. The number of children born to colored mothers has undergone little change, but the number of children who survive shows a gradual increase in both the Negroes and the colored population as a whole. In order to show the relative family size in these groups in different states I have brought together in Table XXXI (Appendix) data for a few states, North and South, in which there is a fairly large number of Negroes. Data for Negroes as distinct from other colored people are not available for individual states, but in the states selected the colored population is so overwhelmingly Negro that the figures represent very closely the family size in the Negro group. The number of children per mother is markedly larger in the South than in the North. One reason for this is the fact that in the North a relatively large number of children are born to young mothers.

I have also made a comparison of the number of children born to mothers in various age groups of the Negro population in five Southern States and in fourteen Northern States in the census year 1920. The results are shown in table 38. Curiously enough, in 1920, Negro women in age groups 10 to 15, and 15 to 20, produced relatively more children per 100,000 population of these groups in the North than in the South. In the North a little more than half of the Negro children were born to mothers below the age of 25; in the South the mothers of this age produced about 39 per cent of the children. In 1930 much the same relations prevailed, with a slightly larger percentage of children born to young mothers in the North. If we consider the respective age distribution of females in these selected states of the North and the South, we find a conspicuous difference. In the South the most numerous age group is that from 5 to 10 years. In the North it is the age group, 25 to 30. Between 20 and 60, and especially between 20 and 45 years of age, there are relatively many more females in the North than in the South. On the whole, the age composition of northern Negroes is highly

favorable for a rapid rate of annual increase. The volume on Birth
Statistics for 1927 shows that, in that year, the number of children born to colored mothers exceeded those born to white mothers
in every state of the Registration Area for Births. Of course, the
data afford information only concerning the offspring of those

TABLE 38

FEMALE BIRTHS PER 100,000 NEGRO MOTHERS IN FOURTEEN NORTHERN STATES
AND IN FIVE SOUTHERN STATES IN 1920

Age group	Northern females		Southern females	
	Number of births	Births per 100,000 females	Number of births	Births per 100,000 females
10–15...............	34	93.31	152	84.93
15–20...............	1,762	4,603.53	6,784	4,286.48
20–25...............	3,502	6,155.31	12,490	8,406.76
25–30...............	2,685	4,445.07	8,665	7,527.52
30–35...............	1,522	3,118.92	5,270	6,108.37
35–40...............	957	1,953.58	4,220	4,490.13
40–45...............	279	806.87	1,288	1,820.55
45–50...............	31	116.86	206	354.06
50–55...............	2	10.63	10	22.37
Total..............	10,744	21,304.08	39,085	33,101.17
		× 5		× 5
		106,520.40		165,505.85

women who have had a child within the year. They tell us nothing of the proportion of women who have had no children. One
might infer that, since the proportion of children less than 5 years
of age is higher in southern whites than in Negroes, the proportion of childless unions must be greater among the Negroes. We
have relatively little information on this point. The Immigration
Commission, in an investigation of the number of children born to
couples who had been married from ten to twenty years, found
that the percentage of childless unions was 5.3 in foreign born
whites, 13.1 in native born whites, and 20.5 in Negroes. Notwithstanding the high percentage of sterile unions, the average num-

ber of children (3.1) was greater in the Negroes than among native women of native parentage (2.7). These data were derived from Rhode Island, Ohio, and Minnesota. What the data from the South might indicate we do not know.

A little further light on the problem is afforded by Miss Graham's study of family size among the Negroes of Chicago. This study was based on data collected but not published by the Bureau of the Census in 1920. A fairly large random sample was obtained by taking the data for every tenth Negro family. Miss Graham found that "The childless married couples formed a surprisingly large proportion of the total Negro group. Some of them undoubtedly had children at one time, or will have children, although we find a larger proportion of childless wives among the younger women than among those over 55." Only about one-half the families had children of any age. A similar study of the white population of Rochester, New York, showed that over three-fourths of the families had children. "The average number of children in Negro families having any children is just 2.0; for native born white females, 2.1 and for foreign born, 2.8. In counting the children of a family, not only the parents' actual offspring of all ages were included, but also all children under 16 in the family group, whether their own or not." In speaking of the economic pressure and its influence upon family limitation, Miss Graham remarks that "there is marked evidence of family limitation, which although undoubtedly involving other factors, must be at least in part due to this necessity."

So far as the conditions described are typical of the general Negro population of Chicago, it is evident that in 1920 the stabilized increase of this population would be a negative quantity. Such facts indicate that the measure of relative fecundity afforded by the number of children ever born to mothers who had a child within the year are apt to lead to an overestimate of the birth rate of the Negro population.

So far as data on family size go, they indicate a slightly increasing number of children to each colored mother in certain representative states of the North having the largest number of Negro inhabitants. Unfortunately, the data for the single states do not give information concerning Negroes as distinct from other persons of color. Besides, they do not yield indubitable evidence of an actual increase of the birth rate, since the results are influenced not only by the age composition of the female population, but also by the nature of the incoming migrants. As may be seen from Table XXXI (Appendix), for every year from 1917 to the latest report the number of children born to Negro mothers exceeds the number born to all white mothers and much exceeds the number produced by mothers who are native born.

We are in a position to gauge the actual fertility of the Negro female population of the North, making the proper allowances for age composition, only for the census years 1920 and 1930. This I have attempted to do for fourteen Northern States, as has been explained in Chapter III. The result of this investigation shows that the actual fertility of Negro women was somewhat less in 1930 than it was in 1920, as might be conjectured from the declining birth rate. It does not show that the fertility of Negroes in the North did not increase for a number of years after 1920. It is worth noting that the percentage of Negroes under 5 years of age, which has shown a steady decrease in the general population, should be greater in most Northern States in 1930 than it was in 1920.

The data published by the Bureau of the Census since 1917 on the ages of mothers show that Negro women in general begin child-bearing earlier than white women and continue their reproductive functions to a later age. For the year 1926 I have estimated the percentage of children born to Negro and white mothers in the several age groups. This percentage for very young mothers (10–14 years), although very low in both races, is much higher in the Negroes. For mothers from 15 to 19 years old, it is almost twice as great for Negroes as for whites, and a little greater between the ages 20 and 24. The percentage is greater for white women between the ages of 25 and 45, after which it becomes higher again in the Negroes. Although the curve expressing the fertility of women at different ages has a somewhat greater spread in the Negroes, child-bearing in Negro women is relatively more concentrated in the earlier years. The effect of this early child-bearing is to make generations follow one another more rapidly in the Negro population, and, other things equal, to bring about a more rapid multiplication of the Negro race. According to the estimates of Miss Parker and myself, the average length of a generation is about one year less (27.5 in-

stead of 28.5) in the Negroes than in the whites. With the present
birth rates of Negroes and whites, these differences would have a
marked effect in the course of a few generations.

Among Negroes, as among whites, the birth rate commonly varies
greatly between urban and rural areas. In the past, cities have had
a much lower birth rate than have rural districts; the population
of many cities has been kept from actually decreasing only through
the influx of people from the surrounding country. Poverty, disease, intemperance, and vice have increased the death rate of city
dwellers and reduced their birth rate, and, although their age composition is generally more favorable for rapid reproduction than
that of the rural population, city dwellers have had, until recently,
relatively low birth rates measured in terms of the number of births
per thousand inhabitants. At present, especially in the Northern
and Western States, the urban birth rates have, for a number of
reasons, exceeded the rural.

City life in the United States has been especially destructive to
the Negro. A high death rate, both in infancy and later life, coupled
with a reduced birth rate, has caused our cities to become potent
destroyers of black humanity. There is much variation in the Negro birth rates of different cities, and in the relation of urban birth
rates to those of the surrounding rural areas. In the North the Negro birth rate is lower than in the South, and especially the rural
South, but the proportion of rural Negroes in most Northern States
is so small as to make the rural birth rates very unreliable. Also,
one should not place too much confidence in the birth statistics of
particular cities, because migration may lead to serious errors in
the estimates of their Negro population.

In the Birth Statistics, rates for particular cities and for the
urban and rural areas of states are given for all persons of color.
In order to show the respective trends of urban and rural birth
rates in the white and colored populations, I have compiled from
the volumes on Birth Statistics table 39. Rates based on population
estimates calculated from the 1930 census are given from 1928 on.
I had included the data for all the years between 1920 and 1928,
which were based upon estimates made before 1930, but a scrutiny
of the figures shows that so many of the rates are highly improbable and so much at variance with both earlier and later rates that

TABLE 39

Birth Rates of White and Colored Populations in Urban and Rural Areas From 1917 to 1930

	1917		1918		1919		1920		1921		1922		1923		1928		1929		1930	
	Urban	Rural	Urban	Rural	Urban	Rural	Urban	Rural	Urban	Rural	Urban	Rural	Urban	Rural	Urban	Rural	Urban	Rural	Urban	Rural
Connecticut:																				
White	32.0	21.2	30.7	20.9	27.2	19.4	26.7	17.6	25.9	18.0	23.1	16.6	22.3	15.9	20.5	10.6	19.7	9.4	20.2	10.7
Colored	24.4	18.6	25.9	17.9	26.7	19.1	27.1	16.7	27.4	20.5	24.6	20.4	26.4	19.6	25.3	13.1	26.1	15.1	27.0	12.4
Delaware:																				
White	....	....	....	....	....	....	....	....	23.8	21.1	21.8	19.6	19.9	19.2	20.1	15.6	20.3	14.9	21.8	15.1
Colored	....	....	....	....	....	....	....	....	20.2	22.1	18.5	20.8	19.3	21.6	19.3	23.4	20.1	23.6	19.9	23.3
Indiana:																				
White	22.8	21.8	23.0	22.1	20.9	20.1	22.9	21.7	23.3	22.9	21.4	21.6	22.3	21.4	20.1	18.1	20.1	16.9	20.1	16.9
Colored	16.2	17.7	16.6	17.1	17.6	15.1	19.6	11.9	21.4	13.5	19.4	17.0	22.4	15.4	19.2	11.9	18.6	13.4	16.6	12.2
Kansas:																				
White	20.5	22.6	21.1	22.7	20.3	20.9	23.2	22.3	24.0	23.4	22.8	21.4	23.8	21.3	20.2	17.6	20.0	16.8	20.3	17.0
Colored	16.6	16.8	16.7	17.8	15.8	17.0	18.4	15.2	18.7	15.3	19.4	16.6	19.5	17.3	15.4	14.4	13.0	13.5	17.5	16.9
Kentucky:																				
White	19.5	28.2	20.5	28.4	18.4	25.9	22.3	27.8	23.2	29.7	21.9	27.6	24.0	28.1	21.9	24.2	21.3	22.6	20.3	24.2
Colored	13.6	20.6	11.7	18.5	12.2	19.3	13.6	19.3	14.9	20.7	10.4	15.4	15.4	15.6	14.7	16.8	15.0	15.9	14.3	15.4
Maryland:																				
White	24.6	22.6	24.6	22.7	23.9	....	25.0	23.3	24.5	24.2	22.5	22.4	22.7	22.0	19.9	18.3	18.3	16.5	18.4	16.5
Colored	24.1	28.5	22.8	27.3	25.1	....	26.0	28.9	26.5	30.7	25.1	28.4	27.0	28.1	24.2	24.4	22.9	23.9	22.9	23.3
Massachusetts:																				
White	27.1	20.6	26.7	20.2	24.3	18.1	24.7	18.8	24.5	18.7	23.0	17.8	23.2	17.1	20.4	12.5	19.0	11.3	18.6	10.8
Colored	23.8	24.5	26.5	27.7	21.0	26.5	25.6	31.6	24.9	21.5	25.2	23.8	24.6	29.0	20.2	19.5	20.1	15.2	18.9	13.6
Michigan:																				
White	28.0	24.6	27.5	24.6	24.9	21.8	26.8	23.2	25.8	24.8	23.1	23.3	24.0	22.6	23.5	18.3	23.4	17.8	21.9	18.1
Colored	9.3	13.5	13.4	17.1	15.9	16.4	21.3	19.2	25.8	23.8	22.4	24.2	26.5	22.8	20.8	15.3	21.2	16.9	20.0	20.5
Mississippi:																				
White	....	....	....	....	....	....	....	....	27.9	27.5	26.3	24.6	25.8	24.3	26.0	24.1	25.4	21.9	26.1	22.8
Colored	....	....	....	....	....	....	....	....	22.8	24.2	23.6	23.9	21.7	23.6	24.8	24.6	22.8	23.5	23.7	24.6
New York:																				
White	26.1	19.5	25.2	19.4	23.2	17.7	23.5	18.9	23.3	20.1	22.1	19.6	21.7	18.9	19.2	14.5	18.4	13.6	18.0	13.3
Colored	20.3	16.6	21.7	14.6	22.3	14.5	24.2	14.1	25.4	16.1	25.5	16.4	27.4	20.6	22.3	19.2	21.4	18.6	20.9	17.7
North Carolina:																				
White	22.9	31.6	21.9	30.6	22.7	29.9	30.2	31.9	30.9	33.9	29.7	30.4	29.3	31.0	26.5	25.7	24.3	24.1	24.1	23.7
Colored	22.0	31.9	19.4	31.8	20.6	29.4	24.4	32.4	26.4	35.9	25.4	33.4	26.6	33.8	23.8	28.6	21.2	27.0	20.8	25.9
Ohio:																				
White	24.5	19.9	24.5	20.2	21.5	18.2	22.6	19.8	22.3	21.3	20.5	20.2	21.4	20.3	19.6	16.9	19.1	15.7	18.8	16.2
Colored	15.1	17.5	16.2	23.4	17.5	23.6	20.7	19.5	22.6	22.1	21.1	19.3	24.7	19.5	22.1	17.8	21.2	15.7	19.7	14.6
Pennsylvania:																				
White	27.1	26.1	26.5	25.4	24.6	24.6	25.6	24.9	25.4	26.4	22.3	24.7	23.2	24.5	20.1	21.1	20.1	19.3	20.0	19.0
Colored	19.3	17.4	19.4	18.1	21.7	21.7	25.2	21.2	24.3	21.9	22.6	19.4	25.2	23.2	25.1	21.2	23.2	19.0	22.4	17.1
South Carolina:																				
White	....	....	....	....	25.8	25.8	30.0	28.7	32.2	29.6	29.3	26.8	26.7	26.4	26.2	22.9	23.5	20.5	22.7	20.9
Colored	....	....	....	....	22.2	22.2	25.4	27.9	28.5	29.2	28.3	26.5	25.7	24.3	26.3	27.0	25.5	24.9	23.5	26.0
Virginia:																				
White	22.6	28.0	24.1	28.5	24.1	26.4	25.4	28.5	25.3	30.6	23.2	27.7	22.2	27.5	20.4	23.7	19.5	22.4	20.1	22.6
Colored	22.0	29.2	21.8	30.3	24.0	29.0	25.0	31.4	25.6	33.2	23.1	31.1	22.8	30.3	21.7	23.6	20.5	25.5	20.0	25.8

I decided to discard those after 1923. An inspection of table 39 shows that in the Southern States the birth rate of Negroes is usually higher in rural districts than in cities, whereas the reverse relation commonly prevails in the North. This is, for the most part, the result of the peculiarities of age distribution in the Negro female population.

The subject of illegitimate births among Negroes deserves mention because it is closely associated with infant mortality and a

TABLE 40

PERCENTAGE OF ILLEGITIMACY AMONG THE WHITE AND COLORED POPULATIONS, FROM 1925 TO 1934

	1925	1926	1927	1928	1929	1930	1931	1932	1933	1934
Whites	1.54	1.54	1.63	1.67	1.72	1.80	1.92	2.07	2.09	2.04
Colored	11.69	11.77	12.84	13.66	14.05	13.82	14.75	15.75	15.60	15.15

high rate for stillbirths. For this and other reasons it is a factor of no small importance in the biological fortunes of the Negro race. In 1930, for example, the percentage of stillbirths was 11.7 for illegitimate, and 7.4 for legitimate colored children. The fact that stillbirths are more than twice as frequent in Negroes as in whites is naturally associated with the prevalence of illegitimacy, although there are other causes, especially syphilitic infection, which conspire to produce this effect. The marked difference in the prevalence of illegitimacy in the white and colored races is shown in table 40, which gives the percentages for the Birth Registration Area from 1925 to 1934.

Rates for the Negroes alone would be still higher than those for the colored population in general because the percentage of illegitimate children is over twice as high among Negroes (14.34 Negroes : 4.70 colored, in 1930) as in other colored races. It is a striking fact that in the total Registration Area the percentage of illegitimate births is greater in the rural than in the urban areas among the Negroes, and precisely the opposite relation is found among the whites. In 1927 the ratios of illegitimate births to 100 total births were as follows : rural whites, 1.38, urban whites, 1.91, rural colored, 13.35, urban colored, 11.97. In Washington, D. C., birth records from 1879 to 1907 show that the percentage of illegitimate births among Negroes varied from 18.1 to 27.6. The rate was rather higher in the nineties than it was before or has been since. In recent years it has declined somewhat, but it is still high (18.40 in 1930, colored).

If one were to consider the relatively low total illegitimacy rate of the urban Negro as an index of the wholesome moral influence of city life, he would be seriously misled. A comparison of the statistics of individual states shows the untenability of this interpretation. There is a marked difference in the illegitimacy rates in the colored population of the Northern and Southern States. Compare the rates (per thousand total births in 1930) of Alabama, 181.1, Louisiana, 151.6, Maryland, 211.6, Mississippi, 123.9, North Carolina, 175.3, and Virginia, 164.6, with those of New York, 62.0, Illinois, 84.0, Indiana, 96.2, Michigan, 65.8, and Ohio, 81.2, and it will be seen that the illegitimacy rates are roughly about twice as great in the South as in the North. Nevertheless, in each of these Southern States the illegitimacy rate among Negroes in 1927 was higher in the cities than in the rural areas. The relations in the Northern States vary, owing in large part to the presence in several states of a relatively large percentage of colored peoples other than Negroes, especially in the rural districts. The high total illegitimacy of rural districts arises from two circumstances: (1) in the South, where the illegitimacy rate is high, the Negroes are mainly rural; and (2) in the North, where the illegitimacy rates are rather low, the Negroes are mainly urban. When we consider each state separately we find that there is commonly more illegitimacy in the cities than in the country. When we lump all the data together it happens that the rural rate becomes higher than the urban.

Whether or not illegitimacy in the Negro race is increasing it is difficult to ascertain, although migration into the cities naturally tends to increase it. When we compare the earlier and the later reports we find that the illegitimate birth rate has tended to rise in the South and to decline in the North, but there is much fluctuation back and forth. During the past few years the illegitimacy rate among southern Negroes has shown a somewhat increased upward trend. In a study of illegitimacy in North Carolina, W. B. Sanders

has found that illegitimacy rates for Negroes and whites tend to
vary together and that both have increased for the five years preceding 1930. This increase is explained by "an increase in drinking
indulged in by both sexes and perhaps the depression which has
caused a decrease of marriages." One other factor in the increasing

TABLE 41

PERCENTAGE OF ILLEGITIMACY IN WHITES AND NEGROES IN NORTH CAROLINA,
FROM 1921 TO 1930

Year	Negroes	Whites	Year	Negroes	Whites
1921	12.88	1.53	1926	13.36	1.82
1922	13.31	1.55	1927	14.24	1.79
1923	12.49	1.55	1928	15.13	1.80
1924	12.49	1.76	1929	16.17	1.99
1925	10.62	1.49	1930	17.33	2.58

illegitimacy of southern Negroes may be the migration to the North
of the types of Negro women who are less likely to become mothers
of illegitimate children.

The illegitimacy rate in cities is probably increased by the fact
that unmarried women who become pregnant in the country come
to cities where they can have their children without the knowledge
of their friends and relatives. They also find in the city better facilities for confinement and a means for providing care for their infants in the charitable agencies, which are often called upon in
such emergencies. The influence of these considerations is shown
in Miss Reed's study of five hundred records of illegitimacy among
Negro women in New York City. More than one-third of these Negro mothers were born outside of the United States, mostly in the
West Indies, and 35 per cent came from the Southern States; 25
per cent of them were less than 19 years of age, and 76 per cent
were under 25.

The relatively low illegitimacy rate among northern Negroes may
arise in part from the fact that, as a class, they represent a more
enterprising and better educated group than their southern compatriots. The illiteracy rates of Negroes over 10 years of age, as
given in the 1920 census, were nearly four times as high in the

South as in the North. Bias in classification may also affect the proportions of births designated as illegitimate in these two regions, but it is quite hazardous to attempt to estimate the influence of this factor.

One striking peculiarity of illegitimacy in Negroes as compared with whites is its relation to the age of mothers. Of the 1,620 illegitimate births to mothers aged 10–14 years in the Birth Registration Area of the United States of 1930, 1,079 were to Negroes. In the next age group, 15–19 years, Negroes contributed 15,118, or a little over 50 per cent of the total of 30,191 illegitimate births. The percentage of illegitimate children among very young mothers (10–14 years) is naturally high for all nationalities and races. It is a well-known fact that illegitimate births occur with relatively much greater frequency in the earlier years of the child-bearing period. In the Birth Registration Area for 1930, for example, nearly one-half of the total illegitimate births in both Negroes and whites occurred to mothers less than 20 years of age. After age 20 we find that the percentage of illegitimacy is relatively markedly higher for Negro mothers in all age groups. In other words, the distribution of illegitimate births in relation to age is more like the distribution of normal births in Negroes than it is in whites.

The general decline of the birth rate in both Negroes and whites is probably owing in the main to the same causes. Contraceptive methods are no secret to numbers of urban Negroes; and where the inconvenience of large families is acutely felt, reduction of the birth supply is bound to follow. It is significant that a special "Negro Number" of the *Birth Control Review* was issued in June, 1932, containing articles by a number of prominent Negro writers and some white students of problems of population. In this number Elmer A. Carter, the editor of *Opportunity,* states that "Although statistics are not readily available, it would appear that the Negro, aware of the tremendous handicaps which his children must face under the most favorable conditions, is even more impelled to limit their number than his white compatriots similarly placed. . . . There is reason to believe, however, if one is willing to accept the almost universal testimony of Negro physicians, that since the economic collapse birth control of a sort is being attempted on a wide scale among the lower classes of Negroes, who find themselves facing a future of almost certain insecurity and want. Negro women in formidable numbers, without the advantage of contraceptive information, seek relief through abortions performed under highly dangerous conditions by unskilled and sometimes grossly ignorant quacks."

There are a few birth-control clinics serving especially a Negro clientele, and several others that are open to all races. According to Norman Himes, "at Cleveland, Cincinnati and Detroit the Negro rate of clinic attendance is *approximately three times* the rate in which Negroes exist in the respective city populations." Miss Constance Fisher, who has had wide experience in social work among Negroes, states that, although many Negroes are reluctant to inform themselves concerning contraceptive methods, "there are increasing numbers who seek birth control information because they feel that if they go on resenting themselves and their mates for physical, economic, and emotional reasons, greater problems are certain to arise, and the existing tensions in their family life are bound to be stretched to their logical ends—the breaking point."

According to G. S. Schuyler, "there is no opposition to birth control among the twelve million brown Americans. Certainly none has been expressed in writing. On the contrary, one encounters everywhere a profound interest in and desire for information on contraceptive methods among them. . . . If anyone should doubt the desire on the part of Negro women and men to limit their families, it is only necessary to note the large scale of 'preventive devices' sold in every drug store in the various Black Belts, and the great number of abortions performed by medical men and quacks." Dr. M. O. Bousfield, after investigating the attitude of the colored people of Harlem toward the work of the birth control clinic in that part of New York City, reported that "Most physicians and ministers are not only sold to the idea and to the need of the work, but are anxious to advance it."

The studies of Pearl on contraception in women residing in or near several large cities of the Eastern States revealed a widespread practice of birth control among both white and Negro women having babies in large urban hospitals. Cards were filled out giving the reproductive history and various other data concerning 30,949 women who obtained obstetrical service. In the third report of

progress of the extensive investigation under way it was stated
that 10,806, or 42.7 per cent, of the white women, and 925, or 16
per cent, of the Negro women reported that they had practiced
some form of contraception before their last visit to the hospital.
In the sample studied it was evident that contraception was employed far less frequently by Negro than by white women, even in
the lowest income groups. Success in preventing pregnancy was
much greater among the well-to-do and better educated white
women. Attempts at contraception among Negroes were followed
by many more mishaps than among whites, and hence there was a
lower proportion of Negro women who had children only when
they wanted them. To judge from the showing made by the Negro
contraceptors in the group investigated, which from the nature of
the case is a selected one, the future decline of the birth rate will be
less rapid in Negroes than in whites.

Will birth control lead to an actual decrease of our Negro population? Proponents of the birth control movement have often contended that the voluntary regulation of births does not necessarily
involve a reduction of the birth rate. Birth control, it is alleged,
will tend to improve the health, material prosperity, and moral
standards of a people, and therefore the birth supply will simply
come to be better regulated and adapted to promote the general
welfare. Granting that a tendency toward such a desirable adjustment is actually operative, there arises the further question, How
will birth control affect the relative net reproductive rates of whites
and blacks? This is a crucial question in relation to the interracial
struggle for numerical supremacy. So far as may be judged from
present trends, both whites and blacks are rapidly approaching a
condition in which the birth supply will be insufficient to insure an
increase in a stabilized population. The increase of both whites
and blacks will be a sort of hang-over effect of their favorable age
composition.

Even in face of a further decline of the birth rate, both races will
go on increasing in number for several years. When an actual decrease in numbers begins to occur, and perhaps even before this, a
compensatory tendency toward an increased birth rate may come
to assert itself. As Malthus has shown, populations automatically
tend to regenerate their losses. It is not unreasonable, therefore, to

suppose that, even when the birth rate is not sufficient for maintenance of a stabilized population, an actual decrease in numbers
will be prevented through the regulative factors influencing population growth. How whites and blacks will be affected by these factors cannot be foreseen, at least by the present writer. Just now the
advantage of a higher birth rate is in favor of the blacks, and the
influence of mortality is against them. According to the volume on
Birth Statistics for 1930 the birth rate of Negroes in the Registration Area was 21.6 per thousand population, and that of the whites
was 18.7. The birth rate of Negroes per thousand enumerated female population from 15 to 45 years of age was 82.5 for Negroes
and 78.4 for native whites. The average number of children ever
born to mothers who had borne a child within the year was 3.6 for
Negroes, 3.1 for total whites, and 3.0 for native whites. According
to all the measures of fertility we possess, therefore, Negro females
are reproducing more rapidly than their white competitors. And
the actual difference in fertility is probably greater than is indicated by the statistics, because of the larger number of Negro births
which escape being recorded.

One might conjecture that, since the desire for family limitation
may prove stronger in the Negroes than in the whites, the dissemi-
nation of birth control information would cause a relatively greater
fall of the birth rate in the Negroes, but in the light of the way in
which birth control has actually worked out in several countries it
would be unsafe to draw this conclusion. One influence which it is
difficult to measure, but which may prove to be of appreciable importance, is the operation of psychological factors growing out of
the Negro's relation to his social environment. Among the Poly-
nesian and Melanesian races of the Pacific, psychological attitudes,
according to a number of anthropologists, have proved to be an important contributory cause of depopulation. It is not likely that
the Negroes, with their cheerful and buoyant temperament, will be
so strongly affected by such factors as the Polynesians. However, if
we may judge from the sentiments which find frequent expression
in Negro literature, the consciousness of the hardships and injustice of their lot has made numerous Negroes loath to bring children
into the world to share their undesirable social heritage.

Naturally, it is the more intelligent, educated, and enterprising of the Negro population among whom the voluntary limitation of the family is most pronounced. Little attention has been paid to this topic, but what is known of the relative fertility of different stocks among the Negroes indicates that the race is afflicted by the same dysgenic forces which are insidiously working to undermine the heredity of the whites. W. E. B. DuBois, after commenting upon the late marriages and few children among the more intelligent class of Negroes, states that "On the other hand, the mass of ignorant Negroes still breed carelessly and disastrously, so that the increase among Negroes, even more than the increase among whites, is from that part of the population least intelligent and fit, and least able to rear their children properly." The same dysgenic tendency is commented upon by Charles S. Johnson, who cites the findings of Dr. E. F. Frazier to the effect that of 174 Negroes listed in *Who's Who in Colored America,* the number of children per family of those 45 years of age and over was 2.3. Professor Kelly Miller finds that 55 colored teachers in Howard University have produced but 37 children, or, considering only the teachers who are married, the average number of children to a family was 1.6. These same teachers came from families with an average number of 6.5 children. Professor Miller remarks that "From a wide acquaintance with the upper life of the Negro race under a wide variety of conditions and circumstances, I am fully convinced that this Howard University group is typical of a like element throughout the race so far as fecundity is concerned. The upper class is headed toward extinction unless reinforced from the fruitful mass below. There are some of sensitive and kindred spirit who shirk the responsibility of parenthood because they do not wish to bring into the world children to be subject to the proscription and obloquy of the Negro's social status." How far the attitude described has led to a deliberate restriction of the Negro birth rate we do not know, but it will probably exert a greater influence as education becomes more widespread.

Chapter VIII

WILL THE WHITES ABSORB THE BLACKS?

THE DESIRABILITY of race mixture from the biological point of view is a subject upon which one meets with the most diverse opinions. Many writers contend that, whether a fusion of races is approved or condemned, it is bound to come anyway, and that whatever may be done to prevent it will merely delay its eventual consummation.

Race mixture has gone on ever since the Negroes were first brought to America. Even a considerable proportion of African Negroes (one-half, according to one estimate) were infiltrated to a certain degree with Caucasian blood before they were imported as slaves. During the period of slavery, miscegenation seems to have occurred more extensively in towns, where there were more opportunities for contacts of whites and blacks, than on the larger plantations, where the Negroes were relatively isolated and more closely supervised. Mulattoes were found in greater abundance in the Border States and the cities of the North. Being more intelligent and adaptable, they were more in demand for personal and domestic service than the husky blacks, who were relegated to work on the plantations. As Reuter remarks, "Slave owners frequently freed their mulatto progeny and sent them into free territory. There were also in these northern regions a large number of freed Negroes and mulattoes whose behavior was not supervised as was that of the slaves. . . . In the northern tier of slave states, the percentage of mulattoes and their increase was greater than in states farther south."

After emancipation, the percentage of mulattoes as compared with blacks continued to increase. Negro women were no longer forced to bear children to their white masters, but they were left unprotected from unscrupulous whites who were ready to take advantage of their lack of any well-developed code of sexual ethics. Partly as an aftermath of slavery, it was customary in many parts of the South for men of prominence in social and political circles to have a family of mulatto children by a Negro mistress. Some of the best blood of the South courses in the veins of mulattoes. Many of these were educated by their white fathers, and even sent to college. Ray Stannard Baker (1908) remarks, "In making my inquiries among colored colleges, I found to my astonishment that in nearly all of them mulatto boys are being educated, and well educated, by their white fathers." And he states that "Wilberforce College ... was largely supported in slavery times by Southern white men, who felt a moral obligation to educate their colored sons and daughters." If we could obtain veracious records of these individuals, the mental ability of many of the intellectual leaders of the colored race could probably be traced to the more prominent whites of the South.

Now that miscegenation is becoming less respectable, it is more nearly confined to the worst elements of both races, and especially of the whites. Many writers who are in a favorable position to judge, have expressed the conviction that unions of whites and blacks are much less frequent than in former years. Mr. A. H. Stone, of Mississippi, who had an intimate knowledge of the colored people of the South, stated in 1903.that "There was a vast amount of amalgamation up to perhaps 20 years ago. Since then there has been a decided change of sentiment on the part of southern white men. I know that not long ago it was not an uncommon thing to find an overseer or superintendent on the plantation who would have from one to half a dozen concubines. This practice has practically been done away with. The planters will not permit their overseers to do such things, and the overseers themselves will not offend in this regard, although they are placed in an extraordinary position, frequently being the only white person in a great multitude of colored people." Mr. Raymond Patterson, in his book *The Negro and His Needs*, states that he finds the opinion "over all the South, that amalgamation of the black and white races is rapidly disappearing"; and Dowd says, "The concensus of opinion among competent observers supports the view that sexual intercourse between whites and blacks is everywhere diminishing."

Sentiment against miscegenation appears to be growing in both whites and blacks, and probably this sentiment was an important factor in causing the diminished proportion of mulattoes which was shown by the census of 1920. As is indicated in table 42, the proportion of mulattoes to blacks increased from 1850 to 1910. Unfortunately the figures understate the number of persons of mixed blood because some very light mulattoes were doubtless classed as whites, and the very dark ones were often classed as blacks. Even in the blacks, there are frequently evident signs of white admixture. In a study of presumably pure-blood and mixed-blood Negroes recently carried on by Hrdlička (1928) in Washington, D. C., the

TABLE 42

COMPARATIVE NUMBERS OF NEGROES AND MULATTOES IN THE UNITED STATES, FROM 1850 TO 1920

Year	Total	Negro	Mulatto		Mulattoes to 1,000 negroes
			Number	Per cent	
1850	3,638,808	3,233,057	405,751	11.2	126
1860	4,441,830	3,853,467	588,363	13.2	153
1870	4,880,000	4,295,960	584,049	12.0	136
1890	7,488,676	6,337,980	1,132,060	15.2	179
1910	9,827,763	7,777,077	2,050,686	20.9	264
1920	10,463,131	8,802,577	1,660,554	15.9	189

proportion of pure blacks was reckoned as less than 30 per cent. This, however, was an urban population; a sample from the black belt would probably have yielded a much higher percentage of unmixed blacks. To how great a degree the Negroes have been bleached, whether a fifth, a third, or even more, cannot be definitely ascertained. The census figures of 1910 and the observations of trained anthropologists indicate that our Negro population was then well on its way toward eventual absorption. Hrdlička has expressed the opinion that "Outside the colored belt in the large cities, approximately three-fourths of the older colored population may today be recognized by the student to have some admixture of white blood."

Mulattoes arise in part from the unions of blacks and whites, in part from the unions of mulattoes among themselves, and in part from the matings of mulattoes with members of either pure race. One might infer, therefore, that, even though race crossing no longer furnishes many new recruits to the mulatto population, the whites, blacks, and mulattoes would continue to maintain about their present relative proportions, and that whatever racial mixture went on, would add to the percentage of mixed bloods until in time all the groups would be completely amalgamated. Owing to the Mendelian segregation of traits, however, the process would not work out in quite this way. Mulattoes commonly produce offspring some of which are lighter and some darker than their parents. Many such children might be classed by the census enumerator as black and others as white. These would be black or white in skin color only, since the other hereditary factors in which the races differ would be distributed in a quite different manner. According to the standards of the census enumerator, the mulattoes would be continually supplying recruits to both the Negro and white races. The mixture might appear to become unscrambled, but this would be to outward appearances only. At the same time, the blood of each race would go on diffusing more widely into the other.

Where two races are intimately associated, amalgamation would seem to be the inevitable outcome. Although the fertile unions of whites and blacks may be few, there are many more such unions between whites and light mulattoes, between light and dark mulattoes, and between mulattoes and pure Negroes. Thus a mingling of the races might slowly be effected. Dr. E. B. Reuter, in his work *The American Race Problem* (1926), tells us that "as a result of intermixture, the Negroes as such will disappear from the population and the race problem will be solved." In his book entitled *Heredity and Human Affairs* (1927), Dr. E. M. East, of Harvard University, states that "the pure Negro will gradually die out and the remaining members of our population will vary imperceptibly from black to white. In the social sense, the black race will be absorbed. In the genetic sense the black germ plasm will remain because the inheritance of genes *is* alternative."

If the blacks are destined to be absorbed by the whites, the fact is not indicated by the census of 1920, which showed a smaller percentage of mulattoes in relation to blacks than in 1910. The enumerators in both these censuses were given virtually the same instructions with respect to classifying blacks and mulattoes. A larger proportion of Negro enumerators was employed in the census of 1910 than in any other census, and a study of the influence of the color of the enumerators on the character of the returns was made in order to test the accuracy of the proportions of blacks and mulattoes indicated. The study showed that this factor "was not the sole nor the principal cause of the indicated decrease." Professor Kelly Miller expressed the conviction that the decrease in mulattoes in 1920 "may be accounted for by the probability that part of the number returned as mulattoes in 1910 were classed as whites in 1920, and partly by the probability that many more of them had been swallowed up by the mass-life of the race and returned as blacks." This, however, is a mere surmise, based on the assumption that the census returns must be wrong. Although there is much uncertainty with respect to the accuracy of the classification of members of the colored population as Negroes or as mulattoes, this would probably affect one census much as it would another. There is, I believe, no adequate reason for doubting the approximate accuracy of the census returns, and for refusing to accept the reduced proportion of mulattoes as an actual fact. It is unfortunate that the census of 1930 made no separate tabulations of Negroes and mulattoes. Such a grouping, even though quite inaccurate, would have been especially valuable at this time.

The decrease in the relative proportion of mulattoes is, I believe, the effect in part of the Mendelian segregation of color factors, but in greater part of the comparative low birth rate of the mulattoes. It is a regrettable fact that our birth and mortality reports make no distinction between mulattoes and blacks, for even a rough classification would be useful. That the mulatto birth rate has been lower than that of the blacks is indicated by several facts. The mulattoes are more common in the North, where the Negro birth rate has been low. In 1920 the percentage of mulattoes in the colored population was highest in the northernmost states, namely, Maine (32.5), New Hampshire (29.3), Vermont (42.8), Minnesota (25.5), and Washington (42.0). There was a high percentage also in South Dakota (36.2), Oregon (31.0), and Ohio (35.2). Taking states by groups, we find the percentage of mulattoes highest in the Pacific States; then follow the East North Central States (20.7), New England (19.4), and the West North Central States (18.7). In the South the percentage is low: South Atlantic States (16.1), East South Central States (15.0), and West South Central States

(15.5). The Middle Atlantic States have the lowest percentage of all (11.6), and the Mountain States have a little less than the average, namely, 18.1.

Perhaps the best rough index of the birth rates in these groups of states from 1910 to 1920 is afforded by the proportions of children under 1 year and under 5 years of age. If we compare these proportions with the percentages of mulattoes in the total Negro population of each state, we shall find that where the proportion of mulattoes is high the total Negro birth rate tends to be low. In the Southern States, the percentage of mulattoes is below the average, and the proportion of Negroes under 5 years is above the average. The Pacific States, which have the highest percentage of mulattoes, have next to the lowest percentage of children under 5 years, the lowest per cent being credited to the Middle Atlantic States.

In the cities, where the mulattoes tend to congregate, the proportion of Negro children under 5 years in 1920 was 8.5 as compared with 12.7 for the rural areas. This, of course, does not indicate that the mulattoes have a low birth rate because their mixed parentage has affected their fertility, but because they live predominantly in areas where the birth rate tends to be low in other classes of the population as well. The same features of regional distribution also tend to enhance the mulatto death rate. These circumstances, I believe, account in large measure for the reduced proportion of mulattoes shown by the census of 1920. Whatever may be the present balance of births and deaths among them, it is improbable that previous to 1920 the northern and urban mulattoes constituted a self-perpetuating group. These form a large part of the mulatto population, and with the diminution of new recruits from the crossing of whites and blacks, it is not surprising that there should have been a decrease in the proportion of mulattoes to blacks between 1910 and 1920. The great source of the natural increase of Negroes is the rural South, and there the mulattoes from a relatively low percentage of the Negro population.

Since the peculiarities of their distribution make the mulattoes a relatively sterile group, it may happen in the future that the white and Negro races will become on the whole more widely divergent. Should this occur, the process of race assimilation would be very much delayed. Some black genes would still pass into the whites and some white genes into the blacks, but with the numerical reduction of the intermediate group which now serves as a sort of bridge between the two races, this transfer would be greatly checked. The mulatto population, so far as it escapes extinction, will probably be slowly absorbed into the blacks and very slightly into the whites, giving the blacks a somewhat lighter color and producing in time a more homogeneous race.

The views I have ventured to set forth, although with some hesitation, are based on the assumption that the census returns are approximately correct in respect to the decreasing proportions of the mulattoes. These returns are probably very wide of the mark as an expression of the actual proportion at any one time. The proportions may be grossly understated or overstated without vitiating one's conclusion concerning the general trends provided they are wrong in the same direction and in about the same degree. If the ratio of mulattoes to blacks is 50 per cent below the mark, or even more, unless there was some very widespread change in the standards of classification between 1910 and 1920, despite essentially the same instructions which were given to enumerators, there would not have been the very marked reduction of reported mulattoes which the census revealed. Such changes of standards might affect the proportions of Negroes and mulattoes reported from local areas, but these discrepancies would tend to balance up in the total returns. Northern enumerators might be held to possess different standards from those of the South, but this would have affected the grouping in the 1910 census much as it did in 1920. There is, in spite of the effect of migration, a broad general agreement in respect to the geographical distribution of mulattoes revealed by the last two censuses. Although there are certain reported changes in local distribution which I am compelled to look upon with extreme suspicion, I can hardly believe that the census returns have been vitiated by so uniform and extensive a bias as to give an entirely wrong index of the trend of race mixture between 1910 and 1920. Besides, the reported change is not improbable *a priori* when we consider the factors reducing the ratio of mulattoes to blacks.

If we grant that the two races will eventually fuse, there are some features of the process as it is now working out which possess appreciable biological significance. The mixture of white and colored races in the United States is chiefly the result of illicit relations between white men and colored women. Throughout the South and in many states of the North and West, the intermarriage of whites and Negroes is prohibited by law. The prohibitions extend to marriages between whites and colored people having one-fourth, one-eighth, or, as in Virginia and Georgia, even any trace whatever of Negro blood. The production of children by a Negro or a mulatto man and a white woman is relatively rare; in the South it may even lead, as it has on several occasions, to the lynching of the father. In the few states of the North in which the marriage of whites with Negroes is legalized, the number of such marriages is small and seems to be decreasing notwithstanding the migration of Negroes into the Northern States. The studies of Hoffman showed that such marriages in Michigan (1874 to 1892), Rhode Island (1881 to 1893), Connecticut (1883 to 1893), and the city of Boston (1885 to 1890) were in every place declining in number. It is a curious fact that most of these racial intermarriages are between white women and Negro men. The women who enter into such unions are usually either unsophisticated recent immigrants or women of very low class. An investigator of Negro-white marriage in Minneapolis states that "Outside the innocent and ignorant foreign-born country girls, none of these women are to be pitied, for, leaving out the exceptions referred to, the majority are social degenerates or moral outcasts." In Hoffman's study of 37 unions of whites and Negroes, 8 were between white men and Negro women, and 29 were unions, legal or otherwise, between Negro men and white women. The white men were in general a worthless lot. Of the 29 white women, 12 were known prostitutes, 3 were of ill repute, charged, in addition, with cruelty and abuse of children, 2 were murdered by their colored husbands, 1 committed suicide, 1 became insane, 2 sued for divorce, 2 deserted their husbands, 5 were apparently satisfied with their choice, while for 4 the information could not be obtained." The Negro husbands were not altogether exemplary either. There was one Negro, a barber, of good character. "Five were of fair repute; nine were idlers, loafers, or drunkards; eleven were of proven criminal and anti-social tendencies; while for three the character could not be ascertained." Fortunately few children resulted from these unions.

From what is known of the extent and the effects of marriages between whites and Negroes, it is evident that we may dismiss them as of very minor biological importance. The fact of outstanding significance in respect to race mixture is that, since it is mainly the result of illicit unions between white men and colored women, it brings about a kind of race fusion which substitutes white germ plasm for black without causing a corresponding loss to the whites. The Negro woman who bears a child to a white father is precluded for a time at least from bearing a child to a black father, but the white father is not prevented from producing children by white women. Mulattoes are thus substitutes for Negroes, but not for whites. One may say that the blacks have been bleached without the accompaniment of a corresponding darkening of the white race. Were it not for miscegenation, the blacks might have been more numerous by the number of the mulatto population, but the white population would have been little, if at all, reduced in number. Race assimilation has thus been largely a one-sided process at the expense of the black race.

So long as miscegenation occurs on this basis, there will be a gradual substitution of white germ plasm for black in our population. If we look upon the interracial struggle as a struggle between genes, or hereditary factors, the way in which race mixture has been taking place is notably favorable for the survival of white heredity. There is, however, a limit to this one-sided method of race assimilation. It comes when the blacks are sufficiently bleached to be indistinguishable from whites, or when their remaining color is no longer a bar to intermarriage. Then there will be nothing to hinder the remaining black genes from becoming distributed to an indefinite extent throughout the white population. Some Negro germ plasm has thus passed across the line into the presumably pure whites. But before the white race takes in all the black genes, if it ever does, the latter will be greatly reduced by a process of dilution. Or, in other words, if the white race is destined eventually to engulf the blacks the latter will first be considerably bleached before they are absorbed.

Having treated briefly of the course of race mixture, we may now consider its effects. One might quote a variety of opinions on the influence of race crossing, ranging from the view that it is a com-

176   *The Negro's Struggle for Survival*

mon cause of the downfall of nations to the claim that the highest
achievements of civilization occur only among peoples of mixed
origin. A favorite description of the crossbreed is that he inherits
the vices of both races and the virtues of neither. Many of the
shortcomings of hybrid stock are doubtless the result of social and
economic factors which operate quite independently of heredity.
According to a very prevalent opinion, the physique of the mulatto
is inferior to that of both blacks and whites. Dr. F. L. Hoffman, in
his paper on "Race Traits and Tendencies of the American Negro
(1896)," quotes from the report of the Provost Marshal in the
Civil War, several opinions of examining surgeons, most of which
are to the effect that the mulattoes have much less vitality than the
pure blacks. According to Gould, the lung capacity of mulatto recruits (158 cubic inches) was less than that of either the whites
(184.7 cubic inches) or the Negroes (158.9 cubic inches). The chest
circumference averaged 35.8 inches for the whites, 35.1 for the Negroes, and 34.97 for the mulattoes. The numbers of respirations
per minute were found to be as follows: whites, 16.4; Negroes,
17.7; mulattoes, 19.

Verdicts in respect to the fertility of the mulattoes have been
equally unfavorable. Nott (1843) found the mulattoes of South
Carolina decidedly infertile. Woodruff (*Expansion of Races,* 1909,
p. 251) tells us that "The mulatto invariably dies out unless new
black blood is infused into the mixed race, and, though some families survive a few generations, as a rule there is absolute extinction
of such feeble offspring." A quite contrary opinion is expressed by
Dr. H. E. Jordan (1913), to the effect that "the mulatto is probably
more prolific than the normal average of either white or Negro."
The recent studies of Frazier (1933) also showed that mulattoes
were not less fertile than the blacks, but the numbers dealt with
were not very large. The fact is that we have no adequate data on a
sufficiently large scale to enable one to decide how the mixed origin
of the mulatto affects fertility, if it affects it at all.

One might conjecture that the crossing of such distinct races as
the Negroes and the whites might produce various inharmonious
combinations of characteristics, especially in the second and subsequent generations. Dr. Mjoen (1926) concludes, both from his experiments on rabbits and his observations on the relation between

hybrid origin and mortality in human beings, that the crossing of distinct races produces many disharmonies of organization in the second generation of hybrids. Professor W. E. Castle (1926) takes issue with these conclusions and considers that the evidence for disharmonies among hybrids is quite inadequate. It is of little value to appeal to experiments on plants and animals in this connection, because one can find in this way data to support almost any conclusion. Our only resource is the study of the actual phenomena of race crossing observed among human beings, and such studies carried on in anything like a scientific manner are rare. Perhaps the best investigation on the results of unions between whites and blacks is that made by Dr. Eugene Fischer (1913) on the Boer-Hottentot hybrids of South Africa. These hybrids constitute a vigorous and prolific stock, but they are quite variable, as one might expect in accordance with the principles of Mendelian segregation. To judge from the many illustrations included in Dr. Fischer's volume, there are not a few rather queer and apparently incongruous jumbles of racial characteristics in this hybrid people.

One might expect that the mulatto population of the United States would exhibit an appreciable segregation of traits, and would therefore be more variable than either of its two chief component races, but Herskovits (1928), who has made numerous measurements of whites, blacks, and mulattoes, has come to a contrary conclusion. He believes that he has shown that the American Negro race is an amalgam of white, black, and a small percentage of Indian elements. "From this mixture," he says, "is being welded, and is already discernible, a definite physical type which may be called the American Negro. It is not like any type from which it has come; it is not white; it is not Negro; it is not Mongoloid. It is all of them and none of them."

The conclusion of Herskovits that pure Negroes, instead of being in the majority as our census figures might imply, are really in the minority, may possibly be true. Certainly the proportion of pure blacks is less than the census returns indicate. The statement that the mixed blacks constitute a type less variable than either the whites or the relatively pure blacks is one which a geneticist would be strongly disposed to question, and Herskovits has therefore supported his thesis by a large amount of anthropometric data. These

were drawn mainly from Negroes of various colleges, Harlem in
New York City, and rural sections of West Virginia and Mississippi. The chief characters measured were stature, sitting height,
width of hips and shoulders, height, width and depth of nose,
thickness of lips, height and width of face, length and width of ear,
height and breadth of head, cephalic index, and skin color. In some
of these characters the mixed Negroes showed a greater degree of
variability than the samples of whites used for comparison; in
other characters, whites were the more variable. But in some characters the differences in the sigmas indicating the variability of the
two races were less than three times their probable error, and therefore of doubtful significance.

In considering the problem of whether the American Negro population has become more variable as a result of the admixture of
white blood, it must be borne in mind that both whites and pure
Negroes include several types which differ in a number of anthropometric characters. It we could compare the variability of the
original Negro and white American stocks with the variability of
the mixture resulting from their union, we could form some estimate of the degree in which the variability of the hybrid population was affected. Our present white population, with its various
ethnic elements differing in height, body build, cephalic index, and
various other physical characters, is an unusually diversified group.
Perhaps the old Americans measured by Hrdlička are as close to
the white ancestry of the mulatto population as any group of which
we have anthropometric measurements. It is safe to assume that
the present white population of the United States is anthropologi-
cally more heterogeneous than the white elements who contributed
to the generation of our mixed Negroes. If, for example, we should
find that certain characters were less variable in American Negroes
than in the present white population with its greatly diversified immigrant stocks, it would by no means follow that race crossing had
not enhanced the variability of our mixed Negroes. In cephalic index, for example, to take a much used characteristic of race, the
Negroes are predominantly dolichocephalic, as are some groups of
the whites, but American whites also include a large proportion of
brachycephalic types, especially among recent immigrants. In cephalic index Nordic and Slav differ more than Nordic and Negro,

and a mixture of Negroes with a predominantly Nordic stock might be less variable in head form than many large samples of the white population of the United States.

Nor can we obtain conclusive evidence on the problem by comparing the variability of American mixed Negroes with the variability of relatively homogeneous groups, such as the Scandinavians or particular African tribes, because both the white and the black contributors to our mulatto population were probably more diversified than these groups. The problem presents many difficulties, because we have no very good average standard measurements of either of the two chief ancestral components of the mixed Negroes, and because it is difficult to separate accurately the mixed from the unmixed Negroes, and especially to estimate the various degrees of mixture. We have to infer what the variability of these components was like from comparisons with existing groups which are more or less different from them.

Herskovits in his extensive paper on "The Anthropometry of the American Negro" has not only given numerous measurements of his own, but has also made a useful compilation of other data bearing on this problem. From the facts presented it will be instructive to make two sets of comparisons. We may compare the variability of American Negroes as a whole, assuming that they represent in a large measure a mixed group, with the variability of such other white or black groups as have been measured on a sufficiently extensive scale. We may also compare the variability of American Negroes known to be of mixed origin with the variability of relatively purebred American Negroes, on the one hand, and with that of whites, on the other. In considering the variability of the Negro population, it should be pointed out that, according to the principles of Mendelian segregation, we should expect hybrids to show enhanced variability only in those characters in which the two races present hereditary differences. In respect to stature, for example, whites and blacks in the United States differ on the whole very little. The average stature of 95,596 white recruits for the World War was 171.99 cm., and that of 6,454 Negroes was 171.97 cm. The average heights of different white stocks such as Norwegians and Italians differ much more than this. The Negroes in the United States Army, however, show a slightly greater variability in stature than the white recruits show, the standard deviations being 6.91 and 6.66, respectively. The variability of the 887 Negroes measured by Herskovits and his coworkers was somewhat less, namely, 6.40.

In sitting height we have a character in which Negroes are relatively shorter than whites, but the degree of variability of this character in Negroes and whites is much the same. Using the coefficient of variation as an index, which is preferable to the standard deviation for most traits, we find that in 6,433 Negroes in the Army the variability was 3.98, and that in 96,239 whites the variability was 3.88, a number precisely the same as that derived from 840 Negroes in Herskovits' series.

In general, Negroes differ from whites in having somewhat broader shoulders and narrower hips, and in both these characters the Negro Army recruits and the 476 Negroes measured at Howard University were a little less variable than the white recruits. In length of head, width of head, and cephalic index the American Negroes measured by Herskovits were more variable than most of the white and colored groups with which they were compared and, with the exception of the cephalic index in 167 skulls measured by Todd, more variable than any of the ethnic groups represented by more than one hundred individuals. In height of head 839 American Negroes proved to be less variable than 727 old Americans, but in minimum forehead width, the variability of 535 American Negroes and 100 Negro cadavers was greater than that of old Americans, Swedes, or any other group. Height of ear in Negroes is less variable, but width of ear more variable, than they are in old Americans. Taking the characters whose variability was measured by Herskovits, we find that, as compared with old Americans, Negroes were more variable in nine characters and less variable in two. In Todd's measurements of seventy-five traits in 100 male Negro and 100 male white cadavers, Negroes were more variable in thirty-six traits, whites were more variable in thirty-six traits also, and the variability was the same in only three traits.

The anthropometric measurements made in the United States Army supply a large material for comparison since they include thousands instead of hundreds of persons. As both Negroes and whites were drawn from numerous localities and consisted of adults selected on a common basis of fitness for military service, they af-

ford valuable material for comparisons. As indicated by the coefficient of variability, the Army Negroes proved to be the more
variable in stature, sitting height, weight, height of sternal notch,
knee height, and forearm; the whites were more variable in chest
measurements, shoulder width, length of arms, circumference of
waist, hip, and thigh, and transverse pelvic diameter. So far as the
Army measurements go, the variability of Negroes, as indicated by
the coefficient of variability, does not differ greatly from that of
the whites, and in several of the traits measured the two races show
on the average but little difference.

In determining whether mixed American Negroes are more variable than the relatively unmixed types, we have to rely mainly
upon Herskovits' measurements made at Howard University. In
this study Negroes were classed in eight groups according to the
proportions of black and white in their ancestry. Some traits were
found to vary more or less consistently with the proportion of white
blood, but others did not. I have calculated from the sigmas given
by Herskovits the coefficients of variability for various traits in
the relatively pure Negroes and in the various classes of mixed
groups, and I find that the mixed Negroes are the more variable in
stature, sitting height, width of hips, height of head, head length,
head width, cephalic index, distance between both the inner and
the outer angles of the eyes, interpupillary distance, nasal height,
nasal width, upper facial height, total facial height, bizygomatic
width, thickness of lips, width of mouth, width of hands, length of
middle finger, and black, yellow, and white pigmentation. The unmixed Negroes proved to be somewhat more variable in shoulder
width, nasal depth, height and width of ear, minimum forehead
width, and amount of red pigment. On the whole, therefore, the
obviously mixed American Negroes are somewhat more variable
than those which are relatively purebred, as we might expect in
accordance with the principles of Mendelian segregation, although
even the relatively pure Negroes have probably been made somewhat more variable through the admixture of white blood.

From a careful consideration of the evidence presented by Herskovits, the Army anthropometric data, and such other fragmentary
materials which bear on the problem, I am unable to accept the conclusion of Herskovits that "the type which the American Negro

seems to be evolving in this country is a relatively homogeneous one." The imperfect evidence at our disposal indicates rather that, as populations go, it is relatively heterogeneous. It is more variable in most traits that most African tribes. It is more variable than most samples of European peoples that have been measured, such as Swedes, English and Scottish students, etc., or the soldiers of various European nations in the United States Army. It is more variable, also, in most traits, than the old Americans measured by Hrdlička. It may not be much more variable than the present exceedingly heterogeneous white American population. If we compare the mean values of the traits measured in the Army for various foreign groups, we find that for most traits there are greater differences between these means than between the means for American Negroes and for total American whites. For most traits the variability of the white soldiers as a whole is, as one would expect, greater than the variability in most of the individual groups, such as the Germans, English, or Italians. Apparently immigration, and especially the more recent immigration, has contributed to make us an anthropometrically diverse people. I cannot see anything in the evidence submitted by Herskovits that must "cause us to reconsider the Mendelian mechanisms operative in a large number of crosses between individuals of racial groups as diverse in the traits measured as are the ancestral races of the American Negro." If, as most of the evidence indicates, the traits measured by the anthropologists depend upon a fairly large number of genetic factors, the facts are roughly about what one might expect according to Mendelian theories.

As K. Wagner has pointed out in his paper on "The Variability of Hybrid Populations," the relation between variability and hybrid origin presents a complex problem for the solution of which adequate data are not available. Possibly the American Negro population will become more homogeneous with the lapse of time, but if it incorporates new white blood to any great degree, it will probably become more variable. At any rate, it will be exposed to two opposing tendencies, namely, inbreeding, which will make for homogeneity, and outbreeding with a highly varied white population, to say nothing of Indians and Mexicans, which will make for diversity. Probably the lighter and the darker elements will be combined to form a more nearly uniform brown color, but the Mendelian segregation of color factors which is observed in most Negro-white crosses will keep up almost indefinitely.

From such data as we possess, it seems evident that, as Herskovits points out, American Negroes are more or less intermediate in their physical characteristics between such African natives as have been measured and white Americans or Europeans. In this process of fusion, a rôle of greater or less importance may be played by sexual selection. Negro men prefer to select the lighter-colored women of their race. This tendency was unmistakably revealed by the studies of Herskovits and has been found also by Davenport in his studies of matings in Jamaica. Among the students of Howard University, the mother was lighter than the father in 56.5 per cent of the students; about the same in color, in 13.2 per cent; and darker than the father, in 30.3 per cent. In his measurements of skin color, Herskovits found that among the Negroes of Harlem the wife was the lighter in 56.5 per cent of the cases; about the same in color, in 14.5 per cent; and darker than the husband, in 29.0 per cent. There is, however, a tendency for like to mate with like in the matter of color. How sexual selection works out depends, of course, upon the kinds of individuals who remain unmated. Herskovits asks, "What happens to the dark woman? I confess I do not know. It may be that they become the wives in second marriages. I note a tendency, where the wife is older than her husband, to find her darker than he is." That women are not as a rule darker than the men is indicated by Herskovits' measurements of a series in Harlem, which gave an average of 69.5 for the men and 69.8 for the women. Whether the black girls are likely to be outbred by their fairer sisters, we do not yet know. If we had adequate data on the reproductivity of the two types in rural and in urban areas, I suspect that the black girl would be found to be more than holding her own.

CHAPTER IX

NEGRO MIGRATION AND ITS BIOLOGICAL EFFECTS

IN THE FLUX AND TURMOIL of racial change which has gone on throughout the course of human history, migration has played an important rôle. Usually peoples migrate from one of two causes: (1) they are forced out by unfavorable circumstances, such as over-population, climatic changes, or the pressure of hostile invaders, or (2) they are lured by the superior opportunities afforded by other lands. Very often migration is the outcome of a combination of both of these causes. With the development of rapid and relatively cheap means of transportation, the movements of peoples become more quickly responsive both to pressure from within and to allurements from without—as in migration of Negroes in the United States, especially during and after the Great War.

It is only within the last two decades that the migration of Negroes in the United States has assumed a magnitude that has made it a disquieting problem, for such it soon became to both the North and the South, although for quite different reasons. It was given a powerful impetus by the Great War, and it was further stimulated by the restriction of foreign immigration. Nevertheless, even under normal conditions, it was bound to become greater in volume as a result of the factors which have led to its gradual increase ever since emancipation. Before 1860, Negro migration in the United States was mainly involuntary. Being mostly slaves, the Negroes went where they were taken, and as slavery became more restricted to the South, the Negro population came to be more concentrated in this region. From 1790 to 1830, there was a slight increase in the proportion of Negroes in the South and a relatively more rapid decrease in the North. After 1830, the percentage of Negroes in the South slowly decreased and that of the North increased; but this was owing to the growth of the slave population in one Northern State, namely, Missouri. Were it not for the existence of slavery in this state, there would have been a continuous concentration of Negroes in the South and a corresponding decrease in relation to total numbers in the North from 1790 to 1860.

The free Negroes in the United States are of interest in relation to the effects of migration because they constituted over 10 per cent of the total Negro population from 1800 to the emancipation in 1863. From 1790 to 1860 the distribution of free Negroes between the North and the South varied relatively little, being between 40 and 50 per cent in the North and 50 and 60 per cent in the South. More free Negroes would doubtless have gone into the North were it not for the restrictive legislation passed by a number of northern states.

The vital statistics of the free Negroes make a very poor showing. Mr. Cummings, in his volume, *Negro Population* (1918), remarks that "The increase of the free colored population, although in this class natural growth was continuously supplemented by accessions from the slave population, was nevertheless insufficient in the decades immediately preceding the Civil War to produce a rate of growth equal to the natural increase of the Negro population as a whole. In the decade 1840 to 1850, the percentage increase of the slave population was more than double and in the decade following nearly double that of the free colored. The *Compendium of the Seventh Census* (1850) commented upon the 'declining ratio of the increase of the free colored in every section,' which in New England 'is now almost nothing,' and in the Southern States 'only one-fourth as great as between 1800 and 1810.' The report of 1860, also, noted that the rate of increase of the free colored had been gradually declining for several decades, 'to 1860, when the increase throughout the United States was but 1 per cent per annum.' "

Apparently the free Negro population did not constitute a self-perpetuating group. As Mr. Cummings points out, this was probably owing in part to the fact that the free Negroes were somewhat older than the slaves, "less normally distributed by sex, and, therefore, probably characterized by a marital condition less favorable to rapid increase." Free Negroes were also more abundant in the North, where until recently deaths have been more numerous among the Negroes than births; they were also more urban in their distribution than the slaves of the South. The free Negroes as a group probably suffered much from the effects of migration into colder climates and urban areas.

The emancipation of slaves in the Civil War naturally resulted in the exodus of many Negroes into the North. Between 1860 and 1870, the increases of Negroes as compared with the increases from 1850 to 1860 were as follows for the different areas of the North and West:

TABLE 43

COMPARATIVE INCREASE IN NEGRO POPULATION, 1850-1870

States	1850–1860	1860–1870
New England.............	1,690	6,994
Middle Atlantic...........	4,549	16,743
East North Central........	18,504	66,798
West North Central........	30,128*	22,043
Mountain.................	163	1,320
Pacific...................	3,075	581
Total..................	58,109	114,479

* Mainly because of the increase of 28,463 Negroes in the slave state of Missouri.

Although the Negro population of the North increased from 1860 to 1870 much more than in any previous decade, the percentage of Negroes in the South was not greatly affected, being reduced from 92.2 per cent to 90.6 per cent, or 1.6 per cent. The percentage would have been reduced still more were it not for the surplus of deaths over births in the North and the rapid increase of Negroes in the South in this prolific period. From 1860 to 1870 the Negro increase in the North and West was 32.2 per cent as compared with an increase of 20.1 per cent between 1850 and 1860. From 1870 to 1910, the Negro population gradually increased though at a slackening rate in both the North and the South. Relative to the Negro population of 1870, the increase in the North and West was the more rapid, namely, 135 per cent as compared with 97 per cent in the Southern States, although, of course, the actual numerical increase was much less. In the West, where there were very few Negroes, the increase was proportionally still more rapid, but even in 1910 the total Negro population of that region was only 50,662.

Notwithstanding the migration of many Negroes, the geographical center of Negro population moved remarkably little, in fact, only 36 miles, in the thirty years between 1880 and 1910. This slow movement, as was pointed out by Mr. Cummings, is explained by the fact that migrations in opposite directions had a neutralizing effect. Previously this center had been moving southward and westward at the rate of nearly 50 miles a decade from its position near Petersburg, Va., in 1790, to near Fort Payne in northeastern Alabama. Between 1910 and 1920, the center moved for the first time

TABLE 44

TOTAL NATIVE NEGROES LIVING IN THE SOUTH IN RELATION TO STATE OF BIRTH

Date	Born in South		Born in North or West		Born elsewhere	
	Number	Percentage	Number	Percentage	Number	Percentage
1870...........	4,400,132	99.6	11,513	0.4	1,073	....
1880...........	5,926,322	99.6	22,039	0.4	45	....
1890...........	6,667,014	98.1	23,268	0.3	63,635	0.9
1900...........	7,866,807	99.4	30,397	0.2	18,202	0.2
1910...........	8,668,619	99.2	41,489	0.34	28,750	0.34
1920...........	8,820,149	99.2	47,223	0.32	28,270	0.32
1930...........	9,273,245	99.2	54,716	0.20	19,002	0.20

to the north and east, traveling 9.4 miles east and 19.4 miles north into the northwestern corner of Georgia.

Much of our knowledge of the migration of our Negro population has to be deduced from the data collected by the census on place of birth of the population of the several states. Tables 44 and 45 giving the percentage of native-born Negroes living in the general region in which they were born shows that a very high percentage of northern Negroes were born in the South, whereas a very small percentage of southern Negroes were born in the North.

The actual numbers born in the South and living in the North and West have been over ten times as great as the numbers born in the North or West and living in the South. The proportion of northern Negroes born in the South very slowly increased up to 1890, after which it more rapidly rose from about one-third to considerably over one-half—an index of the ever increasing influx from the South into the North. Of the native Negro population born in the South, 95.2 per cent were living in the South in 1910, 4.6 in the North, and 0.3 per cent in the West. Of the native Negro population born in the North, 91.8 per cent were living in the North in 1910, 6.3 per cent in the South, and 1.9 per cent in the West. These relative proportions were not much changed in the next decade. In 1920, of those born in the North, 91.7 per cent were living in the North, 6.2 per cent were living in the South, and 2.1 per cent were

TABLE 45

TOTAL NATIVE NEGROES LIVING IN THE NORTH AND WEST IN RELATION TO STATE OF BIRTH

Date	Born in South		Born in North or West		Born elsewhere	
	Number	Percentage	Number	Percentage	Number	Percentage
1870..........	149,100	32.9	304,073	67.0	403	....
1880..........	198,029	32.1	420,318	68.0	23	....
1890..........	241,855	33.8	457,833	64.1	15,092	2.1
1900..........	349,651	38.9	539,692	60.1	8,909	1.0
1910..........	440,534	42.0	595,401	56.8	12,631	1.20
1920..........	780,894	52.3	694,568	46.5	18,324	1.22
1930..........	1,426,213	58.3	985,305	40.3	33,956	1.39

living in the West, thus indicating a somewhat greater tendency of northern Negroes to move west. In 1930, of those born in the North, 92.9 per cent were living in the North, 5.2 per cent were living in the South, and 1.8 per cent were living in the West.

It is obvious that the growth of the Negro population of the Northern States is, in large part if not mainly, the direct result of migration from the South. The age composition of the Negroes has been more favorable for natural increase in the North than in the South, owing to the larger percentage of women in the child-bearing period. Nevertheless, the North did not compare with the South in the propagation of Negroes. In 1910, deaths outnumbered births in the Negro population of all the states and larger cities of the North, and this despite the immigration of persons whose ages were on the whole favorable for a rapid natural increase.

In respect to reproductivity, the Negro population of the North has stood in sharp contrast to our foreign immigrants. The birth rate of our foreign born has greatly exceeded that of the nat.. born stock and has yielded a surplus of births over deaths which gives our immigrant population a greater net rate of increase than our native-born inhabitants. The foreigners have had to cope with conditions in our northern cities which have often been as unfavorable as those which confronted the northern Negro. But the foreigners have flourished while the Negroes have fared much less happily. The failure of the Negro is attributable to a low birth rate combined with a high death rate. These again are chiefly traceable to two sets of factors which may be subsumed under the headings of climate and urbanization. At least it is these two sets of factors which were most active in causing the differences in the vital statistics of northern and southern Negroes in the decade from 1910 to 1920.

This decade, and especially the last four years of the period, saw a remarkable and unprecedented influx of Negroes into the North. How extensive this invasion was cannot be accurately ascertained, because many Negro migrants subsequently returned to the Southern States. In the war period, various estimates were made of the number of Negroes who had gone north. Mr. W. T. Jones, President of the Colored Patriotic League, calculated that more than 300,000 Negro laborers had moved from twelve Southern States in less than a year (in 1917). DuBois estimated that 250,000 Negro laborers had left the South up to June, 1917. Estimates based on insurance records, numbers of railway tickets sold to Negroes, and on various other sources vary from 150,000 to 750,000. In the *Bulletin on Negro Migration in 1916–17*, issued by the Department of Labor, Mr. Dillard states : "I should be inclined to set the limits at 150,000 and 350,000, and my guess would be 200,000. The number of those who have returned South is equally uncertain. Some say 10 per cent; some say as much as 30 per cent." H. G. Duncan remarks that "after weighing all the estimates the result seems to show that from 400,000 to 500,000 Negroes had traveled north during the period of migration which ran at high tide during the years 1916–1917. Of course, these estimates are not much more than a guess. How many of these Negroes returned South no one knows. But, after all is said, I think we can say that there are nearly 2,000,000 Negroes now living in the North."

When the returns of the 1920 census became available, they showed that the number of Negroes living in the North and West was 1,550,900. This represents a gain in these sections of 472,564 Negroes in the decade 1910–1920 as compared to that of 167,311 from 1900 to 1910. Since our data indicate that in this period there were more deaths than births in the northern Negro population,

TABLE 46

INCREASE OF NEGRO POPULATION IN NORTHERN CITIES

	1910	1920	Percentage of increase	1930	Percentage of increase
Chicago...........	44,103	109,458	148.18	233,903	113.7
Cincinnati.........	19,639	30,079	53.15	47,818	59.0
Cleveland.........	8,448	34,451	307.80	71,899	108.7
Detroit............	5,741	40,838	611.34	120,066	194.0
Indianapolis.......	21,816	34,678	58.96	43,967	26.8
Kansas City, Mo...	23,566	30,719	30.35	38,574	25.6
New York.........	91,709	152,467	66.25	327,706	114.9
Philadelphia.......	84,459	134,229	48.9	219,599	63.6
Pittsburgh.........	25,623	37,725	47.2	54,983	45.7
St. Louis..........	43,960	69,854	58.9	93,580	34.0

it is probable that, were it not for migration, there would have been fewer Negroes in the North in 1920 than there were in 1910, instead of 472,564 more. By a conservative estimate, at least a half-million Negroes must have entered and remained in the Northern States in the decade 1910–1920.

As a result of this wholesale trek of black humanity, a number of Southern States (Delaware, Kentucky, Tennessee, Alabama, Mississippi, and Louisiana) had actually fewer Negroes in 1920 than in 1910. The greatest loss in this period was sustained by Mississippi (namely, 74,303), but 25,718 were lost by Kentucky, 21,330 by Tennessee, 13,617 by Alabama, 7,630 by Louisiana, and 846 by Delaware, although in the South as a whole there was a gain of 162,804 Negroes. In this same decade the Negro population of several Northern States and cities showed a phenomenal growth. In New York City the Negro population was increased by 60,758 Negroes, or 66.3 per cent; in Philadelphia, by 49,770, or 58.9 per cent:

in Chicago, by 65,355, or 148.2 per cent; in Cleveland, by 26,003, or 307.8 per cent; and in Detroit, by 35,097, or 611.3 per cent. The increase of Negroes in a few of the larger cities of the North is shown in table 46.

The earlier Negro migrants went mainly into the Border States and the states directly adjoining these on the north. There was relatively little migration from the extreme South. But the later influx drew Negroes from all parts of the Southern States, as was indicated by the data on the birthplaces of northern Negroes given in the 1920 census, and the losses in the Negro population in some of the Gulf States. The fact that multitudes of Negroes were drawn from so great a distance resulted in part from the efforts of northern employers to attract Negro laborers. Agents were sent throughout the South to recruit Negro employees and to arrange for their transportation. Even special trains were provided to carry the Negroes north free of charge, with the understanding, of course, that the laborer would have to reimburse his employer for the price of his ticket. The prospect of earning from two to five times as much pay as they had been receiving made a strong appeal to workers who were ambitious to improve their economic status. Coincident with the demand for labor in the North was a condition of unusual unemployment in the South. For this there were two chief reasons: the invasion of the boll weevil from Mexico, which caused serious losses to the cottongrowers; and the extensive floods which occurred at about the same time. In the resulting disturbed economic circumstances, the Negro population was more than usually willing to seek its fortune elsewhere.

The departure of so many Negroes, however, created a serious inconvenience and financial loss in several parts of the South and led to determined efforts on the part of white employers to keep Negro laborers from migrating. In several states and municipalities, laws were passed to check or prevent the recruiting of laborers by northern employers. The economic loss sustained by the South as a result of this exodus of workers has been estimated at $200,000,000 (Duncan). The desire to retain Negro laborers in the South had its effect in raising wages and in leading to efforts to improve the living conditions of the colored population. As Woodson remarked: "The migration northward has been a great stimulant to municipal improvements in southern Negro neighborhoods. Wishing to keep the Negroes who were moving to better their conditions, southern municipalities became more willing to improve their colored communities. When Negroes moved to the larger industrial centers, they learned that they could find better houses there, better neighborhoods, better recreations, and better schools. As a rule, these first comers to northern cities occupied quarters where immigrants formerly lived; and these neighborhoods had not been neglected as wantonly as Negro neighborhoods in southern cities."

The success of their compatriots in the North naturally created the desire for better living conditions among the Negroes of the South. At the same time the southern whites at last awakened to the fact that it was to their own interest to do something more for their colored neighbors. When the neglect, unjust discrimination, and ruthless exploitation which the southern Negroes had so long endured were found to be causing the emigration of laborers which the South was loath to lose, the conclusion became apparent, and it was widely voiced by the southern press, that more effort should be made to improve the condition of the Negroes if they were to be induced to resist the allurements of the North. The Negro went north not for economic reasons alone, but because he found there a greater measure of freedom, political rights which were frequently denied him in the South, better schools for his children, and no Jim Crow cars. Occasionally the outrages committed in a race riot or a series of lynchings would send a group of Negroes into the North, as was illustrated by the exodus of Negroes from Wilmington, N. C., in 1898, and from Atlanta, Ga., after the riot of 1906. In commenting on a letter written to the *Economic World,* in which it was stated that "burning Negroes at the stake, lynching them, night-riding them, bad Jim-Crow cars, bad schools, general insecurity of person and property, and other meannesses of the southern whites are driving the Negro man cotton producing power out of the South and into the mills, foundries, and factories of the North and West," the editor of this journal remarks that "much southern literature passes over our desks every week, and we find it unanimous in holding that the Negro will certainly leave the South as time goes on, and with a corresponding detriment to southern agriculture and industry, unless the traditional attitude of mind of the less enlightened part of the white population and the traditional manner of treating them are speedily abandoned in favor of a more sympathetic, a wiser, and a juster appreciation of the economic and social dues of his race."

During the World War, much was made of these injustices by the northern Negro press, which lent its influence to inducing the southern Negroes to avail themselves of the northern haven of refuge. The press of the South carried on a strong contrary propaganda, which dwelt upon the wretched conditions of the deluded migrants in the northern cities, their high death rate, and their inability to find employment; but this had little effect in checking the stampede.

On the whole, the injustices suffered by the southern Negroes were probably a very minor factor in causing migration. Certainly, the treatment of southern Negroes was no worse when migration was at its height than it was in previous decades when relatively few Negroes left their homes. The various other causes of migration taken together were probably less effective than the economic factor. Dr. E. E. Lewis has attempted to estimate the relative strength of the industrial demand and the failure in agricultural crops in causing Negroes to leave the South, and he has come to the conclusion that in general the demand of northern industry for workers was the stronger influence.

The greatest rush of Negroes into the North occurred in 1917. After the Armistice and the return of the soldiers from Europe, the migrations still continued, although in a less noticeable degree. According to the careful study of Dr. Lewis, there was relatively little migration in 1919 and 1920. There was some return migration to the South from 1920 to 1922 followed by a pronounced northward migration from the latter half of 1922 to 1924, the extent of the movement varying with conditions of employment north and south. The increasing use of Negroes in northern industrial plants is indicated among other things in the *Negro Survey of Pennsylvania,* which was begun in 1924 and published in 1927. An attempt was made with the aid of several enumerators to ascertain the number of Negroes living in ninety-one of the largest cities of the state in 1925. Since over 95 per cent of the Negroes lived in these cities at the time of the 1920 census, the enumeration has virtually the value of a mid-census count. According to the estimates made, the

Negro population of Pennsylvania was 339,284 as compared with 284,568 in 1920, thus showing a gain in five years of 54,716 Negroes. In the same five years, the Negro population of Philadelphia increased from 134,229 to 158,565; that of Pittsburgh, from 37,725 to 45,166; that of Chester, 7,125 to 9,261; and that of Harrisburg from 5,248 to 6,293. In some of the smaller cities the increase was more striking. Thus the Negro population of Newcastle increased from 867 to 3,000; of Monongahela, from 593 to 1,400; and of East Pittsburgh, from 598 to 1,200.

The continued increase of Negroes in Pennsylvania after 1920 was typical for several other states of the North. DuBois has called attention to a renewal of northward migration of Negroes, and quotes the *Memphis Commercial Appeal* (December 24) to the effect that within 90 days more than 12,000 Negroes had left the cotton fields of Mississippi and Arkansas. The Department of Agriculture estimated that 32,000 Negroes emigrated from Georgia to the industrial centers of the North in 1922. Mid-census enumerations in Kansas and in Iowa in 1925 showed that there had been some migration of Negroes into these states since 1920.

One of the reasons why Negroes continued to migrate to the North was that they found employment there in many occupations from which they were formerly excluded. Instead of being restricted to working as waiters, porters, barbers, house servants, and common unskilled laborers, Negroes came to be employed by the thousands in mills and factories. In 1918 Chicago employed more than 10,000 in the stockyards, and Detroit used more than 3,000 Negroes in the automobile factories. Large numbers came to be employed by the railroads, steel mills, and shipbuilding plants. Having worked into such occupations during the shortage of white labor and having proved on the whole satisfactory to their employers, Negroes have held their jobs, and other Negroes have been employed in similar pursuits. It is true that Negroes as a rule performed the tasks in all these occupations which require less expert knowledge and skill, but they also pushed forward in increasing numbers into the ranks of skilled labor. In the report, *The Negro Survey of Pennsylvania,* after a statement that "Until the outbreak of the World War, the majority of the factory gates of Pennsylvania were closed against the black man,"this comparison is made. "In 1910 there were 23,797

Negroes in the manufacturing and mechanical industries of Pennsylvania. In 1920 this number had increased to 59,774, an increase of 151.1 per cent. For the first time in the 300-odd years that Negroes had lived in Pennsylvania, there were more Negroes in manufacturing and mechanical industries than there were in domestic and personal service." In fact, there was an actual decrease of Negroes in the latter occupations from 75,566 in 1910 to 57,908, or 23.3 per cent. "In 1910," the report continues, "there were 5,410 Negroes in transportation in the State. In 1920, there were 16,616 . . . a percentage increase of 207 per cent. Negroes increased 103.5 per cent in public service; 43.4 per cent in clerical occupations; and 47 per cent in the extraction of minerals."

According to the same report, the number of Negroes in these same occupations has decreased somewhat since 1920 owing to the "recession from the abnormally high peak reached during the war period and which continued until early in 1920." Nevertheless: "In the steel industry about Pittsburgh the proportion of Negroes working today is higher than during the war. A prominent steel and wire company which employed only 25 Negroes at the peak of war production today employs 300. Another wire company which employed 200 at the peak of war production now employs 260. A tube company, never employing more than 100 Negroes before the war, used 250 in wartime and uses 306 today. A pressed steel car company, never exceeding 25 Negro employees before or during the war period, today employs 632."

What has happened in Pennsylvania has been repeated in several other Northern States, such as New York, Illinois, Indiana, Ohio, Michigan, and, in a lesser degree, in states farther west. Negroes continued to come north because they were working more and more into the principal industries of that region, and because, at the same time, their living conditions were improving. The suffering and the high death rates which attended the first great rush of Negroes into northern cities have in a measure passed, although the urban blacks are still inadequately housed, and many have to put up with very unsanitary surroundings. But so long as conditions in the North offer better economic, educational, and social opportunities than are enjoyed in the South, there will continue to be a steady influx of black humanity from the Southern States.

That Negro migration into the North must have continued on a very extensive scale after 1920 is clearly shown by the last census (1930). This movement has excited far less comment than the mass migration of the war period. Subtracting the 52,338 Negroes born in the North and living in the South from those (1,355,789) born in the South and living in the North leaves as the net gain of the

TABLE 47

MIGRATION MOVEMENT, NEGROES AND WHITES

	1920		1930	
	Negroes	Whites	Negroes	Whites
Born east, living west, of Mississippi.......	342,931	4,882,520	320,589	4,820,182
Born west, living east, of Mississippi.......	96,110	939,017	117,158	1,458,154
Net gain of West over East	246,821	3,943,503	143,431	3,362,028

North in 1930, 1,303,451 Negroes, as compared with a net gain of 692,887 in 1920. These figures must be interpreted with caution. One can obtain only a very rough approximation to the number of Negroes who migrated north between 1920 and 1930 as compared with the number that migrated in the preceding decade. Of course, the census returns take no account of the number of Negroes who may have migrated north or south and subsequently returned to their original state of residence between these two dates. Neither is any account taken of the number of migrants who have died. The number, 1,355,789, of southern Negroes living in the North represents all the survivors of all the migrants from the South who were on hand when the census enumerators took account of them in 1930. The difference between the net gain of the North in 1930 and 1920, namely, 610,564, must be much less than the number who migrated from south to north within the decade. Of the 692,887 southern-born Negroes living in the North in 1920, a fairly large number had come north before 1910. Besides, many of these 692,887 must have died between 1920 and 1930. It seems probable, therefore, that the number of migrants who became relatively permanent residents in the North was greater between 1920 and 1930 than it was between 1910 and 1920. There may have been more migration back and forth in the earlier decades; of this we have no adequate records.

Although the movement of Negroes has been mainly from South to North, there are other movements, especially immigration into the West, which are of some extent and importance. The extent of this migration may be inferred from the following data on regions of residence and birth. (See also table 47, p. 196.)

Most of the Negroes went into the West South Central States, having been attracted, as were numerous whites, by the developing agricultural resources of this region. The Mountain and Pacific States have by far the largest percentage of Negroes (79.4 and 80.0 per cent, respectively) who were born in other parts of the United States. The Mountain States have shown a slight decrease in their Negro population between 1920 and 1930, but the Negroes of the Pacific States have increased by 88.6 per cent, the largest increase being in California, where the Negro population has increased in this decade from 38,763 to 81,048, or 101.1 per cent. The northern part of the west coast has not as yet proved very alluring to the Negro. It is noteworthy that within this decade New Mexico lost heavily in its Negro population, namely, 50.3 per cent. The chief reason for this decrease of Negroes in New Mexico and to a lesser degree in the northern Mountain States was probably the invasion of Mexican laborers, who were employed in many localities in preference to the Negro.

The western Negroes not only comprise, in large part, persons born in other states, but they also come from regions where the Negroes are more prone than the Negroes of other regions to leave their state of birth. The Negroes who have moved least are those of the more southern of the South Atlantic States and the Gulf States. Formerly, the Negroes constituted a relatively stable element of the population, but their mobility has rapidly increased in the last three decades. In 1910, when they were, on the whole, less migratory than the whites, a larger percentage of Negroes who left their state of birth was to be found mostly in the Northern and Western States. At present, Negro mobility has come to exceed that of the white population. According to the census of 1930, 24.9 per cent of our native Negro population and only 20.5 of our native

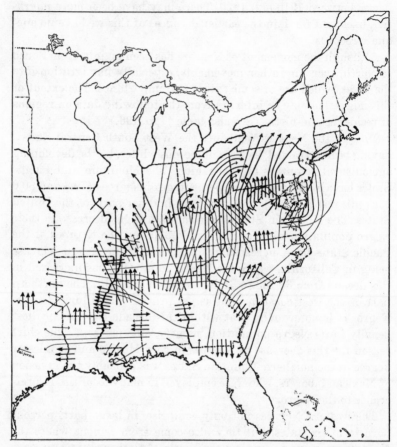

Fig. 8. Migration of Negroes up to 1920. Each line shows origin and destination of group. Heavy lines represent 10,000 Negro migrants; light lines represent 5,000 Negro migrants.

white population were born in some other state than that in which they were residing. Of the persons born in a given state, 25.3 per cent among the Negroes and 22.4 per cent among the whites came to live in some other state. In the South the mobility of the Negroes, as indicated by interstate migration, is usually much less than that of the whites, but it is much greater than that of the whites in the North and West.

In order to give a graphic representation of the general trend of Negro migration, I have prepared two maps indicating the course of migration up to 1920 and 1930, respectively. Each heavy line indicates 10,000 Negro migrants, and each light line 5,000 Negro migrants, and the direction of travel is shown by the arrow points; the two ends of the line indicate respectively the origin and the destination of the group. Thus the two heavy lines and one light line extending from Maryland to Pennsylvania in figure 9 indicate that about 25,000 Negroes born in Maryland were living in Pennsylvania in 1930. In a certain measure, the maps represent the cumulative effect of the movement of the Negro population. The larger number of lines in figure 9 is owing in part to the inclusion of migrants before 1920, many of whom would not be recorded in the later map because they died before 1930. A glance at the maps apprises one of the striking fact that the general direction of Negro migration has been more or less directly northward. The Negroes of Illinois come mainly from Kentucky, Tennessee, Mississippi, Alabama, and, in a lesser degree, Louisiana and Georgia. New York State drew most of its numerous migrants from the Southern States of the Atlantic seaboard, namely, Virginia, the Carolinas, and Georgia. Ohio and Michigan drew relatively more from the intermediate states of Alabama, Georgia, Tennessee, and Kentucky. Only in Florida was the predominant migration from north to south, by far the greater number of the migrants coming from the contiguous state of Georgia.

The northward trek of Negroes, as has been stated, represents their reaction to the opportunity for increasing employment in industrial pursuits and for an abandonment of agricultural labor. From table 48, which gives the number and percentage of Negroes in various classes of occupations from 1910 to 1930, it may be seen that the number of Negroes over 10 years of age who were gainfully employed in agriculture has decreased from 2,834,969, or 54.6 per cent of the Negro population in 1910, to 2,133,135 in 1920, and to 1,987,839, or 36.1 per cent of the total Negro workers, in 1930. There has been an increase of Negroes in domestic and personal service, transportation and communication, trade and clerical occupations, and professional service. The proportion of Negroes engaged in manufacturing and mechanical industries increased between 1910 and 1920 from 655,906 (12.6 per cent) to 901,181 (18.7 per cent), but although the actual number of Negroes so employed

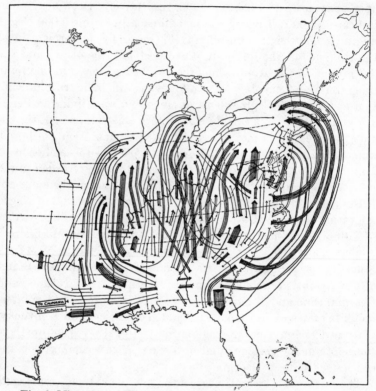

Fig. 9. Migration of Negroes up to 1930. Each line shows the origin and destination of the group. Heavy lines represent 10,000 Negro migrants; light lines represent 5,000 Negro migrants.

in 1930 increased to 1,024,656, the percentage decreased slightly to 18.6 per cent. Slightly decreasing proportions in this class of occupations were also shown in the same decade by both the native-born and the foreign-born whites.

After the immigration of southern Europeans was restricted, northern industrialists found in the Negro a welcome asset. The stockyards of Chicago, the iron and steel mills of Pennsylvania, and the automobile factories of Detroit now teem with thousands of Negro workers. More and more the Negroes are entering upon new employments. They are still virtually excluded from a number of occupations, partly because of traditional customs, and partly as a result of the policy of certain trade unions. The greater number

TABLE 48

NEGROES MORE THAN TEN YEARS OF AGE GAINFULLY EMPLOYED IN
LEADING OCCUPATIONS, FROM 1910 TO 1930

	1910		1920		1930	
	Number	Per-centage	Number	Per-centage	Number	Per-cengate
Agriculture.......	2,834,969	54.6	2,133,135	44.2	1,987,839	36.1
Extracting minerals........	61,129	1.2	73,229	1.5	74,972	1.4
Manufacturing and mechanical in-dustries........	655,906	12.6	901,181	18.7	1,024,656	18.6
Transportation and locomotion.	256,098	4.9	312,538	6.5	397,645	7.2
Trade...........	119,775	2.3	141,119	2.9	183,809	3.3
Public service.....	22,229	0.4	50,436	1.0	50,203	0.9
Professional service.........	68,350	1.3	81,771	1.7	135,929	2.5
Domestic and per-sonal service....	1,121,251	21.6	1,063,008	22.0	1,576,205	28.6

of trade unions are not openly hostile to the Negro laborer, but they find that he presents a number of embarrassing problems. The American Federation of Labor has repeatedly expressed itself as opposed to any kind of discrimination on racial grounds, but, as is commonly true in this sordid world, considerations of practical policy have proved stronger than idealistic sentiment in determin-ing the attitude of labor unions toward Negro workers. Negroes were and are very commonly excluded from membership in local chapters in the South, where the whites have been pretty gener-ally successful in keeping the more remunerative employments for themselves. In the North, there is less discrimination. Nevertheless, many unions in the North either explicitly exclude Negro members or discourage their affiliation. The unions having the largest Negro membership are those including the semiskilled or unskilled workers. Labor unions are often reluctant to bring Negro workers into their fold on an equal footing with white members. However, they recognize that the presence of large numbers of unorganized Negro workers constitutes a menace to the maintenance of a satisfactory scale of wages. Negroes have not infrequently been brought in as strikebreakers, as was done in the stockyards strike in Chicago in 1904. Hence the tendency, as was exhibited after this episode, to seek greater security by organizing the Negro. In many unions, the Negroes are admitted to full membership on the same terms as the whites. In other unions, the Negroes are confined to separate but affiliated organizations. Sometimes the Negroes form independent unions; at other times they are discouraged in various ways. Several unions which include the more skilled white workers have clauses in their constitutions excluding Negroes from membership. Not infrequently, in unions that admit Negro laborers to membership, preferential treatment is given to the whites in obtaining employment, and the same policy is followed by white employers, who do not wish to offend their white laborers by compelling them to work alongside of Negroes. Even in the North, Negro workers suffer from many handicaps in competing with the whites. The result is to force the Negroes down into the lower and more poorly paid employments.

With respect to probable survival, the most important element in the migratory movement of the Negroes is their concentration in cities. During slavery and for many years following this period, Negroes were mostly confined to rural areas. In 1870 only 750,000 Negroes lived in cities. The population of the states containing the largest percentage of Negroes was, and still is, predominantly rural, although much over half of the total population of the United States is urban. Cityward migration is a general phenomenon exhibited by all elements of the population.

The remarkable growth of American cities is also attributable to the fact that most of our foreign immigrants have lodged in cities; in 1930, 80.3 per cent of the foreign born was urban. Immigration has affected the cities of the North much more than those of the

South, although the proportion of the foreign born in the South is very much greater in the cities than it is in the country. In the South the foreigner and the Negro are competitors for the opportunities of urban life. The Negro has had some measure of success in keeping the foreigner out of the cities, and in a greater degree out of the rural districts of the Southern States. However, before the World War the presence of the foreigner reduced the Negroes' opportunity to gain a livelihood in the cities of the North. Negroes had already been driven from certain occupations, such as those of bootblacks, waiters, barbers, janitors, and elevator boys. With the restriction of foreign immigration, the Negroes' opportunities for gainful employment were greatly increased, and at the present time Negroes are found by thousands in occupations formerly manned chiefly by foreigners.

Between 1900 and 1910, the increase of Negroes in cities was relatively less rapid than that of the whites, but in the following decades the tables are turned. Between 1910 and 1920, urban Negroes increased by 32.6 per cent; the urban whites increased by 28.5 per cent. In the previous decade (1900–1910), rural Negroes had increased by 310,980, or 4.5 per cent, the rural whites, by 3,848,876, or 10 per cent. Between 1910 and 1920, the number of Negroes in rural areas actually decreased by 239,308, or 3.4 per cent. This decrease was mainly in the rural South, which lost 233,710 Negroes, but the country districts of the North and West combined also lost 5,598 Negroes. In this decade, the rural Negro population decreased in most of the Northern as well as the Southern States. While this extensive depletion of rural areas was going on, the Negro population in cities (1910–1920) increased by 874,676. The loss of 15,143 rural Negroes in the North represents simply a continuation of an earlier exodus which occasioned an even greater loss, namely, 25,819, or 9.4 per cent, between 1900 and 1910. The actual loss of rural Negroes in the South, however, stands in rather striking contrast to the gain in their number in the preceding decade, which amounted to 336,799. In the Northern States, the urban Negroes increased by 459,778 (1910–1920), and the total urban Negro population increased by 874,676. Between 1920 and 1930, the urban Negroes of the United States increased from 3,559,473 to 5,193,913, or from 34.0 per cent to 43.7 per cent of the total Ne-

gro population. At the same time the urban whites increased
from 53.4 per cent to 57.7 per cent. In the same decade, the Negro
rural population decreased from 6,903,658 to 6,697,230, thereby
losing 206,428.

It is a striking feature of Negro migration that it goes relatively
more to the very large cities than to the smaller ones. This tendency

TABLE 49

PERCENTAGES OF URBAN AND RURAL NEGROES AND WHITES IN SELECTED
NORTHERN STATES, 1930

	Urban		Rural	
	Whites	Negroes	Whites	Negroes
New York............	83.2	94.6	16.8	5.4
Massachusetts........	90.2	88.5	9.8	11.5
Pennsylvania.........	66.9	86.6	33.1	13.4
New Jersey...........	82.6	83.8	17.4	16.2
Ohio.................	66.8	87.9	33.2	12.1
Indiana..............	54.0	92.0	46.0	8.0
Illinois..............	72.9	92.4	27.1	7.6
Michigan.............	67.2	94.2	32.8	5.8
Minnesota...........	49.1	96.5	50.9	3.5

has been much more evident in recent decades, especially in the
North. Between 1910 and 1920, the growth of the Negro population of small cities (2,500 to 10,000) in the North and West was
very slight, and in 1900 to 1910 there was an actual loss of 3,496, or
3 per cent, but in cities of over 100,000 population, the increase
was 41.5 per cent from 1900 to 1910 and 89.4 per cent between
1910 and 1920. In the process of urbanization, the Negro is being
exposed to conditions which are more and more unlike those found
in a relatively wholesome rural environment. Naturally, therefore,
urban migration tends to be all the more deadly to the Negro.

Throughout the North the proportion of Negroes living in cities
is noticeably greater than the proportion of whites, even in those
states which have received the largest numbers of recent foreign immigrants. Taking a few of the more important states of the North,
we find the following percentages of urban and rural Negroes liv-

ing in cities as compared with similar percentages of the white
population (tables 49 and 50).

These percentages contrast sharply with those from the South,
as is illustrated by the data from a few representative Southern
States for the year 1930, presented in table 50.

Cities both North and South draw people in the wage-earning
period of life and the period of highest rate of natural increase.

TABLE 50

PERCENTAGES OF URBAN AND RURAL NEGROES AND WHITES IN SELECTED
SOUTHERN STATES, 1930

	Urban		Rural	
	Whites	Negroes	Whites	Negroes
Alabama.............	31.5	29.6	68.5	70.4
Mississippi...........	20.5	13.3	79.5	86.7
South Carolina........	24.6	17.4	75.4	82.6
North Carolina.......	25.2	26.8	74.8	73.2

Thus the birth rate of the country is lowered, and the city migrants
become exposed to unsanitary and demoralizing conditions which
check fertility and undermine vitality. As has been remarked
earlier, cities both North and South have been potent destroyers of
black humanity. Hitherto it has been the rural South which provided the increase in the colored population. If the vital statistics
of the urban Negroes come to be as bad as they were a few years
ago, and if agricultural conditions of the South should ever lead
to the replacement of Negroes by white laborers so that the Negroes would be forced into the centers of industry, the race problem
might be on its way to a fairly rapid solution. This possibility, however, does not seem to be very imminent. The rural South will continue to be a prolific breeding ground for the blacks, although to a
somewhat diminishing degree, and in the future cities may not continue to be so heavy a drain upon the Negro. The vital prospects of
urban Negroes have much improved, although, as we have seen in
Chapter III, it is fallacious to conclude that in cities in which the
birth rate exceeds the death rate the population is growing through

its own natural increase. The excess of births over deaths may result from the incoming of people in the fertile period of life, since these may cause an excess of total births even in a city where the native population is not reproducing itself. The age composition of the Negro inhabitants in certain cities as shown by the returns of several censuses is such as to produce just this result, and it is quite clear that this anomalous age distribution is largely caused by migration.

We may confidently state that for the past few years births among the urban Negroes in the North have appreciably exceeded deaths. The increase of the Negro birth rate in northern cities, which we have discussed in Chapter VII, is perhaps partly spurious, but that the balance of births and deaths has become less unfavorable to the urban Negro is not open to doubt. One very important factor in this change is the reduction of the Negro death rate, especially in infancy and childhood. The Negroes have long suffered a fearful decimation of their ranks in these early years. According to the life tables of 1910, out of every 100,000 Negro males born in the Original Registration States, 32,490 die before the end of the seventh year, and of the same number of white males born there are only 17,749 deaths before the end of the seventh year. In the early years of life, most of the excess Negro mortality is clearly preventable, as is shown by the striking reduction in the death rate in an improved environment. In the 30th Ward of Phila-'delphia, where there are exceptional hospital advantages for Negro children and where special attention has been given to the instruction of Negro mothers, infant mortality among the Negroes has been reduced below that of the whites. A similar reduction in early Negro mortality has also taken place in several of our large cities, and one may reasonably conclude that this decrease will become more widespread and will cover later years as well. What will happen to the birth rate and therefore to the balance of births and deaths, is more uncertain. Here, as we have pointed out, we are concerned not only with biological factors, but also with psychological and social forces.

In the present state of the available information, an attempt to interpret the comparative vital statistics of northern and southern Negroes is fraught with certain difficulties. The problem of how far a northern climate affects the vital fortunes of the Negro is complicated by several circumstances. Northern Negroes are mainly confined to cities; they have an age composition especially favorable to a high birth rate and a low death rate; furthermore, the northern Negro population constitutes in several respects a selected group inasmuch as it contains relatively more mulattoes and these as a rule are better educated and more enterprising than the more nearly pure blacks. Death rates are notoriously high among ignorant people. If we compare the percentages of illiterates in different areas, we find that illiteracy is much more prevalent in the South than in the North, and relatively lowest in the Western States. According to the 1930 census, the percentage of illiteracy among Negroes was 19.7 per cent in the South, 4.7 in the North, and 3.3 per cent in the West. (Throughout the North and the West foreignborn whites are much more unlettered than the Negroes.) Negro illiteracy is much greater in rural areas than in the cities; in 1920 it was over twice as great. We have here, in the greater intelligence of the urban Negro, a strong factor tending to offset the unwholesome influences of urban life and thus to equalize Negro mortality in the urban North and the rural South. Unquestionably the rapid decrease of illiteracy among urban Negroes has been an important force in the decline of the Negro death rate. For some time yet the Negro, it would seem, is destined to enjoy a higher degree of education in the North than in the South, and this circumstance may contribute not a little to the survival of the race in northern climates. The same factor will doubtless check the birth rate, as it always does. And how far the birth rate may sink in urban communities, with their various inducements to family restriction, is something which in these days one cannot safely predict.

By 1920 a few of the Northern States (New York, Connecticut, Massachusetts, Pennsylvania) showed a surplus of births over deaths in their Negro population. If we compare the vital statistics of the northern Negro in 1930 with those of 1920, it will be seen that there is coming to be an increasing preponderance of births over deaths, and that the greatest advance has occurred in urban areas. In the Negro population of all the Northern States included in the Birth Registration Area in 1920 there were, in that year, 21,207 births and 20,601 deaths, leaving a net increase of only 606.

In the Negro population of the same Northern States in 1930, there were 32,913 births and 28,188 deaths, leaving a surplus of births over deaths of 4,725. In 1924 the surplus of births over deaths among northern Negroes reached its maximum of 6,446 for the decade 1920–1930. Northern States admitted to the Birth Registration Area since 1920 show in general a similar improvement in the vital statistics of their Negro populations.

This change is to be attributed chiefly to gains made in the cities. The rural Negroes of the North make a different showing. In 1920, 514 more deaths than births occurred in the rural Negroes of the Northern States in the Birth Registration Area. By 1930 the excess of deaths over births among the rural Negroes in these same states was 589. It seems evident that the northern rural Negroes are not thriving. Their unfavorable vital statistics, however, may reflect the loss of persons in the reproductive period of life, who go into the cities, a circumstance which would reduce the rural birth rate and increase the urban death rate.

When we compare the balance of births and deaths in the cities of the Southern States, we find that apparently there has been less progress in the South than in the North in the saving of Negro lives. In 1927, for example, more deaths than births occurred among the urban Negroes of Kentucky, Tennessee, Arkansas, Delaware, Missouri, Mississippi, West Virginia, and Louisiana. By 1930 there was an excess of deaths over births in the urban Negroes not only in these same states, but also in Georgia, Alabama, Florida, South Carolina, Oklahoma, and Virginia. The birth rate has been falling quite rapidly in the cities of the South, so that the balance of births and deaths has become more unfavorable for the Negroes than it was a decade ago. It is a striking fact that while births exceed deaths in the urban Negroes of the North, we find a marked excess of deaths over births in the urban Negroes of the South, notwithstanding the favorable influence of climatic conditions. Of course, differences in age and sex composition, which vary from city to city, make comparisons of the vital statistics of different urban areas somewhat unsafe. There is, however, some evidence from several sources which indicates that Negroes are faring better in northern than in southern cities, despite the handicap of climate.

Although births exceed deaths among the Negroes of northern

cities, the surplus is not sufficient for the continued propagation of the race in a stabilized population. If, therefore, the Negroes are bred in the rural districts of the South to be consumed by the cities, it may be an ominous circumstance that the rural Negroes, both North and South, have been actually decreasing. The statistics of the rural South have shown a remarkably high excess of births over

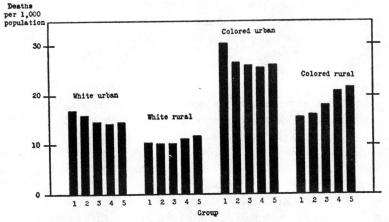

NOTE.—Group I. Florida, Louisiana, Mississippi, North Carolina, and South Carolina
Group II. Tennessee and Virginia.
Group III. Kentucky, Maryland, and Missouri.
Group IV. Illinois, New Jersey, Ohio, and Pennsylvania
Group V. Michigan and New York.

Fig. 10. Urban and rural mortality in certain geographical areas in the white and colored populations, 1920. After Gover.

deaths in the Negro population. Clearly, the cities have been taking the surplus and more. Moreover, the future industrial development of the United States will probably cause the cities to become a still greater drain upon the Negro population of the rural South.

Cities are more of a handicap to the Negroes than to the whites. The differences between urban and rural death rates are enormously greater among the Negroes than in the white population, but urban and rural birth rates show varying relations. One striking recent trend in the birth rates of the white population in the rural North is a tendency to fall below the birth rates of the cities; in the South this tendency is less frequently encountered. In large measure it is a matter of age composition combined, in the North especially, with the influence of foreign immigration.

The fate of the Negro in the North, and to an appreciable degree in the South also, will depend upon how successfully he adapts himself to urban life. According to the recent trend of vital statistics, the Negro has already made sufficient progress to justify his optimistic hopes without affording a definite assurance of racial survival. Just how urban life affects the biological fortunes of the Negro cannot be adequately ascertained from mass statistics on births and deaths. In his volume on *The Negro Family in Chicago,* Dr. E. F. Frazier has given an analysis of the situation that throws much light upon the way in which the Negro population is adjusting itself to an urban environment. One might fittingly describe this volume as a study in human ecology. The earlier migrants concentrated at first around the central business section and in the Loop district. This was an area of deterioration in which rents were cheap in residences that were becoming undesirable because of the expanding business area. Gradually the Negro section spread westward, but mainly southward, until it now includes a section about sixty blocks long and a variable number of blocks in width. Most of the Negroes are concentrated in this "southside community," although there are smaller areas of Negro residence in other parts of the city. This area was divided for the purpose of study into seven zones, each about a mile in length, and numbered consecutively from north to south. According to Dr. Frazier, "As the Negro community has expanded southward, through the process of selection different elements of the Negro population have tended to become segregated in different zones within the community. Although nearly four-fifths of all the Negroes of Chicago were born in the South, the proportion of southern born inhabitants in the population diminishes as one leaves those sections of the Negro community nearest the heart of the city. It is in those zones just outside of the Loop where decaying residences and tottering frame dwellings presage the inroads of industry and business that the southern migrant is able to pay the cheap rents that landlords are willing to accept until their property is demanded by the expanding business area. In these areas of deterioration, the poorer migrant families are often forced into association with the vicious elements of the city." The third zone includes the "bright-light area" with its cabarets, hotels, brothels, clubs, gambling houses, and cheap theaters.

Here mingle the vicious elements of both races, together with many respectable but impecunious Negro families. As the Negroes become more firmly established, they tend to leave the first three zones and travel southward. A professional Negro of the better class who had moved into a better section of the third zone, reported that "The neighborhood rapidly deteriorated. Negroes passing at all times of the night on their way to State, Dearborn, and Federal Streets where they lived, used the vilest language and engaged in fights. The neighborhood became so bad that I was forced to move. . . . We moved out to 51st Street and Michigan Avenue. It was beautiful out there, the lawn well kept, and everything inviting. But the same thing is happening out there. The same class of Negroes who ran us away from 37th Street are moving out there. They creep along slowly like a disease."

This tendency for the Negro population to spread outward in successive waves has led to a gradation in the character of the inhabitants as we pass from the north to the south. The seventh zone at the south end of the area includes the families who have been most successful in adjusting themselves to city life. They consist in large part of the early migrants and their descendants. There is a decrease of southern-born Negroes in passing south and a parallel increase in the proportion of mulattoes. In the first and second zones near the Loop, "where the plantation Negro from the South first settles, only about one out of five Negro men and one out of four women one met in 1920 showed some admixture of white blood. This is due to the fact that the more recent migrants consisted much more than formerly of relatively pure Negroes. Owing to the influx during the war period, the percentage of mulattoes in Chicago decreased from 41.6 in 1910 to 27.4 per cent in 1920. In the third zone, owing to circumstances connected with the prevalence of vice and the various enterprises associated with that district, the high percentage of mulattoes presents an exception to the increasing proportion of mixed bloods that are met with in passing from north to south."

In Zones I and II the percentage of illiteracy in 1920 was, on the whole, about three times as great as in the Negro population of Chicago and about on a par with that of Dallas or Houston. In the sixth and seventh zones illiteracy among the Negroes was about 3 per cent. In these zones there were more professional and skilled workers, more ownership of homes, and a decreased proportion of laborers and persons in domestic service.

Perhaps the most striking differences in these zones of the Negro area are found in the percentage of crime and delinquency. Zone III, as might be expected, has a bad record for criminality. In the first zone near the Loop, according to Frazier, "the thirty-three boys who were arrested for juvenile delinquency in 1926 represented over two-fifths of the boys from ten to seventeen years of age in this area. In the same area 10 per cent of the adult Negro males were in the County Jail in 1921. The next three zones showed only a slight improvement over the first in regard to juvenile delinquency. Three boys out of ten in these areas were arrested for juvenile delinquency, and some of these boys were arrested three or four times during the year. A decided decrease in the delinquency rate appeared in the fifth zone, where police probation officers had complaints against 15 per cent of the boys. In the sixth zone . . . the delinquency rate continued to decline sharply, and in the seventh zone less than 2 per cent of the boys had complaints brought against them for delinquency."

Rates for illegitimacy, broken homes, receipts for charity, desertion, and warrants for nonsupport showed a marked decline in passing from north to south in the Negro area. Of especial significance in relation to the biological adaptiveness of the Negro is the fact that the number of children per hundred women of child-bearing age (15 to 44 years) showed a tendency to increase in the better areas. The third zone, including the bright-light district, contained the smallest proportion of children; the highest proportion was found in Zones VI and VII. This would seem to indicate that as the urban Negro population becomes better adjusted its birth rate tends to rise. There is also evidence that its death rate tends to fall.

Altogether, Negro life in our large cities does not present a pleasing picture. Negroes usually first gain a foothold in the most undesirable and unwholesome parts of the city, where they are brought into contact with the worst elements of the white population. Their children grow up in neighborhoods where they are exposed to demoralizing influences which frequently lead them into delinquency and crime. Wherever possible, the more successful types of Negroes gradually move into better sections, where they can live under more decent conditions. The Negro's struggle for a livelihood is much harder than that of the native American or the European. Nevertheless, Negroes are gradually improving in education, health, and economic status in our northern cities. With better education and a higher economic status, there is apparently no insuperable obstacle to their continued existence in a northern latitude. They may be less well adapted than the white man to live in a cold climate, but their fate will not be decided by death rates alone. If their birth rate continues to exceed that of the whites, as it now does, and if their death rate continues to approach that of the whites, as it has been doing, their net rate of natural increase may come to equal, if not exceed, that of their white competitors. The fact that the Negroes occupy an economic and social status inferior to that of the whites will probably be a positive biological advantage. If carried beyond rather modest limits, prosperity, especially in urban populations, is commonly a prelude to extinction.

CHAPTER X

CONCLUDING CONSIDERATIONS

IN THE PRECEDING PAGES I have dwelt upon some of the chief factors affecting the biological fortunes of the American Negro. I do not venture to forecast the probable future development of the Negro population in the United States, nor to predict how many colored inhabitants there will be in the United States in the year 2000, or even in 1950. I leave this endeavor to more intrepid spirits. The problem is a complex and many-sided one, quite beyond the scope of my feeble powers of vaticination.

Whether the Negro population will increase or decrease relatively to the whites will depend upon many factors. One influence which, we may be sure, will be of prime importance is the course of economic development. What kind of an economic system the future has in store for us is known only to the gods, if even to them. We may be entering upon a period of economic and political experimentation that will prove to be very disquieting to conservative-minded individuals. Changes in social and economic organization inevitably entail changes in the ethnic composition of a people, and they may affect the relative increase of whites and blacks in ways that we do not expect. We are unable to foresee very far what changes in our population are likely to occur, but the trends should be closely studied and we should endeavor to gain insight into their causes.

During the last few years there has been a marked development of interest in problems of population. In the future, nations may come to be concerned over the ethnic composition of their inhabitants much more than they have been in the past, and they may endeavor to exercise a greater degree of control over the course of the population changes occurring in their midst. A very modest attempt in this direction has been made in the United States in federal legislation on immigration. Until recently the United States had no definite policy with respect to population, except to grow big. Now, the government is endeavoring to restrict the entrance of alien peoples and to preserve approximately the present proportions of different national stocks.

There can be little doubt that the exclusion of Europeans has led, directly or indirectly, to an increase of the Negroes. Before the Great War, European immigrants were driving northern Negroes out of a number of occupations in which they were commonly employed. The exclusion of the European became the Negro's opportunity. To a certain degree the increasingly rapid growth of the Negro population in the decade between 1920 and 1930, following upon a long period of decreasing rate of multiplication, is to be attributed to the release from population pressure that followed upon the restricted influx from Europe. Populations always show a considerable degree of resiliency: wherever impediments are removed which hold them in check, they respond by expanding. It is not improbable that, were it not for the limitation of European immigration during and after the war period, the increasing rate of Negro population growth observed between 1920 and 1930 might not have occurred. At least, it would have been much less, although of course other factors were involved in this increase, especially the reduction of Negro mortality in the early periods of life.

That the restriction of foreign immigration might stimulate the growth of our colored population, probably did not occur to the legislators who framed the exclusion acts. If we should open our gates freely and admit large numbers of laborers from abroad to pour into Northern cities and compete with Negro labor, great numbers of Negroes would doubtless return to the South. Negro migration, as shown especially by the waves of migrants that surged into the North during 1917–1918 and 1923–1925 and the smaller return movements between these dates, has been very responsive to both economic opportunity and economic pressure. There is no immediate prospect that we will admit large numbers of foreigners into the United States, so that the Negroes need have no fear of a greatly increased competition for jobs in the near future at least. It is more likely that immigration will be restricted still further, and that the Negro will have a more unobstructed field for expansion.

Among the factors which will favor the future expansion of the Negro race is the decline of the birth rate among the whites. This, like the curtailment of foreign immigration, will reduce the population pressure against which the Negroes must make headway. As the reproductive rate of the whites falls off, that of the Negroes will automatically tend to rise. Hitherto the increase of the whites has been powerfully reinforced by numerous immigrants whose high birth rate helped still further to swell the ranks of the white population. The increasing average age of foreign-born women and the gradual Americanization of the second generation of our immigrants, with the consequent reduction of their birth rate, has brought about a much slower rate of increase in the American whites as a whole. This increase of the whites has so greatly declined that, were it not for their favorable age composition, they would no longer be self-perpetuating. Already, in large areas of the North and East, they fall far short of this goal. Every year sees a decline of the white birth rate to an unprecedented level. Knowledge of birth-control methods is rapidly spreading, but it is still imperfectly disseminated among the lower social classes. To judge from the recent marked decline of the birth rate in these classes in some European countries, one may expect that the practice of contraception will become much more prevalent in the lower economic ranks in the United States, thereby effecting a further reduction of the general birth supply among the whites.

It is the lower economic classes among the whites that constitute the chief competitors of the Negroes. The increasing practice of birth control which seems inevitable in these classes, will therefore relieve the Negroes from pressure just where it has been most acutely felt. Were it not for the past phenomenal growth of the white population of the United States the Negroes might have become very much more numerous than they actually are. In order to be impressed with this fact, one needs only to glance at O. E. Baker's maps showing the distribution of the white and colored farm population in the United States. As a rule, where the white population is dense the colored population is scarce, and vice versa. In the region bordering the Mississippi River in Mississippi and Arkansas, across the middle regions of Alabama and Georgia, in the northeastern part of North Carolina, and in the southeastern part of Virginia, the rural Negroes are numerous and the whites are correspondingly few. These areas would surely contain many more whites were they not so thickly settled by Negroes. Just as surely, were it not for the competition of the whites, the rural Negroes in the North would be more numerous.

Because of this tendency to mutual exclusiveness, the future increase of the Negroes in the United States will be strongly influenced by what happens to their white rivals. We may expect that, owing to the advancement of medical science and improvements in public hygiene and sanitation, the mortality of the whites will continue to decrease, but any increase in numbers from this cause will probably not compensate for the diminishing number of births. Gains in average longevity will come more and more slowly as the natural limit of the span of life is approached. Since the whites are much nearer to this goal than the Negroes, they may be expected to make less gains in the average duration of life.

That the birth rate of the whites may be expected to continue still further on its downward course is indicated by several facts. Aside from their growing urbanization and the prospect of a still greater depletion of rural areas, the whites are undergoing changes in age composition which will inevitably entail a reduction in their normal fertility. Thompson and Whelpton have endeavored to obtain an approximate measure of the comparative effectiveness of the various factors involved in the fall of the birth rate between 1920 and 1929. They conclude that in the total population of the United States about 10.1 per cent of the reduced birth rate is attributable to the higher proportion of city dwellers; 7.5 per cent is owing to the increased average age of women, and 1.7 per cent is the result of the larger proportion of native white women and the reduced ratio of the foreign born. This leaves the larger part of the loss of births, 80.7 per cent, to be accounted for as the result of an actual reduction of age-specific birth rates. Probably the strongest factor in this loss is the voluntary restriction of births.

One very noteworthy phenomenon in relation to Negro expansion and increase is the recent fall of the birth rate in the rural whites of the South. The rural South has always been a notoriously prolific area. But consider the following facts: Between 1920 and 1930 the birth rate of the rural white population fell in Virginia from 28.5 to 22.6, in North Carolina from 31.9 to 23.7, in South Carolina from 28.7 to 20.9, in Maryland from 23.3 to 16.5, and in Mississippi (since 1921) from 27.5 to 22.8. In these same states of the South, between 1920 and 1930 the birth rate of the rural colored population fell in Virginia from 31.4 to 25.8, in North Caro-

lina from 32.4 to 25.9, in South Carolina from 27.4 to 26.0, and in
Maryland from 28.9 to 23.3; in Mississippi, however, there is recorded an actual rise from 24.2 in 1920 to 24.6 in 1930, a fact which
I am inclined to attribute to the increasing registration of births.
The South is in the grip of a birth-control movement which is affecting all social classes. Between 1920 and 1929 the birth rate of
the native-born whites of five states of the South, namely, Maryland, Virginia, North Carolina, South Carolina, and Kentucky,
fell from 124 to 95, or 23.0 per cent (as measured by the number
of children born to 1,000 women of child-bearing age). The corresponding decline was 13.1 per cent in the North Central States,
and 12.3 in Massachusetts, Connecticut, and New York. In these
same five Southern States the birth rate of the Negroes in this
period fell from 115 to 98, or 15.3 per cent.

The fall in the crude birth rate of Southern rural Negroes has
been much accelerated by the exodus into the cities of persons in
the reproductive period of life, a circumstance which accounts in
part for the relatively slow reduction in the fertility of the urban
Negro population. The ratio of children under 5 years to women
in the child-bearing period has fallen off much more in the whites
than in the Negroes in both the rural farm and rural nonfarm
groups. As Lorimer and Osborn remark, "The comparatively slow
decline in the fertility rates for Negroes in the rural South is probably . . . associated with the slow tempo of all social changes in this
group." We may expect that contraception will, in the near future
at least, affect the fertility of Southern rural Negroes less than that
of any other class.

So far as the birth rate is concerned the Negroes will probably
retain their lead over the whites for a long time. The Negroes will
tend to be concentrated in those occupational groups which in every
country contribute the most liberally to the birth supply. If and
when the United States welters through the continuing financial
depression and enters upon a period of industrial expansion which
will call for a greater supply of labor, the Negro population will
probably respond, like the laboring population of Great Britain in
its period of industrial development, by an increase in numbers.

The great handicap of the Negroes in the struggle for existence
is their high death rate. It has often been remarked that the Negro

death rate is about as high as the white death rate was thirty years ago. One might be tempted to conclude, therefore, that at no very distant date Negro mortality will reach the level now attained by the whites. The Negroes have profited greatly from the advances of medical science and improvements in public health administration, and it seems likely that they will continue to do so in increasing measure. The reduction in infant and child mortality in the Negro population of many localities has been rapid and extensive, and much further reduction is quite feasible, if not probable. Since Negro mortality has been greatly reduced in those ages in which it is still relatively high in comparison with that of the whites, there is reasonable ground for expecting that the mortality rates of the two races will differ less in the future than they have in the past.

Other aspects of the situation, however, are less reassuring to the Negro. Except in the younger age groups the reduction in Negro mortality in the last decade has been slight, and in some of the older age groups the death rate has actually risen. The conditions of the Negroes in many cities of the South are still very bad. The differences in mortality from tuberculosis between whites and blacks, despite the decline in the death rate from this disease, continue to be enormous, and will in all likelihood remain so for many years. The greatest enemy of the Negroes, however, is probably venereal disease. If by any miracle the Negroes could be freed from their venereal afflictions they would quickly respond by a reduced mortality and an enhanced fertility. The extent to which venereal infections are disseminated in the Negro population, both urban and rural, is appalling. Were it not for this one handicap, I have little doubt that the Negroes would be increasing at a distinctly more rapid rate than their white rivals. It would be unsafe to assign limits to what medical science may eventually accomplish, but at present the venereal problem in the American Negro shows no prospects of a speedy solution.

Emigration from the rural South into northern and southern cities has markedly increased the mortality of our colored population. The degree to which the Negro suffers from the deleterious influences of urban life varies greatly in different cities. As a rule, more is done to promote the health of the Negro in the North than in the South, but in several localities in the Southern States efficient measures are now being taken to promote the welfare of the Negro population. The Urban League, the Association for the Advancement of the Colored People, the life insurance companies, especially the Metropolitan, the Rockefeller Foundation, the state and city boards of health, the United States Public Health Service, the Children's Bureau, and many other agencies have been giving more and more attention to the conservation of the health of the colored people. In certain localities efforts in the same direction have been fostered even by the Ku Klux Klan. In both North and South there is unquestionably a growing sense of responsibility for the promotion of the welfare of the colored inhabitants. If the Negro population continues to advance in education and in economic status as it has done in the past its mortality will certainly be reduced.

The balance of births and deaths, as we have seen, has come to be relatively more favorable to the Negro. In our attempt to gain a rough measure of the stabilized rates of increase of Negroes and whites, we concluded that these rates are not far apart. In a recent volume on *The Dynamics of Population* (1934), by Lorimer and Osborn, which appeared after this estimate was made, the net reproductive rate of Negroes as compared with that of the whites in 1930 is given as 94 per cent or 98 per cent, according as one or the other of two assumptions is made with respect to the underenumeration of Negro children less than 5 years of age. As these authors remark: "It appears that the reproduction rate of the Negro group as a whole is still slightly below that of the white group as a whole; but any difference in reproduction rates that may now exist between the two groups must be very small, and it may quite disappear or be reversed in the near future. There are, however, so many uncertain elements in the situation that prediction of future population trends for Negroes in this country would be very hazardous."

There is, I believe, no sufficient reason to doubt that the growth of the Negro population was more rapid between 1920 and 1930 than it was between 1910 and 1920. It would be interesting to know the causes of this change in trend. We may be sure that the influenza epidemic of 1918, with the resultant reduction of births, was one important factor, and that the northward migration in the war period and afterward was another. But to these causes of population reduction in 1920 must be added other influences, which also led to an increase in numbers after this date. On the whole, the migration of Negroes into a northern climate, although it has been a march toward extinction, may not constitute so great a drain upon the Negro population as it might appear to be. Let us assume that 25 per cent of a population migrates into another territory, where it does not quite reproduce itself. According to a principle enunciated by Malthus, the population which remains would multiply more rapidly and might produce nearly as many children as before. A region may be continually depleted by emigration, and the migrants may fall short of perpetuating their numbers in a new territory, yet the total effect of migration might be to cause a more rapid natural increase than would otherwise occur.

Our Negro population may be in a situation similar to the one described. The immediate effects of the trek of 1917–18 were bad, but the northern Negroes soon became better adjusted to their environment, and births began to exceed deaths. Unquestionably this exodus meant a loss to the South of many Negroes, but in the long run it may result in a more rapid growth of the Negro population as a whole.

The reader by now may be impressed by the fact that the chief outcome of our inquiries is to bring us face to face with a number of uncertainties. We are uncertain of the degree to which the Negro birth rate will decline, and we do not know what to expect from the spread of birth control, especially in rural Negro communities. We are uncertain how far the Negro death rate will decline, and we do not know what progress may be expected in the conquest of venereal disease. We are uncertain what the future rate of increase of the whites may be, either through immigration or through births. We are uncertain also concerning future economic developments, by which population movements are always profoundly influenced. Unexpected discoveries in science may effect great changes in industry and in the control of disease. To attempt to forecast the future is futile; nevertheless it may be well to take account of possibilities.

It is far from my intention to assume the rôle of an alarmist over the prospect that the blacks may soon come to increase at a more rapid rate than the whites. A few years ago the suggestion of such a possibility would have provoked a smile of incredulity. It may do so now. Since the Negroes had been increasing much more slowly than the whites, they appeared to present a problem of diminishing relative importance. At the present time, however, the two races are running almost a neck and neck race. There is a fair prospect that the blacks may soon be increasing at the faster pace. I do not state this as a confident prediction, because I can lay claim to very little prophetic insight; but from a consideration of the factors influencing the natural increase of the two competing races, such an eventuality seems to me distinctly possible, if not probable.

Should a marked increase in the relative proportion of blacks to whites become unmistakable, the whites may be led to consider seriously the problem of population control. Certainly one very useful function of government, could it be accomplished, would be the proper regulation of numbers in the interest of the general welfare. The topic of population control has been discussed in a number of recent books and in several conferences on population problems, but it is generally treated in vague and general terms. Nations often find it desirable to control the ethnic composition of their inhabitants, but the achievement of this end usually presents many difficult and embarrassing problems. The Turks went at the business in Armenia in a fashion that brought them little credit in the eyes of the civilized world. There is a good deal of discussion in Germany over the curtailment of the increase of Poles, Jews, and other elements not in the good graces of the present régime. The expulsion of the Moors from Spain, of the Greeks from Turkey, and of the Turks from Greece, are examples of population control by drastic methods which it is not likely the United States will ever be led to adopt. At one time several prominent American statesmen advocated the deportation of the entire Negro population, but the time is past when this proposal is likely to be given much consideration, although it still has its advocates. The twelve million Negro inhabitants are here through no fault of their own, and their right to remain may be considered to have as sound a basis as that of the whites. Quite aside, however, from the legal and practical difficulties of this colossal undertaking, there is the fact that a very large proportion of the whites would be as strongly opposed to this solution of the problem as the Negroes themselves. The South was very reluctant to lose Negro migrants during the war period, and as American industries come to be more dependent upon Negro labor, as it seems likely they will, the stronger and more general will be the opposition to such a proposal. Ever since the emancipation, when some four million slaves were suddenly thrown upon their own resources, the Negroes have gradually become more thoroughly incorporated into our economic life. Most of those who loudly bewail the presence of the Negroes, if they found themselves suddenly confronted with the prospect of losing them, would do their utmost to keep them from going.

The relations of Negroes and whites will have to be worked out on American soil. The task will be made more difficult if the ratio of blacks to whites increases. This possibility may not happen, of course, but one cannot help speculating what the whites will be likely to do about it if it does. Very likely they will do nothing, and will allow matters to just drift. Population problems usually do work out in this way. As a result of the struggle for survival, which for the most part proceeded in a very peaceful manner, the people of Haiti and Jamaica have become almost wholly black. Parts of the Southern States have followed much the same course, and the rest of the country would probably offer no effective opposition to an extensive continuation of the same process of racial replacement. Peoples will fight to the death to maintain their rights against a hostile invader, but they will allow themselves to be outbred and supplanted by rival stocks without the slightest attempt to forestall their fate. The half-instinctive group pugnacity of human beings is a very inadequate protection against some of the common dangers to which they are exposed in their struggle to perpetuate their kind.

Possibly the future may see the beginning of population policies which are intelligently and consistently directed toward the promotion of human welfare. Hitherto the greater number of such efforts as have been made for the control of population have been dictated by racial animosity, religious fanaticism, fear, or some other essentially unintelligent impelling force. What the Germans may accomplish—and many of their best minds are giving serious thought to the problem—remains to be seen. But in Germany, as elsewhere, the influence of forces of the type I have mentioned is only too obvious. The immigration-quota system of the United States represents an attempt at population control that rests more on a basis of sentiment and political expediency than of sound biology.

There is no essential injustice in efforts to regulate the proportionate numbers of the various ethnic elements that make up a nation. Whether or not injustice is involved depends upon the means by which the end is achieved. If a government should decide to regulate the relative proportions of whites and Negroes in the United States, there are various measures which might be employed to achieve this end without violating any fundamental human rights. Just how such a situation should be dealt with is a problem which may sorely tax the ingenuity of future statesmen. At present I am not venturing to give these gentlemen any specific advice; I am merely suggesting the possibility of humane and even feasible means of dealing with it. Whether or not there will be sufficient occasion for undertaking measures of control the future will determine. In the meantime, as the years go on, the biological trend of the Negro should be studied with care in order that whatever is to be done about it, if anything, may at least be done wisely.

APPENDIX

TABLE I

ADMISSIONS AND DEPARTURES OF NEGROES TO OR FROM THE UNITED STATES,
FROM 1921 TO 1932

| | Admissions | | | Departures | | | |
	Immigrants	Non-immigrants	Total	Emigrants	Non-emigrants	Total	Gain or loss
1921	9,873	5,112	14,985	1,807	3,122	4,929	+10,056
1922	5,248	4,041	9,289	2,183	2,970	5,153	+ 4,136
1923	7,554	5,589	13,143	1,525	2,834	4,359	+ 8,784
1924	12,243	7,099	19,342	1,449	3,438	4,887	+14,455
1925	791	2,099	2,890	1,094	2,005	3,099	− 209
1926	894	2,491	3,385	865	1,871	2,736	+ 649
1927	955	2,671	3,626	870	1,585	2,455	+ 1,171
1928	956	2,698	3,654	789	1,556	2,345	+ 1,309
1929	1,254	2,935	4,189	425	1,351	1,776	+ 2,413
1930	1,806	2,726	4,532	776	1,782	2,558	+ 1,974
1931	884	2,048	2,932	737	1,416	2,153	+ 779
1932	183	1,452	1,635	811	835	1,946	− 11

TABLE II

Total Population of the United States, by Color or Race, From 1790 to 1930

	Total	White	Negro	Mexican	Indian	Chinese	Japanese	Filipino	All others
1930	122,775,046	108,864,207	11,891,143	1,422,533	332,397	74,954	138,834	45,208	5,770*
1920	105,710,620	94,820,915†	10,463,131	700,541†	244,437	61,639	111,010	5,603	3,885‡
1920			10,613,131¶						
1910	91,972,266	81,731,957‡	9,827,763	367,510†	265,683	71,531	72,157	160	3,015§
1900	75,994,575	66,809,196	8,833,994		237,196	89,863	24,326		
1890	62,947,714	55,101,258	7,488,676		248,253	107,488	2,039		
1890			7,760,000¶						
1880	50,155,783	43,402,970	6,580,793		66,407‖	105,465	148		
1870	38,558,371	33,589,377	4,880,009		25,731‖	63,199	55		
1870	39,818,449	34,337,292	5,392,172		25,731‖	63,199	55		
1860	31,443,321	26,922,537	4,441,830		44,021‖	34,993			
1850	23,191,876	19,553,068	3,638,808						
1840	17,069,453	14,195,805	2,873,648						
1830	12,866,020	10,537,378	2,328,642						
1820	9,638,453	7,866,797	1,771,656						
1810	7,239,881	5,862,073	1,377,808						
1800	5,308,483	4,306,446	1,002,037						
1790	3,929,214	3,172,006	757,208						

* Comprises 3,130 Hindus, 1,860 Koreans, 660 Hawaiians, 96 Malays, 18 Siamese, and 6 Samoans.
† The white population as classified in 1920 and 1910 included 700,541 and 367,510, respectively (estimated), who would have been classified as Mexican in 1930. If the figures are adjusted by deducting these estimates, the number of white persons in 1920 becomes 94,120,374, or 89.0 per cent of the total, and in 1910, 81,364,447, or 88.5 per cent of the total.
‡ Comprises 2,507 Hindus, 1,224 Koreans, 110 Hawaiians, 19 Malays, 17 Siamese, 6 Samoans, and 2 Maoris.
¶ Estimated corrected figures.
§ Comprises 2,545 Hindus, 462 Koreans, and 8 Maoris.
‖ Exclusive of Indians in Indian Territory and on Indian Reservations, not enumerated at censuses prior to 1890.

TABLE III

NEGRO AGE GROUPS FROM 1910 TO 1930 WITH THEIR RESPECTIVE POPULATIONS
AND RESPECTIVE LOSSES IN EACH SUCCESSIVE DECADE

Age groups as of 1910	Populations			Losses		
	1910	1920*	1930*	1910–20	1920–30	1910–30
0–4	1,263,288	1,236,914	1,203,191	26,374	33,723	60,097
5–9	1,246,553	1,083,215	1,071,787	163,338	11,428	174,766
10–14	1,155,266	1,054,847	864,514	100,419	190,333	290,752
15–19	1,060,416	909,739	890,900	150,677	18,839	169,516
20–24	1,030,795	697,865	687,423	332,930	10,442	343,372
25–29	881,227	773,931	630,065	107,296	143,866	251,162
30–34	668,089	559,701	504,590	108,388	55,111	163,499
35–39	633,449	551,589	309,397	81,860	242,192	324,052
40–44	455,413	399,110	242,169	56,303	156,941	213,244
45–49	385,909	229,980	155,177	155,929	74,803	230,732
50–54	326,070	200,118	99,096	125,952	101,022	226,974
55–59	209,622	137,035	58,711	72,587	78,324	150,911
60–64	186,502	91,579	33,377	94,923	58,202	153,125
65–69	123,550	52,352	14,948	71,198	37,404	108,602
70–74	78,839	28,122	6,332	50,717	21,790	72,507
75–79	44,018	12,281	2,611	31,737	9,670	41,407
80–84	25,579	5,847	2,467	19,732	3,380	23,112
85–89	11,166	2,562	....	8,604	2,562	11,166
90–94	5,850	2,935	....	2,915	2,935	5,850
95–99	2,447	....	....	2,447	......	2,447
100+	2,675	....	....	2,675	......	2,675
Unknown	31,040	....	....	......	......	......

* The numbers under the years 1920 and 1930 represent the survivors ten and twenty years
later, respectively, of the cohorts living in 1910. Thus out of the 1,263,288 individuals aged 0–4
years in 1910, 1,236,914 were alive in 1920, and 1,203,191 in 1930.

TABLE IV

DEATH RATES PER THOUSAND POPULATION, WHITE AND COLORED, IN SELECTED C⟩
FROM 1901 TO 1932

City	Annual average		1910	1911	1912	1913	1914	1915
	1901–05	1906–10						
Alexandria, Va.								
White....................	18.4	17.4	16.9	15.9	13.5	13.6	15.8	13.0
Colored..................	30.0	31.6	32.9	31.0	30.9	27.6	29.1	27.2
Annapolis, Md.								
White....................	....	....	....	....	....	....	....	....
Colored..................	....	....	....	....	....	....	....	....
Atlanta, Ga.								
White....................	16.1	15.6	15.5	15.7	14.6	13.6	13.3	11.8
Colored..................	29.6	26.8	25.5	28.1	25.4	26.4	24.4	23.3
Baltimore, Md.								
White....................	17.8	17.3	17.2	16.1	16.1	16.1	15.8	14.9
Colored..................	32.0	31.5	30.5	30.3	28.3	29.6	27.9	25.9
Charleston, S. C.								
White....................	19.3	17.2	18.9	18.5	19.0	15.7	17.6	16.5
Colored..................	38.2	36.5	39.3	40.0	41.4	37.2	37.0	41.6
Frederick, Md.								
White....................	18.4	17.8	17.3	18.5	19.9	17.9	17.2	15.4
Colored..................	41.1	34.0	34.7	34.3	34.6	25.0	11.7	23.7
Jacksonville, Fla.								
White....................	23.3	17.9	16.7	16.8	15.8	15.7	15.1	14.5
Colored..................	30.5	25.8	23.9	26.1	23.8	22.6	21.9	22 7
Key West, Fla.								
White....................	20.4	20.1	20.9	19.5	17.0	14.0	15.5	11.9
Colored..................	24.4	26.3	26.8	31.5	20.0	17.1	17.4	16.0
Lynchburg, Va.								
White....................	15.3	13.2	12.0	15.1	14.3	14.5	15.0	14.3
Colored..................	28.1	25.9	24.4	27.0	26.7	28.5	26.9	31.5
Mobile, Ala.								
White....................	19.7	18.7	17.8	18.8	16.7	16.9	18.0	15.9
Colored..................	31.2	29.7	29.5	30.7	26.0	25.7	26.4	24.1
New Orleans, La.								
White....................	19.2	18.0	17.2	16.6	16.1	15.6	16.6	16.5
Colored..................	31.0	32.1	32.7	31.2	31.5	32.1	31.9	34.5
Norfolk, Va.								
White....................	14.4	16.9	16.4	14.3	13.7	12.9	12.3	12.0
Colored..................	26.3	33.4	30.9	30.3	27.0	26.0	26.0	23.8
Petersburg, Va.								
White....................	19.9	19.7	20.1	20.7	16.6	16.9	16.5	19.4
Colored..................	31.6	35.5	34.2	31.8	31.0	32.4	33.1	31.0
Raleigh, N. C.								
White....................	21.2	22.7	24.5	27.5	29.8	22.0	24.7	23.6
Colored..................	30.5	33.3	33.6	37.5	33.5	29.7	39.6	34.1
Richmond, Va.								
White....................	18.5	17.4	18.1	16.4	15.9	15.9	14.2	14.8
Colored..................	31.7	29.9	30.3	28.6	28.4	27.5	28.5	25.4
San Antonio, Texas								
White....................	21.5	20.8	22.1	21.0	22.8	20.5	21.5	21.4
Colored..................	20.7	19.9	21.4	21.7	25.1	21.7	20.7	23.0
Savannah, Ga.								
White....................	19.2	17.9	19.4	19.3	18.4	17.3	17.5	14.5
Colored..................	34.5	31.3	34.1	38.8	34.4	32.2	33.0	34.4
Washington, D. C.								
White....................	16.5	15.9	15.8	15.1	14.1	13.4	12.7	13.7
Colored..................	29.5	28.7	29.1	26.5	26.9	24.3	23.2	25.1
Wilmington, N. C.								
White....................	19.9	17.4	15.6	22.0	16.6	16.7	16.8	15.2
Colored..................	31.6	28.7	26.7	38.1	31.7	29.1	31.0	26.3

TABLE IV—(*Continued*)

TH RATES PER THOUSAND POPULATION, WHITE AND COLORED, IN SELECTED CITIES, FROM 1901 TO 1932

	1918	1919	1920	1921	1922	1923	1928	1929	1930	1931	1932	1933
	....	....	14.3	11.8	12.9	12.8	14.6	16.0	12.7	12.0	12.7	11.0
	....	....	29.1	21.6	22.9	27.3	21.3	17.2	21.8	24.2	18.9	17.3
	....	....	9.5	8.8	10.3	10.3	9.1	6.1	9.5	11.8	9.3	9.5
	....	....	25.1	27.7	26.3	30.7	23.4	20.7	24.0	21.1	20.0	18.6
6	15.6	13.3	14.5	12.3	12.0	13.4	12.8	11.9	11.6	11.6	11.1	10.9
6	26.8	21.2	23.0	20.6	24.2	28.7	23.7	23.5	23.2	21.6	19.7	20.4
2	23.6	14.3	13.9	12.7	13.0	13.5	13.7	13.3	12.7	12.9	12.1	12.3
	36.5	23.5	23.5	20.5	21.3	23.5	21.6	20.6	19.6	19.9	18.5	17.2
7	....	....	16.4	13.2	12.4	11.9	14.4	13.7	14.6	14.5	13.0	12.5
7	....	....	31.3	29.9	28.4	30.1	32.3	33.2	33.0	33.6	30.1	29.9
4	....	....	18.2	18.2	17.8	24.2	18.2	15.3	18.8	18.0	14.4	14.8
2	....	....	16.3	21.7	20.4	31.3	11.9	20.9	16.9	11.3	16.3	11.9
2	....	....	14.2	12.2	12.5	13.3	12.3	12.3	11.8	11.5	10.5	11.3
0	....	....	20.1	19.2	19.2	22.2	22.9	23.6	21.0	20.4	21.5	21.9
5	....	....	14.7	11.9	11.8	11.2	13.1	12.3	15.3	14.6	12.7	14.9
4	....	....	20.2	22.2	16.3	12.6	18.9	22.4	24.1	21.9	27.6	27.6
2	....	....	14.1	12.8	11.1	12.5	13.7	13.3	13.2	13.1	12.4	11.4
3	....	....	22.5	19.6	20.9	23.7	22.9	26.0	26.0	23.6	25.0	24.6
6	....	....	14.8	14.6	13.8	13.7	14.9	15.6	15.0	13.3	13.4	13.7
1	....	....	23.5	20.0	20.9	20.7	22.1	23.2	23.9	21.6	20.3	19.6
8	22.0	16.2	14.5	13.7	14.0	14.5	13.4	14.3	14.4	13.5	14.1	13.3
0	37.5	26.7	26.4	23.9	24.5	26.7	22.7	26.4	25.0	23.5	22.8	22.4
3	21.1	12.6	11.8	10.0	9.0	8.3	10.7	10.6	10.1	10.1	10.2	9.8
7	30.8	23.3	20.7	17.7	17.3	17.1	21.2	23.6	20.4	19.1	18.0	19.1
9	....	....	14.1	13.5	13.2	12.1	15.4	15.6	13.5	13.3	12.5	14.2
1	....	....	25.6	23.7	21.6	19.9	28.5	26.2	24.6	21.1	22.9	22.3
5	....	....	20.8	17.5	17.8	21.3	19.7	20.3	18.8	16.2	17.0	16.4
0	....	....	27.2	23.4	26.7	28.1	23.2	22.4	23.7	21.2	20.5	21.0
1	19.6	13.4	13.3	12.3	12.2	12.6	12.5	13.2	12.3	13.1	11.8	11.7
5	29.6	20.6	23.3	19.8	20.6	22.8	22.7	23.1	21.4	21.4	20.2	19.0
4	....	....	16.1	15.7	15.4	14.7	16.3	15.9	....	....	....	....
3	....	....	16.8	14.6	15.6	15.2	16.3	19.3	....	....	....	....
0	....	....	16.4	13.3	12.0	12.0	14.6	13.7	13.6	13.5	13.6	13.2
8	....	....	31.2	28.8	27.1	27.1	28.2	28.6	26.5	26.1	24.9	23.9
4	19.9	12.7	12.6	12.1	12.4	12.3	12.5	13.0	12.9	13.4	14.0	13.3
6	30.7	20.6	20.6	18.9	20.5	22.9	20.9	21.7	21.0	22.0	21.6	22.8
0	....	....	15.5	15.0	11.8	10.4	17.1	15.1	15.7	13.1	13.7	13.5
7	....	....	25.2	21.5	23.3	22.1	23.0	23.9	24.9	23.3	20.5	21.8

TABLE V

Deaths, With Death Rates, in the White and Colored Populations in the Registration States of 1920, From 1920 to 1932

	White		Colored	
	Deaths	Rate	Deaths	Rate
1920.............................	990,859	12.54	127,211	17.41
1921.............................	895,593	11.16	114,080	15.33
1922.............................	929,910	11.40	117,492	15.51
1923.............................	980,294	11.84	129,092	16.75
1924.............................	946,219	11.25	135,586	17.30
1925.............................	971,258	11.38	139,620	17.52
1926.............................	1,021,643	11.79	145,654	17.97
1927.............................	969,239	11.03	138,639	16.83
1928.............................	1,044,210	11.71	147,857	17.67
1929.............................	1,043,291	11.54	148,071	17.42
1930.............................	1,000,570	10.91	146,092	16.92
1931.............................	989,917	10.79	145,376	15.67
1932.............................	988,647	10.71	135,909	14.53

In the foregoing table deaths of Mexicans preceding 1930 are included with the whites. In 1930 and thereafter, Mexicans are included in the colored population, but, as is stated in the *Mortality Statistics* for 1932, "it is evident that very many Mexican deaths are designated as white on the death certificates." The reporting of Mexican deaths seems to be as yet (1936) in a transitional stage, and this fact naturally modifies somewhat the statistics on the relative death rates of the white and colored populations.

TABLE VI

MEASLES: DEATH RATES PER 100,000 POPULATION, WHITE AND COLORED, IN SELECTED STATES, FROM 1915 TO 1927

	1915	1916	1917	1918	1919	1920	1921	1922	1923	1924	1925	1926	1927
Florida													
White					6.5	1.7	0.9		9.2	20.8	0.8	2.1	1.6
Colored					3.3	0.6	0.6	0.6	10.7	20.0	0.5	2.2	1.6
Georgia													
White								0.1	15.4	20.3			
Colored								0.4	8.7	16.1			
Kentucky													
White	3.8	8.4	41.5	18.5	10.2	11.8	7.9	4.3	17.2	12.5	1.4	19.3	6.0
Colored	1.6	4.1	29.7	6.2	6.3	5.1	1.7	6.5	13.7	4.0	1.8	11.7	4.3
Louisiana													
White				21.5	2.5	3.1	7.3	1.0	8.2	22.2	0.4	0.2	13.3
Colored				16.9	1.7	1.3	4.1	0.6	5.0	30.2	0.7	1.0	14.5
Maryland													
White	2.2	7.9	8.0	10.6	3.5	6.8	3.3	4.8	10.1	3.3	1.8	13.7	1.1
Colored	3.8	7.1	10.8	13.6	2.0	4.9	2.4	7.3	11.2	4.8	0.4	15.3	2.3
Mississippi													
White					3.1	0.6	2.0	0.4	9.8	15.5	2.1	5.6	14.1
Colored					1.7	1.4	1.2	0.7	15.5	7.5	0.5	2.2	6.0
North Carolina													
White	0.9	6.9	45.9	17.6	6.6	2.8	6.3	0.6	20.8	17.1	0.6	2.6	9.3
Colored		7.6	33.9	6.9	1.2	1.4	4.1	1.6	24.5	16.0	0.5	5.2	6.5
South Carolina													
White		4.8	53.2	22.1	3.2	4.2	6.9	0.2	12.8	32.2	0.2	0.7	7.9
Colored		4.4	28.6	20.6	3.2	2.4	3.4	0.7	11.3	29.8	0.4	0.6	3.1
Tennessee													
White			35.2	19.8	8.0	12.3	3.7	0.6	21.7	13.1	2.4	13.0	6.5
Colored			29.3	8.3	3.3	3.5	2.2	2.0	22.3	10.4	2.5	8.3	3.5
Virginia													
White	2.5	16.2	17.3	15.8	3.8	4.2	7.9	1.9	23.5	8.1	2.7	4.3	4.6
Colored	2.9	23.1	12.0	9.6	1.9	3.6	6.5	0.4	19.5	10.9	3.9	3.1	4.4

TABLES VII, VIII, AND IX

In the three following tables I have given the statistics of the morbidity from measles, scarlet fever, and diphtheria in the white and colored populations of Baltimore, Md. Other statistical data on morbidity might be compiled, but I have felt so dubious about

TABLE VII

MEASLES: REPORTED CASES, WITH RATES PER 100,000 POPULATION, WHITE AND COLORED, IN BALTIMORE, FROM 1920 TO 1932

Year	Whites		Colored	
	Cases	Rate	Cases	Rate
1920	4,530	722.6	509	461.2
1921	2,181	345.9	55	48.4
1922	4,658	734.5	384	328.2
1923	7,739	1,213.4	550	457.1
1924	3,732	581.9	491	397.1
1925	2,033	315.2	102	80.3
1926	11,614	1,790.6	1,014	778.3
1927	610	93.5	51	38.2
1928	10,986	1,675.1	1,243	907.8
1929	133	20.2	12	8.6
1930	400	60.3	51	35.5
1931	13,654	2,048.2	1,365	929.2
1932	150	22.4	15	10.0

their accuracy that I have hesitated to employ them. Reports of the contagious diseases of children are probably more nearly complete than those for many other maladies. They are obviously very incomplete for tuberculosis and pneumonia. The fact that in Baltimore in 1932 there were reported 488 cases of lobar pneumonia and 538 deaths, or 50 more deaths than cases, naturally destroys all confidence in the morbidity statistics for this disease. It may be that measles, scarlet fever, and diphtheria are less likely to be reported in the Negro population. If we can rely upon the statistics given in the accompanying tables (VII, VIII, IX), colored people are much less likely to contract these diseases than are the whites. I give the data for what they are worth.

TABLE VIII

SCARLET FEVER: REPORTED CASES, WITH RATES PER 100,000 POPULATION, WHITE AND COLORED, IN BALTIMORE, FROM 1920 TO 1932

Year	Whites		Colored	
	Cases	Rate	Cases	Rate
1920.................	1,207	192.5	41	37.2
1921.................	1,023	162.2	42	36.9
1922.................	1,155	182.1	39	33.3
1923.................	2,182	342.1	56	46.5
1924.................	1,890	294.7	99	80.1
1925.................	1,093	169.5	29	22.8
1926.................	1,043	160.8	44	33.8
1927.................	983	150.7	31	23.2
1928.................	993	151.4	44	32.1
1929.................	1,475	223.7	57	40.6
1930.................	1,700	256.4	77	53.6
1931.................	1,171	175.7	74	50.4
1932.................	2,011	300.0	83	55.3

TABLE IX

DIPHTHERIA: REPORTED CASES, WITH RATES PER 100,000 POPULATION, WHITE AND COLORED, IN BALTIMORE, FROM 1920 TO 1932

Year	Whites		Colored	
	Cases	Rate	Cases	Rate
1920.................	1,514	241.5	35	31.7
1921.................	1,365	216.5	58	51.0
1922.................	1,448	228.3	85	72.7
1923.................	1,224	191.9	94	78.1
1924.................	1,047	163.2	63	51.0
1925.................	823	127.6	74	58.3
1926.................	764	117.8	73	56.0
1927.................	1,413	216.6	206	154.2
1928.................	730	111.3	99	72.3
1929.................	476	72.2	71	50.6
1930.................	437	65.9	85	59.2
1931.................	318	47.7	98	66.7
1932.................	196	29.2	58	38.6

TABLE X

TUBERCULOSIS: DEATH RATES, CRUDE AND ADJUSTED, PER 100,000 POPULATION, WHITE AND COLORED, IN THE REGISTRATION STATES OF 1920, FROM 1920 TO 1925

Year	Adjusted	Crude	Year	Adjusted	Crude
1920			1923		
White.......	96.2	99.5	White.........	79.4	82.4
Colored.....	263.0 '	263.5	Colored.......	231.5	232.2
1921			1924		
White.......	82.3	85.3	White.........	75.6	78.3
Colored.....	242.5	243.2	Colored.......	237.8	238.2
1922			1925		
White.......	81.1	84.1	White.........	70.8	73.7
Colored......	237.4	238.2	Colored.......	235.9	236.0

TABLE XI

TUBERCULOSIS: DEATH RATES, PER 100,000 PERSONS INSURED, OF WHITE AND COLORED POLICY HOLDERS OF THE METROPOLITAN LIFE INSURANCE COMPANY, FROM 1911 TO 1930

Year	White		Colored	
	Males	Females	Males	Females
1911..............	230.8	165.4	422.2	415.1
1913..............	218.2	147.7	428.6	363.1
1915..............	201.1	141.5	432.8	394.2
1917..............	194.3	135.0	414.9	371.7
1919..............	145.2	125.2	319.7	328.9
1921..............	99.5	95.2	249.1	285.8
1923..............	97.9	88.2	242.9	245.7
1925..............	84.3	76.7	224.9	228.0
1927..............	77.9	70.9	227.6	228.4
1929..............	73.1	63.0	226.4	220.1
1930..............	68.0	57.1	223.8	213.0

MORTALITY RATES FOR TUBERCULOSIS AND CANCER IN THE
REGISTRATION STATES OF 1920

In calculating the mortality rate for tuberculosis and cancer in the Registration States of 1920 (see Tables XII and XIII) I have taken the Mexicans out of the colored group and added them to the white population of 1930, inasmuch as they were so included in the

TABLE XII

TUBERCULOSIS: DEATHS, WITH DEATH RATES PER 100,000 POPULATION, WHITE
AND COLORED, IN THE REGISTRATION STATES OF 1920,
FROM 1920 TO 1929

Year	White		Colored	
	Deaths	Rate	Deaths	Rate
1920.................	78,479	99.38	18,887	258.52
1921.................	68,179	84.97	17,560	236.07
1922.................	68,157	83.61	17,327	228.86
1923.................	67,684	81.76	17,017	220.90
1924.................	65,335	77.73	17,720	226.13
1925.................	63,169	74.03	18,004	225.93
1926.................	63,740	73.61	18,426	227.44
1927.................	59,507	67.72	17,799	216.17
1928.................	59,393	66.63	17,944	214.47
1929.................	57,249	63.32	17,417	204.93

census for 1920 and also in the mortality statistics. The data for the whites for the several years between 1920 and 1930 are therefore on a comparable basis.

In calculating mortality rates for the colored population for the several years, I have adopted the Census Bureau's estimate of 150,000 as the undercount of Negroes in 1920. In obtaining a population base for the calculation of rates, I have therefore added to the colored population of 1920 that part of 150,000 obtained by dividing it in the ratio of the Negro population of the Registration States of 1920 to the entire Negro population of the United States. This would increase the enumerated colored population of the Registration States of 1920, which was 7,239,519, by 98,485, making a total of 7,337,999.

TABLE XIII

CANCER: DEATHS, WITH DEATH RATES PER 100,000 POPULATION, WHITE AND
COLORED, IN THE REGISTRATION STATES OF 1920,
FROM 1920 TO 1929

Year	White		Colored	
	Deaths	Rate	Deaths	Rate
1920	68,266	86.44	3,490	47.77
1921	71,491	89.09	3,622	48.69
1922	74,454	91.34	3,901	51.52
1923	77,346	93.43	4,159	53.98
1924	80,870	96.21	4,371	55.78
1925	83,982	98.43	4,641	58.24
1926	87,578	101.14	4,922	60.75
1927	90,034	102.47	5,069	61.56
1928	93,864	105.31	5,136	61.38
1929	95,278	105.39	5,227	61.50

AGE-SPECIFIC DEATH RATES FROM CANCER IN THE WHITE AND COLORED POPULATIONS OF THE REGISTRATION STATES of 1920, FROM 1920 TO 1929

In Tables XIV to XXI, giving the age-specific death rates for the white and colored populations of the Registration States of 1920, certain adjustments were made for the Mexican population. The Mexicans were taken out of the colored group and added to the whites. Mexicans were classed as white in the census of 1920, but in 1930 they were given a separate enumeration for the first time, being included along with Negroes, Chinese, Indians, Japanese, etc., in the total colored population. Populations for each year were estimated as of July 1 according to the usual assumption of a uniform arithmetic rate of increase during the ten-year interval.

Since the Mexicans over 35 years of age were classified only in ten-year groups instead of five-year groups, I have divided the numbers in each ten-year group in the ratio in which the total colored population is distributed in the two quinquennia in each group. This gives a close approximation to the Mexican population in each five-year age interval. The numbers of Mexicans in each five-year age group were deducted from the total number of colored in the corresponding age group and added to the corresponding age group of the whites. The result of this distribution of the Mexicans was to reduce the age-specific mortality rates for the whites very slightly and to increase the rates for the colored by a larger percentage. The Mexicans apparently do not die of cancer as frequently as the whites and Negroes—at least not officially. Not improbably this is owing in part to faculty diagnosis of the cause of death, and partly to the fact that many Mexicans suffering from cancer return to their native country.

In making the estimates for the colored population, no allowance was made for the undercount of Negroes in 1920. This was done advisedly for the reason that we are dealing with populations over 20 years of age, and, according to Arner's estimates, most of the underenumeration of Negroes in 1920 occurred in children under 10. Because of the tendency of Negroes to overstate their age, the omissions may have been balanced by the inclusions of individuals in the age groups over 20 who did not belong there. Owing to the uncertainty with respect to what adjustments of the Negro population should be made, it was deemed best to take the figures as they are given in the census for 1920.

Age-specific death rates are naturally affected by errors in reporting ages. Many of these errors may be corrected by making a smoothed distribution of ages in the general population. To obtain a quite accurate result there should also be a smoothed age distribution of reported deaths, and this would be a most unsatisfactory undertaking. It may be questioned if ages given on death certificates are any more accurate than those reported to the census enumerator. If not, little is gained by using a smoothed age distribution in the population base. If, for example, too many people are given in the census as of age 40, and too many are reported in the mortality statistics as dying at that age, the death rate for age 40 may not be very far wrong. For the sake of accuracy in the vital statistics we may cherish the hope that misstatements of age given to the census taker and misstatements of age at death are both wrong to approximately the same degree and in the same direction.

TABLE XIV

CANCER: DEATHS, WITH DEATH RATES PER 100,000 POPULATION, IN THE
REGISTRATION STATES OF 1920, FROM 1920 TO 1929

Age groups	Deaths		Rate	
	Whites	Colored	Whites	Colored
20–24				
Male...............	1,691	173	4.76	4.69
Female............	1,554	307	4.21	7.45
25–29				
Male...............	2,509	234	7.19	6.83
Female............	3,612	805	10.28	21.71
30–34				
Male...............	4,002	387	12.09	13.48
Female............	8,191	1,407	25.46	48.26
35–39				
Male...............	7,943	705	23.97	22.60
Female............	17,479	2,709	56.47	93.57
40–44				
Male...............	13,529	1,237	47.52	51.37
Female............	29,020	3,670	109.48	171.62
45–49				
Male...............	21,723	1,681	84.48	71.67
Female............	40,465	4,338	174.23	246.76
50–54				
Male...............	33,345	2,185	153.88	121.73
Female............	51,167	4,126	257.56	317.47
55–59				
Male...............	44,282	2,006	262.77	181.19
Female............	56,546	3,245	360.46	415.40
60–64				
Male...............	55,267	1,919	399.93	221.93
Female............	61,459	2,961	473.28	451.64
65–69				
Male...............	59,582	1,613	606.23	285.78
Female............	60,960	2,192	642.88	483.16
70–74				
Male...............	52,898	1,237	791.24	351.22
Female............	52,385	1,601	785.76	496.69
75–79				
Male...............	38,032	756	993.09	377.54
Female............	38,783	991	957.44	523.83
80–84				
Male...............	19,373	376	1,130.93	380.64
Female............	22,285	608	1,105.77	550.72
85–89				
Male...............	7,368	201	1,187.86	469.29
Female............	9,743	330	1,208.73	666.93

TABLE XV

CANCER OF STOMACH: DEATHS, WITH NUMBERS, AND RATES PER 100,000 POPULATION, WHITE AND COLORED, FROM 1920 TO 1929

Age groups	White		Colored	
	Deaths	Rate	Deaths	Rate
20–24				
Male..............	213	.60	39	1.06
Female............	183	.50	46	1.12
25–29				
Male..............	497	1.42	64	1.87
Female............	453	1.29	94	2.53
30–34				
Male..............	1,113	3.36	165	5.74
Female............	1,181	3.44	169	5.80
35–39				
Male..............	2,915	8.80	346	9.35
Female............	2,709	8.75	416	13.37
40–44				
Male..............	5,654	19.86	623	25.87
Female............	5,039	19.01	584	27.31
45–49				
Male..............	9,949	38.69	925	39.44
Female............	8,141	35.04	775	44.08
50–54				
Male..............	15,875	73.26	1,220	67.97
Female............	12,316	62.00	885	68.10
55–59				
Male..............	21,363	126.77	1,091	98.54
Female............	16,261	103.66	842	107.79
60–64				
Male..............	26,762	193.66	985	113.94
Female............	20,667	159.15	861	131.33
65–69				
Male..............	28,648	291.48	839	148.65
Female............	22,944	241.96	619	136.44
70–74				
Male..............	24,415	365.19	651	184.83
Female............	21,324	319.85	502	155.74
75–79				
Male..............	16,531	431.66	348	173.79
Female............	15,903	392.59	322	170.20
80–84				
Male..............	7,498	437.71	171	173.11
Female............	8,587	426.08	187	169.38
85–89				
Male..............	2,472	398.53	82	191.45
Female............	3,279	406.79	111	224.33

TABLE XVI

CANCER OF PERITONEUM, INTESTINE, AND RECTUM: DEATHS, WITH DEATH
RATES PER 100,000 POPULATION, WHITE AND COLORED,
FROM 1920 TO 1929

Age groups	White		Colored	
	Deaths	Rate	Deaths	Rate
20–24				
Male...............	328	.92	28	.76
Female............	236	.64	40	.97
25–29				
Male...............	550	1.58	59	1.72
Female............	565	1.61	110	2.97
30–34				
Male...............	907	2.74	62	2.16
Female............	1,061	3.30	133	4.56
35–39				
Male...............	1,630	4.92	104	3.33
Female............	1,972	6.37	229	7.91
40–44				
Male...............	2,415	8.48	152	6.31
Female............	3,149	11.88	261	12.20
45–49				
Male...............	3,442	13.39	196	8.36
Female............	4,537	19.53	319	18.52
50–54				
Male...............	4,886	22.55	228	12.70
Female............	6,514	32.79	322	24.78
55–59				
Male...............	6,716	39.85	243	21.95
Female............	7,842	49.99	277	35.46
60–64				
Male...............	8,336	60.30	241	27.88
Female............	9,304	71.65	237	36.15
65–69				
Male...............	8,661	88.12	132	28.70
Female............	9,742	102.74	171	37.69
70–74				
Male...............	7,492	112.06	123	34.92
Female............	8,731	130.96	154	47.77
75–79				
Male...............	5,292	138.18	86	42.94
Female............	6,871	169.62	103	54.44
80–84				
Male...............	2,486	145.12	37	37.45
Female............	3,779	187.51	45	40.76
85–89				
Male...............	828	133.49	18	42.02
Female............	1,551	192.41	23	46.48

TABLE XVII

CANCER OF FEMALE GENITIVE ORGANS: DEATHS, WITH DEATH RATES PER 100,000 FEMALE POPULATION, WHITE AND COLORED, FROM 1920 TO 1929

Age groups	White		Colored	
	Deaths	Rate	Deaths	Rate
20–24................	460	1.24	127	3.08
25–29................	1,375	3.91	435	11.73
30–34................	3,289	10.22	790	27.10
35–39................	7,085	22.89	1,528	52.77
40–44................	11,229	42.36	1,966	91.94
45–49................	14,054	60.47	2,170	123.44
50–54................	15,614	78.60	1,865	143.50
55–59................	14,663	93.47	1,289	165.01
60–64................	13,579	104.57	1,155	176.17
65–69................	11,834	124.80	836	184.27
70–74................	8,426	126.38	505	156.67
75–79................	5,331	131.60	283	149.59
80–84................	2,653	131.64	187	169.38

TABLE XVIII

CANCER OF BREAST: DEATHS, FEMALES ONLY, WITH DEATH RATES PER 100,000 FEMALE POPULATION, WHITE AND COLORED, FROM 1920 TO 1929

Age groups	White		Colored	
	Deaths	Rate	Deaths	Rate
20–24................	74	.20	20	.48
25–29................	397	1.13	68	1.83
30–34................	1,422	4.42	176	6.04
35–39................	3,534	11.42	392	13.54
40–44................	6,237	23.53	531	24.83
45–49................	8,980	38.66	667	37.94
50–54................	10,301	51.85	641	49.32
55–59................	10,258	65.39	479	61.32
60–64................	9,505	73.20	400	61.02
65–69................	7,869	82.98	312	68.77
70–74................	6,321	94.81	233	72.28
75–79................	4,641	114.57	150	79.28
80–84................	3,007	149.20	105	95.10
85–89................	0	0	0	0

TABLE XIX

CANCER OF BUCCAL CAVITY: DEATHS, WITH DEATH RATES PER 100,000 POPULATION, WHITE AND COLORED, FROM 1920 TO 1929

Age groups	White		Colored	
	Deaths	Rate	Deaths	Rate
20–24				
Male...............	44	.12	11	.30
Female.............	19	.05	9	.22
25–29				
Male...............	76	.22	8	.23
Female.............	35	.10	10	.27
30–34				
Male...............	119	.36	17	.59
Female.............	57	.18	14	.48
35–39				
Male...............	371	1.12	32	1.03
Female.............	105	0.34	23	0.79
40–44				
Male...............	806	2.83	86	3.57
Female.............	159	0.60	30	1.40
45–49				
Male...............	1,440	5.60	99	4.22
Female.............	230	0.99	50	2.84
50–54				
Male...............	2,309	10.66	122	6.80
Female.............	330	1.66	49	3.77
55–59				
Male...............	2,894	17.17	99	8.73
Female.............	418	2.66	36	4.61
60–64				
Male...............	3,474	25.14	85	9.83
Female.............	487	3.75	38	5.79
65–69				
Male...............	3,558	36.20	95	16.83
Female.............	597	6.30	36	7.93
70–74				
Male...............	3,197	47.28	57	16.18
Female.............	628	9.41	28	8.68
75–79				
Male...............	2,444	63.81	40	19.97
Female.............	553	13.65	22	11.62
80–84				
Male...............	1,572	91.76	17	17.20
Female.............	477	23.66	9	8.15
85–89				
Male...............	707	113.98	15	35.02
Female.............	301	37.34	14	28.29

TABLE XX

Cancer of Skin: Deaths, With Death Rates per 100,000 Population, White and Colored, From 1920 to 1929

Age groups	White		Colored	
	Deaths	Rate	Deaths	Rate
20–24				
Male	38	0.11	1	0.03
Female	31	0.08	8	0.19
25–29				
Male	51	0.15	5	0.15
Female	50	0.14	6	0.16
30–34				
Male	107	0.32	13	0.45
Female	77	0.24	12	0.41
35–39				
Male	189	0.57	13	0.41
Female	115	0.37	20	0.69
40–44				
Male	325	1.14	18	0.75
Female	210	0.79	26	1.21
45–49				
Male	522	2.03	32	1.36
Female	250	1.08	26	1.48
50–54				
Male	787	3.63	44	2.45
Female	376	1.89	41	3.15
55–59				
Male	1,066	6.33	40	3.61
Female	495	3.15	34	4.35
60–64				
Male	1,492	10.80	32	3.70
Female	710	5.47	21	3.20
65–69				
Male	1,998	20.33	43	7.62
Female	948	10.00	34	7.49
70–74				
Male	2,382	35.62	23	6.53
Female	1,270	19.04	29	8.99
75–79				
Male	2,445	63.84	22	10.98
Female	1,338	34.26	17	8.98
80–84				
Male	1,921	112.14	8	8.09
Female	1,451	71.99	12	10.86
85–89				
Male	1,141	183.95	7	16.34
Female	1,087	134.85	3	6.06

TABLE XXI

CANCER OF UNSPECIFIED ORGANS: DEATHS, WITH DEATH RATES PER 100,000 POPULATION, WHITE AND COLORED, FROM 1920 TO 1929

Age groups	White		Colored	
	Deaths	Rate	Deaths	Rate
20–24				
Male..............	1,063	2.99	94	2.54
Female............	551	1.49	57	1.38
25–29				
Male..............	1,333	3.82	97	2.83
Female............	737	2.09	82	2.21
30–34				
Male..............	1,745	5.27	129	4.49
Female............	1,104	3.43	113	3.87
35–39				
Male..............	2,816	8.50	209	6.70
Female............	1,959	6.32	182	6.29
40–44				
Male..............	4,277	15.02	346	14.37
Female............	3,097	11.68	272	11.72
45–49				
Male..............	6,312	24.55	423	18.04
Female............	4,282	18.44	331	18.83
50–54				
Male..............	9,382	43.29	561	31.26
Female............	5,716	28.77	323	24.85
55–59				
Male..............	12,127	71.96	524	47.33
Female............	6,609	42.13	288	36.87
60–64				
Male..............	15,059	108.97	568	65.70
Female............	7,210	55.52	249	37.98
65–69				
Male..............	16,579	168.69	467	82.74
Female............	7,026	74.09	189	41.66
70–74				
Male..............	15,294	228.76	375	106.47
Female............	5,685	85.27	150	46.53
75–79				
Male..............	11,212	292.76	257	128.34
Female............	4,096	101.11	104	54.97
80–84				
Male..............	5,826	340.10	141	142.74
Female............	2,331	115.66	63	57.06
85–89				
Male..............	2,183	351.94	76	177.44
Female............	1,019	126.41	36	72.75

TABLE XXII

NEPHRITIS: DEATH RATES, PER 100,000 POPULATION, WHITE AND COLORED, IN
THE REGISTRATION AREA OF 1920, FROM 1920 TO 1927

	1920		1921		1922		1923	
	White	Colored	White	Colored	White	Colored	White	Colored
All ages								
Adjusted.........	78.8	131.1	74.6	130.9	74.4	137.3	78.8	140.9
Crude...........	86.7	111.5	82.5	111.7	86.3	116.7	88.3	120.6
Under 1 year.......	29.9	50.5	25.0	47.0	24.8	51.2	18.7	39.0
1 to 4.............	8.5	14.8	8.1	18.6	6.8	19.7	6.7	19.2
25 to 34.............	18.4	45.4	17.0	52.9	16.1	41.4	17.2	52.5
65 to 74.............	643.9	933.8	609.7	876.9	646.0	940.5	668.7	967.0

	1924		1925		1926		1927	
	White	Colored	White	Colored	White	Colored	White	Colored
All ages								
Adjusted.........	76.4	158.0	84.9	179.0	88.5	147.1	82.2	174.2
Crude...........	86.2	137.1	93.3	150.1	97.3	130.3	90.5	146.1
Under 1 year.......	21.7	44.9	18.5	33.8	15.9	25.8	14.4	28.3
1 to 4.............	6.3	16.1	5.8	20.5	5.4	10.9	4.7	13.6
25 to 34.............	16.4	52.3	15.8	58.7	15.6	53.7	15.3	60.1
65 to 74.............	644.5	1075.1	734.2	1212.1	783.5	940.5	723.9	1126.6

TABLE XXIII

DEATHS FROM DIARRHEA AND ENTERITIS (UNDER 2 YEARS), AND FROM PRE-
MATURE BIRTH (INT. LIST NO. 159), IN BALTIMORE, FROM 1910 TO 1932

Year	Diarrhea and enteritis*				Premature birth			
	White		Colored		White		Colored	
	Deaths	Rate per 100,000 popula- tion	Deaths	Rate per 100,000 popula- tion	Deaths	Rate per 100,000 popula- tion	Deaths	Rate per 100,000 popula- tion
1910........	435	91.7	163	190.6	486	102.4	169	197.6
1911........	451	93.8	117	133.7	411	85.5	138	157.7
1912........	386	79.3	115	128.4	567	116.5	135	150.8
1913........	451	91.6	107	116.9	476	96.6	155	169.3
1914........	459	92.1	105	112.2	411	82.5	168	179.6
1915........	400	79.3	80	83.7	385	76.3	107	112.0
1916........	430	84.3	151	154.8	354	69.4	104	106.6
1917........	483	93.6	152	152.7	341	66.1	94	94.4
1918........	610	116.8	185	182.1	445	85.2	75	73.8
1919........	497	80.1	119	110.6	339	54.6	106	98.5
1920........	532	84.9	131	118.7	394	62.8	116	105.1
1921........	346	54.9	83	73.0	334	53.0	82	72.1
1922........	370	58.3	112	95.7	279	44.0	70	59.8
1923........	214	33.6	84	69.8	263	41.2	81	67.3
1924........	233	36.3	68	55.0	266	41.5	88	71.2
1925........	231	35.8	71	55.9	240	37.2	84	66.2
1926........	152	23.4	81	62.2	233	35.9	88	67.5
1927........	132	20.2	59	44.2	209	32.0	102	76.3
1928........	128	19.5	56	40.9	218	33.2	105	76.7
1929........	103	15.6	33	23.5	206	31.2	101	72.0
1930........	107	16.1	35	24.4	194	29.3	80	55.7
1931........	95	14.3	46	31.3	182	27.3	72	49.0
1932........	64	9.6	35	23.3	170	25.4	95	63.2

*The decreasing mortality from these diseases explains the remarkable decline in the infant mortality in both whites and blacks which has occurred in Baltimore in the past two decades.

TABLE XXIV

INFANT MORTALITY RATES PER THOUSAND LIVE BIRTHS, WHITE AND COLORED, IN SELECTED STATES AND CITIES, 1916 TO 1934

STATES

	1916	1917	1918	1919	1920	1921	1922	1923	1924	1925	1926	1927	1928	1929	1930	1931	1932	1933	1934
Mass.																			
White	100	98	112	87	90	75	81	77	67	72	73	64	64	61	60	54	52	52	49
Colored	164	131	158	142	128	115	109	134	98	107	102	98	97	85	98	81	84	79	78
New York																			
White	93	90	95	82	85	74	76	71	68	66	68	57	63	59	57	55	51	52	50
Colored	169	176	175	151	159	138	124	121	114	119	132	109	123	111	103	104	93	90	90
Ohio																			
White	...	91	92	88	81	73	70	72	64	67	73	60	64	66	58	58	57	51	52
Colored	...	158	178	157	153	122	111	139	113	127	128	103	113	120	107	106	97	88	81
Maryland																			
White	101	101	124	92	90	81	81	80	76	76	74	68	67	69	63	66	57	55	60
Colored	209	201	215	160	164	147	147	155	128	146	137	134	128	120	121	132	110	104	107
Michigan																			
White	96	88	88	89	90	78	73	79	71	73	76	66	68	65	61	56	53	50	51
Colored	199	158	159	147	179	125	127	147	126	149	124	102	126	109	95	94	68	71	72
Mississippi																			
White	...	...	...	...	...	53	56	53	55	53	59	55	61	58	51	44	44	51	55
Colored	...	...	...	...	...	85	79	82	88	85	81	78	86	85	83	67	62	75	74
No. Car.																			
White	...	85	85	74	73	66	70	70	70	67	71	66	75	67	67	60	57	55	67
Colored	...	133	140	109	113	95	101	106	110	105	107	109	109	107	105	102	87	90	101
Virginia																			
White	...	80	86	78	72	68	65	71	66	67	72	62	64	67	65	64	58	59	62
Colored	...	137	141	120	110	103	102	115	104	111	111	106	104	107	107	108	90	90	98

(Continued on next page)

TABLE XXIV—(Continued)

CITIES

	1916	1917	1918	1919	1920	1921	1922	1923	1924	1925	1926	1927	1928	1929	1930	1931	1932	1933	1934
New York																			
White....	92	87	90	79	83	69	73	65	66	62	65	53	62	56	55	52	48	50	50
Colored..	169	176	171	145	157	135	117	116	106	118	131	108	128	111	105	106	93	95	90
Boston																			
White....	104	98	113	96	100	77	92	82	74	84	83	76	77	68	69	60	59	58	55
Colored..	193	167	173	115	129	106	90	108	97	118	117	99	79	92	90	78	85	82	66
Philadelphia																			
White....	102	103	118	86	84	75	79	73	68	70	70	58	63	56	58	58	47	45	48
Colored..	160	192	214	146	178	121	135	138	131	128	134	103	117	99	100	103	83	76	87
Detroit																			
White....	..	..	..	..	..	81	85	84	76	77	82	68	74	66	62	53	51	49	50
Colored..	..	..	..	..	..	116	122	141	118	128	114	95	122	106	90	85	63	70	61
Chicago																			
White....	..	..	..	..	..	..	82	84	73	72	65	61	61	58	51	55	48	46	46
Colored..	..	..	..	..	..	..	114	143	126	115	94	89	98	86	77	75	58	77	65
Baltimore																			
White....	104	103	137	89	95	80	84	75	76	72	71	70	70	62	57	64	53	53	58
Colored...	219	197	215	143	105	123	134	136	124	122	128	127	124	111	94	111	94	87	88
Richmond																			
White....	..	74	105	91	81	80	77	75	69	67	76	61	59	55	51	57	49	53	54
Colored..	..	219	236	139	180	142	112	177	124	132	164	113	133	131	119	119	90	83	107
Washington																			
White....	83	71	85	67	72	68	64	71	62	67	67	49	46	48	52	44	56	49	43
Colored ..	158	160	188	132	139	122	134	143	108	132	123	109	107	117	110	115	108	101	108
Louisville																			
White....	..	87	96	81	73	67	66	82	67	75	83	64	75	66	63	67	61	60	69
Colored ..	..	166	251	219	190	117	178	153	99	126	170	80	129	108	96	144	102	98	91

TABLE XXV

NUMBERS AND RATIOS OF DEATHS OF WHITE AND COLORED INFANTS IN THE
REGISTRATION AREA, FROM 1911 TO 1923

Causes of death	Number of deaths		Ratio of white to colored
	White	Colored	
All causes..........................	1,447,538	193,658	7.474
General diseases................	158,206	31,565	5.012
Typhoid fever.................	431	182	2.368
Malaria.......................	1,265	1,378	.918
Measles......................	14,276	1,305	10.939
Scarlet fever..................	1,500	54	27.77
Whooping cough..............	36,394	6,696	5.435
Diphtheria and croup.........	8,047	1,128	7.133
Influenza.....................	35,375	6,817	5.189
Dysentery....................	5,381	2,433	2.2117
Erysipelas....................	7,498	248	30.23
Poliomyelitis.................	2,008	168	11.95
Meningococcus meningitis.....	3,078	214	14.38
Tetanus......................	1,798	1,575	11.41
Tuberculosis..................	18,743	3,129	5.990
Respiratory tuberculosis.......	5,507	1,715	3.211
Tuberculous meningitis........	8,981	863	10.40
Abdominal tuberculosis.......	1,508	147	10.25
Disseminated tuberculosis.....	617	271	2.276
Syphilis......................	14,598	4,967	2.939
Gonococcus infection..........	486	81	6.0
Purulent infection and septicemia..................	1,525	91	16.75
Cancer and malignant tumor...	520	......	......
Diseases of the nervous system...	35,064	5,207	6.734
Simple meningitis.............	7,983	569	14.03
Cerebral hemorrhage..........	1,330	147	9.048
Epilepsy......................	817	258	3.166
Convulsions...................	1,613	3,448	.468
Diseases of the ears...........	2,940	171	17.19
Diseases of the circulatory system.....................	11,046	675	16.36
Acute endocarditis............	2,949	125	23.59
Other diseases of the heart....	5,293	368	14.38
Diseases of lymphatics........	1,771	110	16.10

(*Continued on next page*)

TABLE XXV—(*Continued*)

Causes of death	Number of deaths		Ratio of white to colored
	White	Colored	
Diseases of respiratory system...	221,889	33,032	6.717
Diseases of the larynx.........	1,375	199	6.91
Bronchitis....................	27,587	3,341	8.257
Broncho-pneumonia (capillary bronchitis since 1921).......	129,342	16,348	7.911
Pneumonia, lobar and undefined	56,194	11,251	5.058
Pleurisy.....................	1,634	123	13.28
Diseases of digestive system.....	320,993	34,670	9.258
Diarrhea and enteritis........	284,381	29,635	9.596
Hernia......................	1,440	261	5.52
Intestinal obstruction.........	8,832	745	11.85
Nonvenereal diseases of the genitourinary system: Nephritis, acute and chronic...	4,646	683	6.803
Diseases of the skin............	5,844	275	21.25
Malformations..................	109,047	4,675	23.32
Hydrocephalus...............	7,722	478	16.15
Congenital malformations of the heart...................	66,806	2,759	24.21
Other congenital malformations	34,519	1,428	24.17
Early infancy..................	517,314	54,949	9.414
Congenital debility, atrophy, marasmus.................	89,685	13,793	6.502
Premature birth..............	313,425	33,223	9.434
Injuries at birth..............	67,603	3,309	20.43
External causes................	17,106	3,299	5.185
Homicide....................	1,231	175	7.034
Ill-defined diseases..............	32,902	19,061	1.726
Sudden death................	1,517	614	2.47
Not specified, or unknown.....	25,371	20,067	1.264

TABLE XXVI

MORTALITY RATES FOR WHITE AND NEGRO INFANTS IN THE BIRTH REGISTRATION AREA, FROM 1916 TO 1934

(DEATHS PER THOUSAND LIVING BIRTHS)

Causes of death	1916	1917	1918	1919	1920	1921	1922	1923	1924	1925	1926	1927	1928	1929	1930	1931	1932	1933	1934
Measles																			
White.....	1.4	1.2	1.0	0.5	1.0	0.5	0.6	1.2	0.7	0.3	1.1	0.4	0.6	0.3	0.4	0.4	0.2	0.2	0.6
Negro.....	.9	2.2	.8	0.2	0.4	0.4	0.5	1.8	1.4	0.2	1.0	0.4	1.1	0.2	0.4	0.3	0.1	0.3	1.1
Scarlet fever																			
White.....	0.1	0.1	0.1	0.1	0.1	0.1	0.1	0.1	0.1	0.1	0.1	0.1	0.1	0.1	0.1	0.1	(1)	(1)	(1)
Negro.....	0.1	...	...	(1)	(1)	0.1	(1)	(1)	(1)	(1)	(1)	(1)	(1)	(1)	(1)	(1)	(1)	(1)	(1)
W'ping cough																			
White.....	2.2	2.2	3.1	1.2	2.9	2.0	1.3	2.1	1.8	1.6	2.1	1.7	1.4	1.7	1.4	1.1	1.4	1.0	1.8
Negro.....	5.6	5.8	8.1	3.2	4.7	4.4	2.9	5.2	5.1	3.1	3.8	4.3	2.8	3.3	2.7	2.1	2.7	2.5	4.1
Diphtheria																			
White.....	0.5	0.5	0.4	0.4	0.4	0.4	0.5	0.4	0.3	0.3	0.2	0.2	0.3	0.2	0.2	0.2	0.2	0.2	0.1
Negro.....	1.1	0.9	0.7	0.7	0.6	0.8	0.6	0.7	0.5	0.4	0.4	0.3	0.4	0.4	0.4	0.3	0.2	0.3	0.2
Dysentery																			
White.....	0.2	0.3	0.3	0.3	0.3	0.3	0.2	0.2	0.2	0.3	0.2	0.2	0.3	0.2	0.3	0.2	0.2	0.3	0.3
Negro.....	0.4	1.8	1.9	2.0	1.9	1.2	1.3	1.1	1.1	0.9	0.8	0.8	1.0	0.8	0.9	0.8	0.4	0.6	0.8
Influenza																			
White.....	0.8	0.8	6.3	3.7	2.3	0.6	1.6	2.0	1.0	1.6	2.2	1.3	2.5	3.0	1.2	1.6	1.6	1.6	1.0
Negro.....	1.3	1.0	13.0	10.6	6.9	1.2	2.9	4.7	2.4	3.3	4.7	2.6	4.6	6.0	2.5	3.1	2.9	3.2	2.2
Erysipelas																			
White.....	0.6	0.5	0.4	0.4	0.4	0.4	0.4	0.4	0.4	0.4	0.4	0.4	0.4	0.4	0.3	0.3	0.3	0.3	0.3
Negro.....	0.5	0.2	0.2	0.1	0.2	0.2	0.1	0.1	0.2	0.2	0.2	0.1	0.1	0.1	0.1	0.1	0.1	0.1	0.1
Meningitis																			
White.....	0.8	0.8	0.8	0.7	0.6	0.2	0.1	0.1	0.1	0.1	0.1	0.1	0.2	0.3	0.2	0.2	0.1	0.1	0.1
Negro.....	1.0	0.9	0.8	0.7	0.7	0.1	0.1	0.1	0.1	0.1	0.1	0.1	0.1	0.2	0.3	0.2	0.1	0.1	0.1

(1) Less than one-tenth of 1 per 1,000 births.

(Continued on next page)

TABLE XXVI—(Continued)

Causes of death	1916	1917	1918	1919	1920	1921	1922	1923	1924	1925	1926	1927	1928	1929	1930	1931	1932	1933	1934
Tetanus																			
White	0.1	0.1	0.1	0.1	0.1	0.1	0.1	0.1	0.1	(1)	(1)	0.1	0.1	(1)	(1)	(1)	(1)	0.1	(1)
Negro	0.4	0.7	0.6	0.7	0.7	0.4	0.5	0.6	0.5	0.5	0.4	0.5	0.5	0.3	0.3	0.3	0.3	0.3	0.3
Respiratory tuberculosis																			
White	0.5	0.5	0.4	0.4	0.3	0.2	0.2	0.2	0.2	0.2	0.2	0.1	0.1	0.1	0.1	0.1	0.1	0.1	0.1
Negro	2.3	1.4	1.6	1.2	1.0	0.8	0.7	0.7	0.7	0.6	0.6	0.7	0.6	0.3	0.6	0.4	0.4	0.3	0.3
Tuberculous meningitis																			
White	0.8	0.7	0.6	0.6	0.5	0.4	0.4	0.4	0.3	0.3	0.3	0.2	0.2	0.2	0.2	0.2	0.1	0.1	0.1
Negro	1.9	0.8	0.5	0.5	0.5	0.4	0.4	0.5	0.3	0.4	0.4	0.3	0.3	0.2	0.2	0.2	0.1	0.2	0.2
Other forms																			
White	0.2	0.2	0.2	0.2	0.1	0.2	0.1	0.1	0.1	0.1	0.1	0.1	0.1	0.1	0.1	0.1	0.1	(1)	(1)
Negro	0.3	0.3	0.2	0.1	0.2	0.2	0.3	0.3	0.2	0.2	0.2	0.2	0.3	0.2	0.2	0.2	0.2	0.2	0.2
Syphilis																			
White	1.2	1.0	0.8	0.8	0.7	0.7	0.7	0.6	0.7	0.5	0.5	0.5	0.5	0.5	0.5	0.5	0.4	0.4	0.4
Negro	7.9	3.9	3.5	2.8	2.8	2.8	2.7	3.0	2.8	3.0	2.9	3.2	3.3	3.4	3.5	3.3	3.2	3.0	2.9
Convulsions																			
White	1.2	1.0	1.1	0.9	0.9	0.7	0.7	0.6	0.6	0.6	0.5	0.4	0.4	0.4	0.3	0.3	0.3	0.2	0.2
Negro	3.2	2.8	2.7	2.3	2.1	2.0	2.1	1.7	1.7	1.3	1.2	1.1	1.0	1.0	1.0	0.8	0.8	0.7	0.7
Bronchitis																			
White	2.5	2.1	1.9	1.8	1.7	1.0	1.2	1.0	0.8	0.7	0.7	0.5	0.5	0.4	0.4	0.3	0.3	0.3	0.3
Negro	6.0	3.6	4.2	2.4	2.7	1.3	1.3	1.7	1.4	1.3	1.2	0.9	0.8	0.7	0.8	0.6	0.5	0.3	0.3
Pneumonia																			
White	3.9	3.9	4.5	3.0	2.8	2.2	2.7	2.5	2.4	2.3	2.6	1.9	2.4	2.2	2.1	2.0	1.8	1.7	1.8
Negro	7.5	9.2	10.2	6.7	7.8	5.1	6.5	6.5	6.6	5.6	6.5	5.1	6.3	5.2	5.2	5.2	4.3	4.6	5.2
Broncho-pneumonia																			
White	9.2	8.0	8.6	7.6	7.6	6.0	7.5	7.3	6.5	6.4	7.4	5.3	6.4	6.1	5.9	5.8	5.2	4.9	5.3
Negro	3.8	13.6	15.7	9.6	12.7	9.0	10.6	12.9	12.1	12.6	14.1	10.3	10.4	9.8	9.8	9.2	8.1	7.1	9.0

TABLE XXVI—*(Concluded)*

Causes of death	1916	1917	1918	1919	1920	1921	1922	1923	1924	1925	1926	1927	1928	1929	1930	1931	1932	1933	1934
Diarrhea & enteritis																			
White	23.7	19.5	18.6	15.4	14.6	13.3	11.4	11.2	8.8	10.7	9.3	7.3	7.2	6.6	7.2	5.9	6.7	4.8	5.3
Negro	39.6	28.7	25.2	20.0	19.8	16.3	15.1	15.3	14.4	17.0	14.4	12.2	11.7	10.5	11.2	9.7	7.1	7.6	8.8
Malform.																			
White	6.8	6.4	6.6	6.5	6.5	6.4	6.7	6.6	6.8	6.5	6.5	6.0	5.8	5.9	5.7	5.8	5.7	5.6	5.6
Negro	6.5	3.5	3.7	2.9	3.2	2.8	2.6	2.9	2.9	3.2	3.1	2.4	2.2	2.2	2.2	2.4	2.1	2.0	2.3
Con. deb.																			
White	9.9	8.4	8.9	7.8	7.3	4.1	3.7	3.7	3.3	3.2	3.1	2.6	2.6	2.9	2.2	2.2	2.8	2.0	2.0
Negro	18.7	15.4	15.8	13.2	13.2	7.2	6.6	6.8	6.1	6.3	5.9	4.9	5.6	5.3	4.9	4.6	4.3	4.3	4.6
Prem. birth																			
White	19.1	19.0	20.1	18.6	18.9	17.6	17.8	17.5	17.2	16.9	17.4	16.6	17.2	17.1	16.2	15.6	15.3	15.3	15.8
Negro	31.6	21.7	21.3	26.7	26.3	22.3	22.1	22.2	23.6	21.3	21.3	19.2	20.5	20.5	20.0	18.9	19.1	19.6	19.5
Inj. at birth																			
White	4.2	3.9	3.4	3.5	3.9	4.4	4.7	4.8	5.0	5.1	5.1	5.0	4.9	5.0	5.0	5.0	4.8	4.8	4.7
Negro	4.3	2.4	2.4	2.3	2.2	2.2	2.6	2.7	2.9	3.2	3.1	3.2	2.9	2.8	3.3	3.3	3.0	3.3	3.4
Other dis. of infancy																			
White	…	…	…	…	…	2.7	2.5	2.5	2.4	2.3	2.1	1.9	1.9	1.8	2.1	1.9	1.8	1.8	1.9
Negro	…	…	…	…	…	3.2	3.2	3.3	3.2	3.4	3.1	2.9	2.6	2.5	2.9	2.3	2.3	2.3	2.3
Ext. causes																			
White	1.0	1.2	0.9	0.9	1.0	0.9	0.9	0.9	0.9	1.0	1.0	0.9	0.9	0.9	0.9	0.9	0.8	0.9	0.9
Negro	3.0	2.8	2.5	1.9	1.9	2.0	1.8	1.7	2.1	1.9	2.0	2.0	1.9	1.8	1.9	1.7	1.5	1.7	1.8
Unknown																			
White	0.8	2.2	2.0	1.9	1.7	…	1.5	1.4	1.4	1.2	1.3	1.7	2.0	2.1	2.2	2.0	2.0	2.1	1.9
Negro	5.3	15.0	16.6	13.4	12.8	…	15.2	14.5	13.4	13.7	13.3	15.8	17.7	16.9	18.0	16.7	15.2	15.1	14.7
Other causes																			
White	5.6	4.6	4.0	4.0	4.1	6.1	5.0	4.9	4.8	4.9	4.9	4.6	4.6	4.5	3.7	3.5	3.1	3.2	3.2
Negro	9.4	7.8	7.1	7.4	8.1	22.3	7.4	7.2	6.8	7.3	6.5	5.7	6.1	6.0	5.3	6.9	4.0	4.7	4.8

BIRTH RATES IN THE REGISTRATION STATES FOR 1920 FROM
1920 TO 1930

In obtaining a population base for the calculation of birth rates in
the Birth Registration States of 1920, the same procedure was followed as in the construction of Tables XII and XIII. The Mexicans
were removed from the colored population in 1930 and their numbers added to the number of whites. Births in the Mexican popula-

TABLE XXVII

BIRTH RATES OF WHITES AND NEGROES IN THE BIRTH REGISTRATION STATES
OF 1920, FROM 1920 TO 1930

Years	White	Negro	Years	White	Negro
1920...........	23.44	25.86	1926.............	20.44	25.17
1921...........	23.94	27.35	1927.............	20.27	25.05
1922...........	22.34	25.19	1928.............	19.45	23.99
1923...........	21.83	25.25	1929.............	18.45	22.64
1924...........	22.44	26.89	1930.............	18.39	22.36
1925...........	21.38	25.87			

tion have been classed as white in all the volumes on Birth Statistics.
The classification of races in the census of 1930 was adopted too
late for use in the proper classification of births for that year, and
more or less confusion has resulted from this circumstance. Evidently many Mexican births were classified under "other races" in
1930 that had been previously included with the whites. This is
indicated by the fact that in the Birth Registration Area for 1930,
6,938 births were attributed to "other races," and only 537 were
so classed in 1929, and 256 in 1928.

Since births to Negroes, Indians, Chinese, and Japanese were
separately classed, this sudden increase in the category of "other
races" can be attributed only to the inclusion of Mexicans. For the
Birth Registration States of 1920, there were recorded, in 1930,
2,436 births to "other races." About three hundred of these, according to previous records of births, should be assigned to other colored races, such as Filipinos, Hindus, Hawaiians, etc. To make the
data on the white birth rate of 1930 strictly comparable with that

of previous years, at least 2,000 births should be added to the white group. This addition makes only a very slight increase in the birth rate, which becomes 18.39 instead of 18.36.

TABLE XXVIII

Birth Rates of the White and Colored Populations of Selected Northern and Southern States, From 1916 to 1933

	1916	1917	1918	1919	1920	1921	1922
New York							
White	24.4	24.6	23.8	21.9	22.5	22.6	21.5
Colored	19.8	19.8	20.8	21.3	23.1	24.4	24.6
Michigan							
White	26.1	26.1	25.9	23.3	25.1	25.3	23.2
Colored	8.7	10.4	14.4	16.0	20.9	25.5	22.7
Pennsylvania							
White	26.3	26.6	25.9	24.1	25.2	25.9	23.9
Colored	17.5	18.8	19.1	21.3	22.3	23.8	21.9
Indiana							
White	....	22.1	22.4	20.4	22.1	23.1	21.5
Colored	....	16.5	16.7	17.1	18.3	20.1	19.0
Ohio							
White	....	22.2	22.4	19.8	21.3	21.9	20.4
Colored	....	15.8	17.7	18.5	20.4	22.5	20.7
Maryland							
White	23.7	23.6	23.6	22.9	24.3	24.4	22.4
Colored	26.3	26.7	25.3	26.7	27.5	28.7	26.8
Kentucky							
White	....	26.7	27.1	24.7	26.8	28.6	26.6
Colored	....	18.3	16.5	17.2	17.6	19.0	13.9
Virginia							
White	....	26.9	27.6	25.9	27.8	29.4	26.6
Colored	....	27.4	28.2	27.7	29.7	31.1	28.9
North Carolina							
White	....	30.9	30.0	29.3	31.7	33.6	30.3
Colored	....	30.9	30.6	28.5	31.3	34.5	32.2
South Carolina							
White	....	....	....	27.1	28.8	29.9	27.1
Colored	....	....	....	26.2	27.7	29.1	26.7
Mississippi							
White	....	....	....	....	....	27.6	24.7
Colored	....	....	....	....	....	24.1	23.9

(*Continued on next page*)

TABLE XXVIII—(*Continued*)

	1923	1928	1929	1931	1932	1933
New York						
White...................	21.1	18.1	17.4	16.0	15.3	14.3
Colored.................	26.7	22.9	21.1	19.8	14.5	18.6
Michigan						
White...................	23.3	21.1	20.9	18.5	12.2	16.1
Colored.................	26.0	20.0	20.5	17.5	16.2	14.4
Pennsylvania						
White...................	23.8	21.0	19.7	18.4	17.3	16.0
Colored.................	24.8	24.3	22.4	19.3	17.8	17.0
Indiana						
White...................	21.8	18.9	18.3	12.3	16.3	15.4
Colored.................	21.4	18.3	18.0	14.7	14.1	14.0
Ohio						
White...................	20.9	19.6	19.1	16.1	15.1	14.0
Colored.................	23.6	22.1	21.2	15.6	14.5	15.4
Maryland						
White...................	22.1	19.0	17.5	16.5	16.4	15.4
Colored.................	27.6	24.3	23.4	22.3	22.6	21.7
Kentucky						
White...................	27.4	23.7	22.3	22.4	23.3	21.5
Colored.................	15.5	16.1	15.6	14.4	14.7	14.5
Virginia						
White...................	26.2	22.9	21.7	21.2	21.5	19.9
Colored.................	28.2	25.2	24.2	23.1	24.9	24.0
North Carolina						
White...................	30.7	25.8	24.2	22.9	23.5	22.3
Colored.................	32.7	27.7	25.9	24.1	25.3	24.8
South Carolina						
White...................	26.4	23.4	20.9	20.2	20.9	20.3
Colored.................	24.4	26.9	24.9	25.7	27.3	26.5
Mississippi						
White...................	24.5	24.3	22.3	21.5	21.5	20.1
Colored.................	23.5	24.6	23.4	23.1	24.0	23.2

TABLE XXIX

NEGRO BIRTH RATE PER THOUSAND NEGRO POPULATION IN THE BIRTH
REGISTRATION AREA, FROM 1920 TO 1924

	1920	1921	1922	1923	1924
California	16.6	17.6	17.3	19.8	20.9
Connecticut	26.4	26.7	24.3	25.7	28.0
Delaware	....	21.4	20.0	20.7	21.6
District of Columbia	22.6	23.5	24.0	22.6	24.2
Florida	....	....	....	....	21.7
Illinois	....	....	18.4	20.9	26.0
Indiana	18.4	20.2	19.1	21.5	24.1
Iowa	....	....	....	....	15.8
Kansas	17.3	17.3	18.4	18.2	18.4
Kentucky	17.6	19.0	13.9	15.5	19.5
Maine	4.6	5.4	....	....	....
Maryland	27.6	28.7	26.8	27.6	27.5
Massachusetts	26.9	24.7	25.1	24.8	27.4
Michigan	21.3	25.5	22.6	26.4	27.6
Minnesota	14.5	14.2	14.1	13.9	....
Mississippi	....	24.1	23.9	24.2	23.1
Nebraska	9.8	14.9	11.5	12.7	15.7
New Hampshire	9.6	20.7	....	....	....
New Jersey	....	26.9	25.4	28.3	32.0
New York	23.7	25.0	25.1	27.4	32.7
North Carolina	31.2	34.4	32.2	32.6	33.7
Ohio	20.5	22.6	20.7	23.5	27.8
Oregon	12.9	7.6	....	....	....
Pennsylvania	22.4	23.9	22.0	24.8	28.9
Rhode Island	....	26.3	22.9	29.0	26.1
South Carolina	27.6	29.1	26.7	24.4	26.5
Utah	18.8	15.4	....	....	....
Vermont	1.9	1.7	....	....	....
Virginia	29.7	31.1	28.9	28.2	27.9
Washington	12.9	8.0	....	....	....
Wisconsin	16.4	15.3	....	....	....

Birth rates for Negroes as distinct from those of the colored population in general are not given
in the volumes on Birth Statistics after 1924.

TABLE XXX

BIRTH RATES PER THOUSAND MARRIED WOMEN, 15 TO 44 YEARS OF AGE—
NATIVE WHITE AND NEGRO—FOR 1920–1922

	1920		1921		1922	
	Native white	Negro	Native white	Negro	Native white	Negro
Connecticut....	151.6	141.0	152.2	148.7	141.7	134.2
Delaware......	.....	.....	139.6	117.4	127.1	102.3
District of Columbia....	130.2	106.3	127.4	108.1	124.6	106.9
Illinois........	.....	.....	.....	.....	136.0	85.4
Indiana........	149.4	94.5	155.9	102.2	145.5	96.1
Kansas........	156.2	101.1	161.4	98.3	149.3	102.1
Kentucky......	188.1	101.4	199.9	109.1	185.3	78.1
Maryland......	169.2	145.7	169.1	147.2	155.1	138.0
Michigan......	165.0	94.0	167.4	111.5	154.2	99.8
Minnesota.....	187.1	72.0	190.0	66.2	185.0	68.0
Mississippi.....	.....	.....	191.9	134.7	171.0	134.2
Montana......	.....	.....	.....	.....	116.7	65.9
Nebraska......	168.5	63.7	172.4	67.8	164.0	53.7
New Hampshire	166.9	64.1	171.6	164.6	167.3	128.2
New Jersey....	.....	.....	.....	.....	144.7	128.8
New York.....	145.6	110.8	147.8	116.4	142.1	117.8
North Carolina	229.0	198.5	241.5	216.9	217.1	200.6
Ohio..........	139.5	101.6	143.2	110.0	133.8	100.4
Oregon........	124.4	65.5	126.1	38.8	118.7	82.0
Pennsylvania..	170.3	105.4	175.6	112.1	163.4	102.3
Rhode Island..	.....	.....	173.3	181.2	171.7	158.1
South Carolina	203.8	167.1	210.9	175.7	190.8	159.0
Utah..........	229.8	88.9	232.2	67.5	215.5	47.5
Vermont......	158.2	172.4	170.8	.....	162.0	50.0
Virginia.......	201.8	182.5	212.4	187.9	192.6	172.6
Washington....	130.0	68.5	127.9	46.4	117.4	56.1
Wisconsin......	170.7	89.3	177.3	81.7	165.5	74.8
Wyoming......	.....	.....	.....	.....	146.8	73.1

TABLE XXXI

Number of Children Ever Born to Mothers in the Total White, Native White, Foreign-Born White, and Colored Populations, Respectively, of Selected States, From 1917 to 1928

	1917	1918	1919	1920	1921	1922	1923	1924	1925	1926	1927	1928
New York												
Total white	3.1	3.0	3.2	3.1	3.0	3.0	3.0	3.0	2.9	2.9	2.9	2.8
Native white	2.6	2.6	2.7	2.6	2.6	2.6	2.6	2.6	2.6	2.6	2.5	2.5
Foreign white	3.5	3.5	3.7	3.6	3.6	3.5	3.6	3.5	3.5	3.4	3.4	3.3
Colored	3.0	2.9	2.9	2.8	2.8	2.9*	2.9	2.9	2.9	2.8	2.9	2.9
Michigan												
Total white	3.2	3.2	3.4	3.2	3.2	3.2	3.2	3.2	2.1	3.1	3.1	3.1
Native white	3.0	2.9	3.1	2.9	2.9	3.0	3.0	3.0	3.0	3.0	3.0	2.9
Foreign white	3.8	3.9	4.1	4.1	4.0	4.0*	3.9	3.8	3.8	3.7	3.7	3.6
Colored	3.1	3.1	3.0	2.9	3.0	3.2*	3.2	3.2	3.2	3.2	3.4	3.4
Pennsylvania												
Total white	3.5	3.5	3.7	3.5	3.5	3.5	3.6	3.5	3.5	3.5	3.4	3.4
Native white	3.1	3.1	3.2	3.1	3.1	3.1	3.1	3.1	3.18	3.1	3.0	3.0
Foreign white	4.1	4.3	4.5	4.6	4.6	4.6	4.7	4.8	4.8	4.9	4.9	4.9
Colored	3.4	3.3	3.4	3.3	3.3	3.3*	3.3	3.2	3.3	3.3	3.3	3.4
Indiana												
Total white	3.2	3.2	3.3	3.1	3.1	3.2	3.2	3.1	3.2	3.2	3.2	3.2
Native white	3.1	3.1	3.2	3.0	3.0	3.1	3.1	3.1	3.1	3.1	3.1	3.1
Foreign white	4.0	4.1	4.4	4.3	4.4	4.2*	4.1	4.0	4.1	4.1	4.1	4.1
Colored	3.4	3.4	3.4	3.2	3.4	3.3*	3.3	3.4	3.3	3.5	3.5	3.6
Ohio												
Total white	3.0	3.1	3.2	3.1	3.1	3.1	3.1	3.1	3.1	3.1	3.1	3.0
Native white	2.9	2.9	3.0	2.8	2.9	2.9	2.9	2.9	2.9	2.9	2.9	2.9
Foreign white	3.6	3.8	4.1	4.1	4.0	4.0	4.0	4.0	4.0	4.0	4.1	4.0
Colored	3.2	3.2	3.4	3.2	3.3	3.3	3.4	3.3	3.4	3.4	3.4	3.5

* For this year colored = Negro.

(Continued on next page)

TABLE XXXI—(Continued)

	1917	1918	1919	1920	1921	1922	1923	1924	1925	1926	1927	1928
Maryland												
Total white	3.3	3.2	3.3	3.2	3.3	3.3	3.3	3.3	3.3	3.2	3.3	3.2
Native white	3.2	3.1	3.2	3.1	3.2	3.2	3.2	3.2	3.2	3.1	3.2	3.2
Foreign white	3.9	3.9	4.0	4.0	4.1	4.1	4.1	4.2	4.2	4.1	4.2	4.2
Colored	4.1	4.1	4.1	3.9	4.0	4.0	4.0	4.0	4.0	4.0	4.1	4.0
Kentucky												
Total white	3.7	3.6	3.7	3.6	3.6	3.6	3.7	3.6	3.7	3.7	3.7	3.6
Native white	3.7	3.6	3.7	3.5	3.6	3.6	3.7	3.6	3.7	3.7	3.7	3.6
Foreign white	4.0	4.2	4.1	4.1	4.0	3.9	4.1	4.0	4.1	3.8	3.9	3.6
Colored	3.7	3.6	3.8	3.6	3.6	3.6	3.7	3.6	3.8	3.7	3.8	3.7
Virginia												
Total white	3.7	3.7	3.8	3.6	3.7	3.7	3.7	3.7	3.7	3.7	3.7	3.6
Native white	3.7	3.7	3.8	3.6	3.7	3.7	3.7	3.7	3.7	3.7	3.7	3.6
Foreign white	4.0	3.9	3.9	3.8	3.8	3.8	3.6	3.8	3.9	4.0	3.9	4.0
Colored	4.1	4.1	4.1	4.0	4.1	4.0	4.1	4.2	4.2	4.2	4.2	4.1
North Carolina												
Total white	3.9	3.9	4.0	3.8	3.8	3.8	3.8	3.8	3.7	3.7	3.6	3.6
Native white	3.9	3.9	4.0	3.8	3.8	3.8	3.8	3.8	3.7	3.7	3.6	3.6
Foreign white	3.6	3.6	3.4	3.3	3.4	3.4	3.5	3.1	3.2	3.1	3.6	3.0
Colored	4.2	4.2	4.3	4.0	4.1	4.1	4.0	4.0	3.9	4.0	3.9	3.9
South Carolina												
Total white	....	....	3.9	3.6	3.7	3.7	3.7	3.7	3.7	3.7	....	3.8
Native white	....	....	3.9	3.6	3.7	3.7	3.7	3.7	3.7	3.7	....	3.8
Foreign white	....	....	3.4	3.3	3.5	3.1	3.4	3.3	3.2	3.1	....	3.6
Colored	....	....	4.0	3.8	3.9	3.9	4.0	3.9	3.9	4.0	....	4.1
Mississippi												
Total white	....	....	....	....	....	3.6	3.6	3.5	3.5	3.5	3.5	3.4
Native white	....	....	....	....	....	3.5	3.6	3.5	3.5	3.5	3.5	3.4
Foreign white	....	....	....	....	....	4.3	4.8	4.3	5.0	4.4	4.1	4.4
Colored	....	....	....	....	....	3.8*	3.9	3.9	3.8	3.9	3.8	3.8

* For this year colored = Negro.

REFERENCES

THE LITERATURE dealing with the biological status of the American Negro is extensive in amount and published in widely scattered sources. Several bibliographies on Negro problems have been issued from time to time, but they have been superseded by the very full bibliography on all phases of Negro life, compiled by M. N. Work. This volume is indispensable for all serious students of Negro problems. More recently the extensive literature on Negro migration has been brought together by Ross and Kennedy.

The references I have selected are grouped according to the subjects treated in the several chapters. There is no attempt to make a complete bibliography; choice was made of only a few of the more significant contributions bearing specifically on the topics discussed. The books and papers in the short list immediately following deal with more than one aspect of the subject.

The Negro's progress in fifty years. *Ann. Am. Acad. Polit. Soc. Sci.*, **49** (1913), 266 pp.

The American Negro. *Ann. Am. Acad. Polit. Soc. Sci.*, **140** (1928), viii + 359 pp.

The Negro year book (edited by M. N. WORK; Tuskegee, Ala.), 1922–1926; *ibid.*, 1931–1932.

DOWD, J.
   The Negro in American life (New York, Century Co., 1926), xix + 611 pp.

HILL, C. E.
   Negroes in the United States, 1920–1932 (Washington, D. C., 1935), xiv + 845 pp.

HOFFMAN, F. L.
   "Race traits and tendencies of the American Negro." *Publ. Am. Econ. Assoc.*, **11** (1896), 1–329.

HOLMES, S. J.
   "The biological fortunes of the Negro." Chap. 16 of *Studies in evolution and eugenics* (New York, Harcourt, Brace, 1923).
   "The biological trend of the Negro." *Univ. Calif. Chronicle*, **32** (1930): 38–70.

JOHNSON, CH. S.
   The Negro in American civilization (New York, Holt, 1930), xiv + 538 pp.

LORIMER, F., AND OSBORN, F.
   Dynamics of population (New York, Macmillan, 1934), xiii + 461 pp.

REUTER, E. B.
   The American race problem (New York, Crowell, 1927), 448 pp.

STONE, A. H.
   Studies in the American race problem (New York, Doubleday, Page, 1908), xxii + 555 pp.

THOMPSON, W. S.
   Population problems (ed. 2; New York, 1935), xi + 500 pp.
THOMPSON, W. S., AND WHELPTON, P. K.
   Population trends in the United States (New York, McGraw-Hill, 1933),
   415 pp.
WORK, M. N.
   A bibliography of the Negro in Africa and America (New York, H. W.
   Wilson Co., 1928), xxiii + 698 pp.

Discussions bearing upon our subject are often found in *Opportunity; a
Journal of Negro Life,* the *Journal of Negro History,* and less frequently in
The Crisis (edited by W. E. B. DuBois) and *The Southern Workman.* Many
short articles on the mortality and morbidity of Negroes appear in the *Statistical Bulletins of the Metropolitan Life Insurance Company of New York.*
There is a useful selected bibliography on the physical and mental abilities of
the American Negro in the *Journal of Negro Education,* 3 (1934):548–564.

CHAPTER I

THE INTERRACIAL STRUGGLE FOR EXISTENCE

BEALS, C.
   "The black belt of the Caribbean." *Fortn. Rev.,* n.s., 130 (1931):356–368.
BRYCE, J.
   The relations of the advanced and backward races of mankind. Romanes
   Lecture (London, Frowde), 46 pp.
EAST, E. M.
   Mankind at the crossroads (New York, Scribner, 1923), ix + 360 pp. See
   chap. 5.
   Heredity and human affairs (New York, Scribner, 1927), vii + 325 pp.
   See chaps. 9 and 10.
GREGORY, J. W.
   The menace of colour (Philadelphia, Lippincott, 1925), 264 pp.
HAYNES, G. E.
   The trend of the races (New York, Council Women for Home Missions,
   etc., 1922), xvi + 205 pp.
HOFFMAN, F. L.
   "The Negro in the West Indies." *Publ. Am. Statist. Assoc.,* 4 (1895):181–
   200.
HOLMES, S. J.
   "The changing effects of race competition." *Science,* n.s., 75 (1932):201–
   208.
MATHEWS, B. J.
   Clash of color (New York, Doran, 1924), viii + 181 pp.
MILLER, H. A.
   Races, nations and classes (Philadelphia, Lippincott, 1924), xvii + 196 pp.
MONEY, L. C.
   Peril of the whites (London, Collins, 1925), xiii + 207 pp.
MUNTZ, E. E.
   Race contact (New York, Century Co., 1927), xiv + 474 pp.

MURPHY, E. G.
    The basis of ascendancy (New York, Longmans, Green, 1909), xxiv + 250 pp.
PITT-RIVERS, G. H. L. F.
    The clash of colour and the contact of races (London, Routledge, 1927), xiv + 312 pp.
ROBERTS, S. H.
    Population problems of the Pacific (London, Routledge, 1927), xx + 411 pp.
SILBURN, COL. P. A.
    South Africa, white and black, or brown? (London, Allen and Unwin, 1927), 192 pp.
SPEER, R. E.
    Race and race relations (New York, Revell, 1924), 434 pp.
STODDARD, L.
    The rising tide of color (New York, Scribner, 1920), xxxii + 320 pp.
    Re-forging America (New York, Scribner, 1927), viii + 389 pp. See chaps. 11 and 12.
TAYLOR, T. G.
    Environment and race (London, Oxford Univ. Press, 1927), xiv + 354 pp.
WEALE, B. L. P.
    The conflict of color (New York, Macmillan, 1910), ix + 341 pp.

CHAPTER II

THE GROWTH OF THE NEGRO POPULATION

BEALES, LEV.
    "Negro enumeration of 1920. A reply to Dr. Kelly Miller." *Scient. Mon.*, 14 (1922):352–360.
CUMMINGS, J.
    Negro population: 1790–1915 (Washington, D. C., Gov't Printing Office, 1918), 844 pp.
EGGLESTON, E.
    The ultimate solution of the American Negro problem (Boston, Badger, 1913), 285 pp.
FRAZIER, E. F.
    The free Negro family (Nashville, Tenn., Fisk Univ. Press, 1932), 75 pp.
FRY, C. L.
    "The Negro in the United States—A statistical statement." *Ann. Am. Acad. Polit. Soc. Sci.*, 140 (1928):26–35.
GANNETT, H.
    "Was the count of population in 1890 reasonably correct?" *Publ. Am. Statist. Assoc.*, 4 (1895):99–102.
GOVER, M.
    "Increase of the Negro population." *Human Biol.*, 1 (1929):263–273.
HOLMES, S. J.
    "The increasing growth-rate of the Negro population." *Am. Jour. Sociol.*, 42 (1936):202–214.

MILLER, K.

"Enumeration errors in Negro population." *Scient. Mon.,* **14** (1922):167–177.

"Negro in the 15th census." *Springfield Republican,* Aug. 14, 1931.

ROSSITER, W. S.

Increase of populations in the United States, 1910–1920 (Washington, D. C., Gov't Printing Office, 1922), 255 pp.

THOMPSON, W. S.

Population problems (ed. 2; New York, McGraw-Hill, 1935), xi + 500 pp.

THOMPSON, W. S., AND WHELPTON, P. K.

Population trends in the United States (New York, McGraw-Hill, 1933), 10 + 415 pp.

"The population of the nation." Chap. 1 of *Recent social trends* (New York, McGraw-Hill, 1933).

WALKER, F. A.

"Statistics of the colored race in the United States." *Publ. Am. Statist. Assoc.,* **2** (1890):91–106.

WHELPTON, P. K.

"Population of the United States, 1925 to 1975." *Am. Jour. Sociol.,* **34** (1928):253–270.

WILLCOX, W. F.

"Census statistics of the Negro." *Yale Rev.,* **13** (1904):274–286.

"The probable increase of the Negro race in the United States." *Quart. Jour. Econ.,* **19** (1905):545–573.

"Birth rate and natural increase of whites and Negroes in the United States." *Report* of Fifth Internat. Neo-Mal. and Birth Control Conference (London, Heinemann, 1922):138–154.

"Distribution and increase of Negroes in the United States." In *Eugenics in race and state* (Baltimore, Williams and Wilkins, 1923; 2 vols.), 2:166–174.

WOOFTER, T. J.

"What is the Negro rate of increase?" *Jour. Am. Statist. Assoc.,* **26** (1931):461–462.

"The status of racial and ethnic groups." Chap. 11 of *Recent social trends* (New York, McGraw-Hill, 1933), 558–601.

CHAPTER III

THE STABILIZED RATE OF INCREASE AMONG THE NEGRO POPULATION

DUBLIN, L. I., AND LOTKA, A. J.

"On the true rate of natural increase." *Jour. Am. Statist. Assoc.,* **20** (1925):305–339.

"The true rate of natural increase of the population of the United States." *Metron,* **8** (1930):107–119.

FOUDRAY, E.

United States abridged life tables (Washington, D. C., Gov't Printing Office, 1923), 84 pp.

HOLMES, S. J., AND PARKER, S. L.
"The stabilized natural increase of the Negro." *Jour. Am. Statist. Assoc.*, 26 (1930):159–171.

KUCZYNSKI, R. R.
The balance of births and deaths (New York, Macmillan, 1928), xi + 140 pp.
Fertility and reproduction (New York, Falcon Press, 1932), 94 pp.

LOTKA, A. J.
"Modern trends in the birth rate." *Ann. Am. Acad. Polit. Soc. Sci.*, 188 (1936):1–13.

WHELPTON, P. K.
"Population of the United States, 1925 to 1975." *Am. Jour. Sociol.*, 34 (1928):253–270.
"Differentials in true natural increase." *Jour. Am. Statist. Assoc.*, 24 (1929):233–249.
"Population; trends in age composition and in specific birth-rates, 1920–1930." *Am. Jour. Sociol.*, 37 (1932):855–861.
"An empirical method of calculating future population." *Jour. Am. Statist. Assoc.*, 31 (1936):457–473.
"Geographic and economic differentials in fertility." *Ann. Am. Acad. Polit. Soc. Sci.*, 188 (1936):1–19.

CHAPTER IV

THE TREND OF NEGRO MORTALITY

CHASE, T. N.
"Mortality among Negroes in cities." *Atlanta Univ. Publ.*, 1 (1903):1–24.

DAVIS, W. A.
"Some facts relative to Negro mortality in the United States." *Jour. Nat. Med. Assoc.*, 22 (1930):26–29.

DUBLIN, L. I.
The reduction in mortality among colored policy holders (New York, Metropolitan Life Insurance Co., 1920).
"Life and death and the Negro." *Am. Mercury*, 12 (1927):37–45.
"The problem of Negro health as revealed by vital statistics." *Jour. Negro Education*, 6 (1937):268–275.

DUBLIN, L. I., KOPF, E. W., AND VAN BUREN, G. H.
Mortality statistics of insured wage earners and their families (New York, Metropolitan Life Insurance Co., 1919), viii + 397 pp.

DUBLIN, L. I., AND LOTKA, A. J.
Length of life. A study of the life table (New York, Ronald, 1936), xxii + 400 pp.

FRICK, C. S.
"Vital statistics of Baltimore." *Am. Jour. Med. Sci.*, Oct., 1855.

GOVER, MARY
"Mortality among the Negroes in the United States." *Public Health Bull.* No. 174 (Washington, Gov't Printing Office, 1928), vi + 63 pp.
"Trend of mortality among southern Negroes since 1920." *Jour. Negro Education*, 6 (1937):276–288.

HALL, J. B.
"Negro death rate in Boston." *Jour. Nat. Med. Assoc.*, 18 (1926):133–135.
HARRIS, S.
"The future of the Negro from the standpoint of the southern physicians." *Ala. Med. Jour.*, 14 (1901–02):57–68.
HOFFMAN, F. L.
"Causes of death in primitive races." *Metron*, 10 (1932):153–200.
JAFENS, L. S.
"Remarks on the comparative mortality of the white and colored populations of Richmond, Va." *Va. Med. Mon.*, 2 (1875):155–167.
MARTIN, ASA E.
Our Negro population (Kansas City, Franklin Hudson Publ. Co., 1913), 189 pp.
PEARL, R.
"Biological factors in Negro mortality." *Human Biol.*, 1 (1929):229–249.
SIBLEY, E.
Differential mortality in Tennessee (Nashville, Tenn., Fisk Univ. Press, 1930), 152 pp.
SYDNOR, C. S.
"Life span of Mississippi slaves." *Am. Hist. Rev.*, 35 (1930):566–574.
TOBEY, J. A.
"Death rate among American Negroes." *Current Hist.*, 25 (1926):217–220.
WALTER, J. T.
"The comparative mortality of the white and colored races in the south." *Charlotte Med. Jour.*, 10 (1897):291–294.
SYDENSTRICKER, E.
"The vitality of the American people." In chap. 12 of *Recent social trends* (New York, McGraw-Hill, 1933), pp. 602–660.

CHAPTER V

THE SELECTIVE ACTION OF DISEASE

ACKER, G. N.
"Rickets in Negroes." *Arch. Pediat.*, 11 (1894):893–899.
ALLEN, F. J.
"Observations on tuberculosis, cutaneous reactions and tuberculosis." *Tubercle*, 13 (1932):241–254.
ALLEN, F. P.
"Physical impairment among 1,000 Negro factory workers." *Jour. Indust. Hyg.*, 13 (1931):164–168.
ALSOBROOK, H. B.
"One thousand cases of uterine fibroids in the Negro race." *New Orleans Med. and Surg. Jour.*, 84:317–326 (Nov., 1931).
ARONSON, J. D.
"Incidence of tuberculosis infections in some communities in the south." *Am. Jour. Hyg.*, 14 (1931):374–393.
BARKER, J. ELLIS
"Cancer in the black man." *Fortn. Rev.*, 123 (1925):381–393.

BARNES, F. M.
"General paralysis in the Negro." *New York Med. Jour. and Med. Record,* **98** (1913):767–771.

BARNES, I.
"The inheritance of pigmentation in the American Negro." *Human Biol.,* **1** (1929):321–381.

BERTRAM, N. W.
Health conditions in North Harlem in 1923–1927. (Nat. Tub. Assoc., *Social Research Series,* No. 2, 1932), 68 pp.

BLACK, J. B.
"A comparative study of susceptibility to diphtheria in the white and Negro races." *Am. Jour. Hyg.,* **19** (1934):734–748.

BLANC, H. W.
"A review of five years of dermatological practice in New Orleans." *Med. News,* **53** (1888):439–444.

BOAS, E. P.
"Relative prevalence of syphilis among Negroes and whites." *Soc. Hyg.,* **1** (1915):610–616.

BOGEN, E.
"Racial susceptibility to tuberculosis." *Am. Rev. Tub.,* **24** (1931):522–531.

BOINET AND ISEMEIN
"La tuberculose aiguë chez le nègre." *Marseille Méd.,* **64** (1927):387–389.

BORREL, A.
"Pneumonie et tuberculose chez les troupes noires." *Ann. Inst. Pasteur,* **34** (1920):105–148.

BOUSFIELD, M. O.
"Major health problems of the Negro." *Proc. Nat'l Conf. Soc. Work,* **60** (1933):216–226.

BOWCOCK, H. M.
"Diabetes mellitus in the Negro race. A study of one hundred consecutive cases." *South. Med. Jour.,* **21** (1928):994–999.

BRITTEN, R. H.
"The incidence of epidemic influenza, 1918–19." *Pub. Health Repts.,* **47** (1932):303–339.

BROCK, B. L., AND BLACK, H.
"Tuberculosis in the Negro." *Am. Rev. Tub.,* **24**:136–151 (Aug., 1931).

BULLOCH, E.
"Relative frequency of fibroid processes in dark skinned races." *Trans. South. Med. Assoc.* (1894).

BURNETT, SWAN
"The comparative frequency of eye diseases in the white and colored races in the United States." *Arch. of Ophth.,* **13** (1884):187–200.

BUSHNELL, G. E.
A study of the epidemiology of tuberculosis with especial reference to tuberculosis of the tropics and of the Negro race (New York, Wood, 1920), v + 221 pp.

CARLEY, P. S., AND WENGER, O. C.
"Prevalence of syphilis in apparently healthy Negroes in Mississippi as determined by complement fixation reactions in unselected groups." *Jour. Am. Med. Assoc.,* **94** (1930):1826–1829.

CARTER, H. G.
"Inherited immunity in tuberculosis." *Am. Rev. Tub.*, 13 (1926):373–378.
"Deductions drawn from eight years of tuberculosis work among Negroes."
Am. Rev. Tub., 14 (1926):653–661.

CASON, T. Z.
"A comparative study of cardiovascular syphilis in white and colored
races." *Am. Jour. Syph.*, 15 (1931):527–531.

CHADWICK, H. D.
"The Negro and tuberculosis." *Proc. Nat'l Conf. Soc. Work*, 60 (1933):
227–235.

CHURN, W. P.
"Abdominal tumors in the Negro race." *Maryland Med. Jour.*, 19 (1888):
180–183.

CLARK, G. C.
"The immunity of the Negro race to certain diseases and causes thereof."
Maryland Med. Jour., 38 (1897–98):722–724.

CLEMENTS, F.
"Racial differences in mortality and morbidity." *Human Biol.*, 3 (1931):
397–419.

COBB, W. M.
"The physical constitution of the American Negro." *Jour. Negro Education*, 3 (1934):340–388.

COBBETT, L.
"The resistance of civilized white man to tuberculosis; is it racial or individual in its origin?" *Tubercle*, 6 (1925):577–590.

COHEN, J.
"Uterine fibroids; an analysis of 1000 consecutive cases." *South. Med.
Jour.*, 23 (1930):875–880.

COLLINS, S. D.
"The influenza epidemic of 1928–29 in 14 surveyed localities in the United
States." *Pub. Health Repts.*, 49:1–62 (Jan. 5, 1934).

CORSON, E. R.
"The vital equation of the colored race and its future in the United
States." In *Wilder Quarter Century Book* (Ithaca, New York, Comstock
Publishing Co., 1893), pp. 115–175.

CRABTREE, J. A.
"Tuberculosis Studies in Tennessee." *Jour. Am. Med. Assoc.*, 101 (1933):
756–761.

CRABTREE, J. A., AND BISHOP, E. L.
"Syphilis in a rural Negro population in Tennessee." *Am. Jour. Pub.
Health*, 22 (1932):157–164.

CRABTREE, J. A., HICKERSON, W. D., AND HICKERSON, V. P.
"Tuberculosis Studies in Tennessee." *Am. Rev. Tub.*, 28 (1933):1–31.

CRAIG, J. D., AND DUBLIN, L. I.
"The influenza epidemic of 1918." *Trans. Actuarial Soc. Am.*, 20 (1919):
134–156.

CRUM, F. S.
"A statistical study of measles." *Am. J. Pub. Health*, 4 (1914):389–409.
"A statistical study of whooping-cough." *Ibid.*, 5 (1915):996–1017.
"A statistical study of diphtheria." *Ibid.*, 7 (1916):445–477.

CUMMINS, S. L.
"Tuberculosis in primitive tribes and its bearing on the tuberculosis of civilized communities." *Internat. Jour. Pub. Health*, 1 (1920):137–171.

CUNNINGHAM, R. McW.
"The morbidity and mortality of Negro convicts." *Med. News* (Philadelphia), 64 (1894):112–117.

CUTTING, R. A., LORIA, F. L., AND PICKELL, F. W.
"Syphilis among Negro males." *Ann. Surg.*, 91 (1930):269–286.

DAVIDSON, H. M., AND THOROUGHMAN, J. C.
"A study of heart disease in the Negro race." *South. Med. Jour.*, 21 (1928):464–469.

DAY, A. B., AND McNITT, W.
"The incidence of syphilis as manifested by routine Wassermann reactions on 2,925 hospital and dispensary medical cases." *Am. Jour. Syph.* (St. Louis), 3 (1919):595–606.

DAY, G. H.
"Urological and venereal idiosyncrasies." *Jour. Urol.*, 5 (1921):19–27.

DE SAUSSURE, P. G.
"Obstetrical observations on the Negroes of So. Carolina." *Trans. Pan-Am. Med. Cong., 1893*, pt. 1 (1895):917–921.

DONNELLY, J.
"Tuberculosis in Negroes." *South. Med. Surg.*, 95 (1933):78–84.
"Tuberculosis among Negro children." *Trans. Nat. Tub. Assoc.*, 30 (1934): 47–49.

DOULL, J. A.
"Comparative racial immunity to diseases." *Jour. Negro Education*, 6 (1937):429–437.

DOULL, J. A., AND FALES, W. T.
"Carriers of diphtheria bacilli among the school population of Baltimore." *Am. Jour. Hyg.*, 3 (1923):604–639.

DOULL, J. A., FERREIRA, M. J., AND PARREIRAS, D.
"The results of the Schick and Dick tests in Rio de Janeiro." *Jour. Prev. Med.*, 1 (1927):513–527.

DROLET, G. J.
"The inheritance factor in tuberculosis." *Am. Rev. Tub.*, 10 (1924):280–298.

DUBLIN, L. I.
The reduction in mortality among colored policyholders (Annual Conf. Nat. Urban League, Newark, N. J., Oct. 21, 1920. Metropolitan Life Insurance Co., N. Y.).
Recent changes in Negro mortality (New York, Metropolitan Life Insurance Co., 1924), 10 pp.
"The health of the Negro." *Ann. Acad. Polit. Soc. Sci.*, 140 (1928):77–85.
"Incidence of tuberculosis in the industrial population." *Am. Jour. Pub. Health*, 22 (1932):281–291.
The mortality from the principal cardiovascular-renal diseases (New York, Metropolitan Life Insurance Co.), 80 pp.
"Statistics on morbidity and mortality from cancer in the United States." *Am. Jour. Cancer*, 29 (1937):736–742.

DUBLIN, L. I., AND BAKER, G. W.
    "The mortality of race stocks in Pa. and N. Y." *Quart. Publ. Am. Statist. Assoc.*, 17 (1920) :13–44.
DUBOIS, W. E. B.
    "The health and physique of the Negro American." *Atlanta Univ. Publ.*, No. 11 (1906), 112 pp.
DYER, ISADOR
    "Notes on the statistical relation of skin disease in the Negro and white races in New Orleans." *Proc. Orleans Parish Med. Soc.* (1896), 1H, 68–71.
EMERSON, H.
    "Significant differences in racial susceptibility to diphtheria and scarlet fever in New York City, 1921–1925." *Jour. Prev. Med.*, 5 (1931) :317–350. See also *Trans. Assoc. Am. Phys.*, 46 (1931) :303–310.
EVERETT, F. B.
    "Pathological anatomy of pulmonary tuberculosis in the American Negro and in the white race." *Am. Rev. Tub.*, 27 (1933):411–464.
FITTS, J. B.
    "Cancer of the stomach in the Southern Negro. A study of fifty cases." *South. Med. Jour.*, 24 (1931):110–111.
FISHBERG, M.
    Pulmonary tuberculosis (ed. 2; Philadelphia, 1919), xii + 744 pp.
FLETCHER, R. M.
    "Surgical peculiarities of the Negro race." *Trans. Med. Assoc. Ala.*, 1898: 49–57.
FLEURE, H. J.
    The characters of the human skin in their relations to questions of race and health (London, Oxford Univ. Press, 1927).
FOSTER, R. H.
    "Paresis in the Negro." *Am. Jour. Psychiat.*, 5 (1926):631–640.
FOX, R. H.
    "Syphilis in the Negro." *New York State Jour. Med.*, 26 (1926):255–256. See also *Am. Jour. Obst. Gyn.*, 11 (1926):850.
    "Observations on skin diseases in the Negro." *Jour. Cutan. Dis.*, 26 (1908):67–79.
FRANKEL, L. K., AND DUBLIN, L. I.
    "Influenza mortality among wage earners and their families." *Am. Jour. Pub. Health*, 9 (1919):731–742.
FRICK, C. G.
    "Vital statistics of the city of Baltimore." *Am. Jour. Med. Sci.*, n.s., 30 (1855):312–334.
FROST, W. H.
    "Statistics of influenza morbidity." *Pub. Health Repts.*, 35 (1920):584–597.
GAGER, L. T., AND DUNN, W. L.
    "Heart Disease in Washington, D. C." *Med. Ann. Dist. Columbia*, 2 (1933):112–117.
GARRETT, J. B., AND SMITH, L. B.
    "Incidence of syphilis in 5,000 Negro ex-service men." *Mon. Bull. Vet. Admin.*, 8 (1932):38–42.

GARVIN, C. H.
"Immunity to disease among dark skinned people." *Opportunity*, 4 (1926) :
242–245.

GIBSON, J. M.
"The black man and the great white plague." *Social Forces*, 14 (1936):
585–590.

GILL, D. G.
"Syphilis in the rural Negro." *South. Med. Jour.*, 25 (1932):985–988.

GOVER, MARY
"Mortality among the Negroes in the United States." *Pub. Health Bull.*
No. 174 (Washington, Gov't Printing Office, 1928), 63 pp.

GRANDY, C. R.
"Racial characteristics as cause of high tuberculosis rate among Negroes."
Am. Rev. Tub., 10 (1924):275–279.

GRANGER, W. R. R.
"The incidence of syphilis among Negroes." *Am. Jour. Syph.*, 16 (1932):
303–307.

GREEN, E. M.
"Psychoses among Negroes—a comparative study." *Jour. Am. Med. Assoc.*,
101 (1933):2111–2113.

HAYES, H. T.
"Stricture of the rectum with special reference to stricture in the colored
race." *Trans. Am. Proct. Soc.*, 32 (1931) :173–187.

HAZEN, H. H.
"Syphilis among school children." *Wash. Med. Ann.*, 12 (1913):223–230.
"Syphilis in the American Negro." *Jour. Am. Med. Assoc.*, 63 (1914):
463–466.
"Syphilis and skin diseases in the American Negro." *Arch. Dermat.*, 31
(1935):316–322.
"Syphilis in the American Negro." *Am. Jour. Syph. and Neur.* 20 (1936):
530–561.
"A leading cause of death among Negroes: syphilis." *Jour. Negro Educa-
tion*, 6 (1937) :310–321.

HAZEN, H. H., HOWARD, W. J., FREEMAN, C. W., AND SCULL, R. H.
"The treatment of granuloma inguinale in the Negro." *Jour. Am. Med.
Assoc.*, 99 (1932):1410–1411.

HEDLEY, O. F.
"A study of 450 fatal cases of heart disease occurring in Washington
(D. C.) hospital during 1932 with special reference to etiology, race and
sex." *Pub. Health Repts.*, 50 (1935):1127–1153.

HINDMAN, S. S.
"Syphilis among insane Negroes." *Am. Jour. Pub. Health*, 5 (1915):218–
224.

HOFFMAN, F. L.
Race traits and tendencies of the American Negro (New York, Am. Econ.
Assoc., *Publ.*, 11, Nos. 1–3, 1896), 329 pp.
The mortality from cancer throughout the world (Newark, Prudential
Press, 1915), xv + 826 pp.
The malaria problem in peace and war (Newark, Prudential Press, 1918),
101 pp.

The homicide problem (Newark, Prudential Press, 1925), 106 pp.

Cancer in native races (Newark, Prudential Press, 1926), 48 pp.

"Cancer in the North American Negro." *Am. Jour. Surg.*, 14 (1931): 229–263.

"Malaria in Mississippi and in adjacent states." *South. Med. Jour.*, 25 (1932):657–663.

HOLMES, S. J.

"The resistant ectoderm of the Negro." *Am. Jour. Phys. Anthrop.*, 12 (1928):139–153.

"The biological trend of the Negro." *Univ. Calif. Chronicle*, 32 (1930): 38–70.

"Differential mortality in the American Negro." *Human Biol.*, 3 (1931): 71–103, 203–244.

"The differential mortality from cancer in the white and colored population." *Am. Jour. Cancer*, 25 (1935):358–376.

"The principal causes of death among Negroes. A general and comparative statement." *Jour. Negro Education*, 6 (1937):289–302.

HOWARD, D. C., AND LOVE, A. G.

"Influenza in the U. S. Army." *Military Surg.*, 44 (1920):522–558.

HOWARD, W.

The natural history of disease in Baltimore (Maryland Public Health Administration; Carnegie Inst. Wash., 1924), 565 pp.

JASON, R. S.

"On the incidence of syphilis in the American Negro." *Am. Jour. Syph. and Neur.*, 19 (1935):313–322.

JOHNSON, C. S.

"Negro health in the light of vital statistics." *Proc. Nat. Conf. Soc. Work*, 55 (1928):173–175.

JOHNSON, W. M., AND MYERS, J. A.

"Tuberculosis in infants and primitive races." *Am. Rev. Tub.*, 28 (1933): 381–405.

JOHNSTON, C.

"Racial differences in incidence of coronary sclerosis." *Am. Heart Jour.*, 12 (1936):162–167.

JONES, E. K.

"The Negro's struggle for health." *Hosp. Soc. Serv.* (New York), 8 (1923): 126–136.

JONES, F.

"Syphilis in the Negro." *Jour. Am. Med. Assoc.*, 42 (1904):32–34.

JONES, R. F., AND PRICE, K. A.

"The incidence of gonorrhea among Negroes." *Jour. Negro Education*, 6 (1937):364–376.

JONES, T. J.

"Tuberculosis among Negroes." *Proc. Second Ann. Meet. Nat. Tub. Assoc.*, *1906*, 97–113; *Am. Jour. Med. Sci.*, n.s., 132 (1906):592–599. See also *Southern Workman*, 35 (1906):662.

JORDAN, E. O.

Epidemic influenza (Chicago, Am. Med. Assoc., 1927), 599 pp.

KEIDEL, A., AND MOORE, J. E.
"The Wassermann reaction in the Johns Hopkins Hospital." *Bull. Johns Hopkins Hosp.*, **34** (1923):16–20.

KELLER, A. E., LEATHERS, W. S., AND RICKS, H. C.
"An investigation of the incidence and intensity of infestation of hookworm in Mississippi." *Am. Jour. Hyg.*, **19** (1934):629–656.

KELLER, R. L.
"Syphilis and tuberculosis in the Negro race." *Texas State Jour. Med.*, **19** (1924):495–498.

KELLY, F. B.
"Observations on 6,500 cases of lobar pneumonia at Cook County Hospital, Chicago." *Jour. Infect. Dis.*, **38** (1926):24–36.

KNOPF, S. A.
"Tuberculosis, drug addiction and the Negro within our gates." *Med. Jour. and Rec.*, **132**:53–57 (July, 1930).

LANDIS, H. M. R.
"Tuberculosis and the Negro." *Ann. Am. Acad. Polit. Soc. Sci.*, **140** (1928):86–89.

LAWS, C. L.
"The etiology of heart disease in whites and Negroes." *Am. Heart Jour.*, **8** (1933):606–615.

LEHMANN, I. I.
"A study of disease in the Negro." *South. Med. Jour.*, **27** (1934):33–39.

LINDBERG, D. O. N.
"A chest Roentgen-ray study of the adult Negro population of an entire community." *Ann. Int. Med.*, **8** (1935):1421–1426.

LOVE, A. G., AND DAVENPORT, C. B.
"A comparison of white and colored troops in respect to incidence of disease." *Proc. Nat. Acad. Sci.*, **5** (1919):58–67.

MACHT, D. J., ANDERSON, W. T., AND BELL, F. K.
"The penetration of ultraviolet rays into live animal tissues." *Jour. Am. Med. Assoc.*, **90** (1928):161–165.

MALZBERG, B.
"Migration and mental disease among Negroes in New York state." *Am. Jour. Phys. Anthrop.*, **21** (1936):107–113. See also *Human Biol.*, **7** (1935): 471–513.

MARTIN, C. F.
"Stricture of the rectum." *Jour. Am. Med. Assoc.*, **101** (1933):1550–1552.

McCAIN, P. P.
"A report of the study of 25,048 school children for tuberculosis." *South. Med. Jour.*, **22** (1929):310–320.

McCULLOCH, H. D.
"Negro immunity from malaria and yellow fever." *Brit. Med. Jour.*, **1** (1905):103.

MATAS, R.
The surgical peculiarities of the Negro (*Trans. Am. Surg. Assoc.*, **4** [1896]), iv + 130 pp.

MAXCY, K. F., AND BRUMFIELD, W. A.
"A serological survey of syphilis in a Negro population." *South. Med. Jour.*, **27** (1934):891–899.

Medical and Casualty Statistics (Washington, D. C., Medical Dept. U. S. Army in the World War, 1925), 15, *Statistics.*

MILLER, C. J.
"Comparative study in certain gynecologic and obstetric conditions as exhibited in colored and white races." *Trans. Am. Gyn. Soc.,* 53 (1928): 91–106; *Am. Jour. Obst. Gyn.,* 161 (1928):662–675.

MILLS, C. A.
"Susceptibility to tuberculosis: race or energy level?" *Am. Jour. Med. Sci.,* 189 (1935):330–340.

MITCHELL, F. T.
"Incidence of rickets in the South." *South. Med. Jour.,* 23 (1930):228–237.

MOENCH, G. L.
"The etiology of adenomyositis and uterine fibromyoma; an hypothesis." *Am. Jour. Obst. Gyn.,* 17 (1929):682–688.

MOORE, GEO. S.
"Introduction to a study of neuropsychiatric problems among Negroes." United States Veterans' Bureau *Med. Bull.,* 3 (1927):887–897.

MORGAN, J. H.
"An essay on the cause of production of abortion in Negroes." *Nashville Jour. Med. and Surg.,* 19 (1860):117–123.

MORISON, R. B.
"Personal observations on skin diseases in the Negro." *Trans. Am. Dermat. Assoc.,* 1888:29–34.

MOSSELL, S. T.
A study of the Negro tuberculosis problem in Philadelphia (H. Phipps Inst., 1923), v + 29 pp.

MURRELL, T. E.
"Peculiarities in the structure and disease of the ear in the Negro." *Trans. Ninth Internat. Med. Cong., Washington,* 3 (1887):817–824.

NATHAN, W. B.
Health conditions in North Harlem, 1923–27 (Nat. Tub. Assoc., *Soc. Research Series,* No. 2, 1932), 68 pp.

NOTT, J. C.
"Liability of Negroes to the epidemic diseases of the South." *South. Med. Surg. Jour.,* n.s., 14 (1858):253.

OLESON, R.
"Endemic goiter in Tennessee." *Pub. Health Repts.,* 44 (1929):865–897.

O'MALLEY, M.
"Psychoses in the colored race." *Am. Jour. Insanity,* 71 (1914):309–337.

OPIE, E. L.
"Pneumonia following influenza (at Camp Pike, Ark.)." *Jour. Am. Med. Assoc.,* 72 (1919):556–565.
"Active and latent tuberculosis in the Negro race." *Am. Rev. Tub.,* 10 (1924):265–274.
"Epidemiology of tuberculosis of Negroes." *Tubercle,* 12:207–214 (Feb., 1931); *Trans. Nat. Tub. Assoc.,* 26 (1930):243–253; *Am. Rev. Tub.,* 22: 603–612 (Dec., 1930).

OPIE, E. L., AND ISAACS, E. J.
"Tuberculosis in Jamaica." *Am. Jour. Hyg.,* 12 (1930):1–61.

ORNSTEIN, G. G.
"The leading causes of death among Negroes: tuberculosis." *Jour. Negro Education*, 6 (1937):303–309.

PAGAUD, M. V.
"Nursing problems in social hygiene programs." *Jour. Soc. Hyg.*, 15 (1929):475–480.

PARKHURST, E.
"Resident mortality from tuberculosis in urban and rural New York according to age, sex, color, and general nativity." *Am. Jour. Pub. Health*, 23 (1933):901–909.

PAULLIN, J. E., DAVIDSON, H. M., AND WEED, R. H.
"Incidence of syphilitic infection among Negroes in the South, etc." *Boston Med. Surg. Jour.*, 197 (1927):345–350.

PEARL, R.
"The vitality of the people of America." *Am. Jour. Hyg.*, 1 (1921):592–674.
"Biometric studies in pathology. The quantitive relations of certain viscera in tuberculosis." *Johns Hopkins Hospital Repts.*, 21 (1922):157–230.
"Biological factors in Negro mortality." *Human Biol.*, 1 (1924):227–249.

PEARL, R., AND BACON, A. L.
"Biometrical studies in pathology, V. The racial and age incidence of cancer and of other malignant tumors." *Arch. Path. and Lab. Med.*, 3 (1927):963–992. "VI. The primary site of cancers and other malignant tumors." *Ibid.*, 6 (1928):67–89.

PERROTT, G. ST. J., AND HOLLAND, D. F.
"The need for adequate data on current illness among Negroes." *Jour. Negro Education*, 6 (1937):350–363.

PEVAROFF, H. H., AND HINDMAN, S. M.
"The Dick test in white and Negro children resident in a congested section of Cleveland." *Am. Jour. Hyg.*, 19 (1934):749–752.

PHIQUEPAL D'ARUSMONT, L.
"Les tumeurs malignes dans la race noire." *Bull. Soc. Path. Exot.*, 23 (1930):109–114.

PINNER, M., AND KASPER, J. A.
"Pathological peculiarities of tuberculosis in the American Negro." *Am. Rev. Tub.*, 26 (1932):463–491.

PLEHN, A.
Die Malaria der afrikanischen Negerbevölkerung, besonders mit Bezug auf die Immunitätsfrage (Jena, Fisher, 1902), 51 pp.

POLLOCK, H. M.
"Mental disease among Negroes in the United States." *State Hosp. Quart.*, 11 (1925–26):47–66.

POTTENGER, F. M.
"Some observations on inherited physical and psychical characteristics in tuberculosis patients." *Med. Jour. Rec.* (New York), 123 (1926):1–2.

POWELL, T. O.
"The increase of insanity and tuberculosis in the southern Negro since 1860, etc." *Jour. Am. Med. Assoc.*, 27 (1896):1185–1188.

QUILLIAN, D. D.
"Racial peculiarities as a cause of the prevalence of syphilis in Negroes."
Am. Jour. Dermat. and Genito-urinary Dis., 10 (1906):277–279.

REICHENOW, E.
"Zur Frage der Malariaresistenz bei Negern." *Arch. f. Schiffs- und Tropenhyg.*, 33 (Beiheft 3, 1929):58–66.

REINHARD, F. O.
"The venereal disease problem in the colored population of Baltimore city." *Am. Jour. Syph.*, 19 (1935):183–194.

REITZEL, R. J.
"Lobar pneumonia in Negroes and influence of syphilis as a co-existing disease." *South. Med. Jour.*, 21 (1928):469–471.

RITTER, J.
The noticeable difference in the morbidity and the mortality rate (in acute and chronic diseases), of the black race as compared with those of the white (Dept. Pub. Health, Miami, Fla., 1934), 15 pp.

ROBERTSON, J. P., AND LEE, A. B.
"Urology in the colored race." *Urol. and Cutan. Rev.*, 39 (1935):405–418.

ROGERS, J. B.
"Comparison of gross tuberculosis lesions in whites and Negroes as based on 150 autopsies." *Am. Rev. Tub.*, 4 (1920):669–675.

ROSENTHAL, S. P.
"Racial differences in the mental diseases." *Jour. Abnor. and Soc. Psych.*, 28 (1933):301–318.
"Racial differences in the incidence of mental disease." *Jour. Negro Education*, 3 (1934):484–493.

ROSSER, C.
"Rectal pathology in the Negro." *Jour. Am. Med. Assoc.*, 84 (1925):93–97.
"Proctologic peculiarities of the Negro." *Am. Jour. Surg.*, 37 (1923):264–271.

SANDERS, C. B., AND BILLUPS, J. T.
"Tuberculosis necropsy findings in the southern Negro." *Texas State Med. Jour.*, 28 (1932):364–366.

SCHEPPERGRELL, W.
"The comparative pathology of the Negro in diseases of the throat and ear, from an analysis of 11,855 cases." *Am. Ophth. Otol.* (St. Louis), 4 (1895):589–593.

SCHWAB, E. H., AND SCHULZE, V. E.
"Heart disease in American Negro of the South." *Am. Heart Jour.*, 7 (1932):710–717.

SIBLEY, E.
Differential mortality in Tennessee (Nashville, Tenn., Fisk Univ. Press, 1930), 152 pp.
"Statistical view of tuberculosis in the Negro population." *Trans. Nat. Tub. Assoc.*, 26 (1930):261–263.

SLATER, S. A.
"The results of Pirquet tuberculin tests on 1,654 children in a rural community in Minnesota." *Am. Rev. Tub.*, 10 (1924):299–305.

SMILLIE, W. G., AND AUGUSTINE, D. L.
"The intensity of hookworm infestation in Alabama." *Jour. Am. Med. Assoc.*, 85 (1925):1958–1963.
"Vital capacity of the Negro race." *Ibid.*, 87 (1926):2055–2058.

SORSBY, M.
Cancer and race (New York, Wm. Wood, 1931), 120 pp.

STEUBER
"Ueber Krankheiten der Eingeborenen in Deutsch-Ostafrika." *Arch. f. Schiffs- und Tropen-Hyg.*, 6 (1902):111–117; 7 (1903):57–62.

SULLIVAN, M. P.
"The part of the Negro doctor in the control of syphilis." *Jour. Soc. Hyg.*, 19 (1933):435–444.

SULZBERGER, M. B., AND WISE, F.
"Lymphopathia venereum." *Jour. Am. Med. Assoc.*, 99 (1932):1407–1410.

SYDENSTRICKER, E.
"Tuberculosis among relatively neglected groups." *Trans. Nat. Tub. Assoc.*, 25 (1929):262–274.

SYKES, W.
"Negro immunity from malaria and yellow fever." *Brit. Med. Jour.*, 2 (1904):1776–1777; 1 (1905):389.

THOMPSON, J. A.
A treatise on the diseases of Negroes as they occur in the Island of Jamaica (Jamaica, 1820).

THOMPSON, L., AND KINGERY, L. B.
"Syphilis in the Negro." *Am. Jour. Syph.*, 3 (1919):384–397.

TIFFANY, L. McL.
"Comparison between the surgical diseases of the white and colored races." *Trans. Am. Surg. Assoc.*, 5 (1887):261–273.

TRASK, J. W.
"Death rates of the colored population; their trend, significance in the United States." *Pub. Health Repts.*, 31 (1916):705–711.

TURNER, T. B.
"The race and sex distribution of the lesions of syphilis in 10,000 cases." *Bull. Johns Hopkins Hosp.*, 46 (1930):159–184.

USILTON, L. J.
"Prevalence of venereal disease in the United States." *Ven. Dis. Information*, 11 (1930):543–562.

VEDDER, E. B.
"The prevalence of syphilis in the army" (*Bull.* No. 8, Office of the Surgeon General, Washington, D. C.), 110 pp.

VEER, J. B. V., CORMIA, F. E., AND ULLERY, J. C.
"Lymphopathia venereum (*Lymphogranuloma inguinale*)." *Am. Jour. Med. Sci.*, 190 (1835):178–187.

WALKER, J. W.
"Tuberculosis in the Negro." *Jour. Nat. Med. Assoc.*, 22:19–21 (Jan., Mar., 1930).

WALSH, G., AND MASON, H. M.
"Pulmonary tuberculosis in American Negro." *Am. Rev. Tub.*, 31 (1935):413–428.

WEINER, L.
"Tuberculosis among Negroes in New York City." *Med. Jour.* (New York), 136 (1933):27–29.

WELLS, A. S.
"An analysis of 1259 confinements of colored women in Cape Town." *South Africa Med. Rec.,* 23 (1925):398–403.

WILLIAMS, E. Y.
"The incidence of mental disease in the Negro." *Jour. Negro Education,* 6 (1937):377–392.

WILLIAMS, J. W.
"The limitations and possibilities of prenatal care." *Jour. Am. Med. Assoc.,* 64 (1915):95–101.
"The significance of syphilis in prenatal care, and in the causation of foetal death rate." *Bull. Johns Hopkins Hosp.,* 31 (1920):141–145; also *N. Y. State Jour. Med.,* 20 (1920):252.
"The value of the Wassermann reaction in obstetrics, based upon the study of 4,547 consecutive cases." *Bull. Johns Hopkins Hosp.,* 31 (1920): 335–342.

WILLIAMS, P. F., AND KOLMER, J. A.
"The Wassermann reaction in gynecology." *Am. Jour. Obst. Gyn.,* 74 (1916):638–652.

WITCHEN, E.
Tuberculosis and the Negro in Pittsburgh (Pittsburgh, Tuberculosis League, 1934), 120 pp.

WITHERSPOON, T., AND BUTLER, V. W.
"The etiology of uterine fibroids." *Surg. Gyn. Obst.,* 58 (1934):57–61.

WOODY, W. S.
"The incidence of heart disease in the Negro race." *Virginia Med. Mon.,* 50 (1924):784–787.

WRIGHT, L. T.
"The Schick test with special reference to the Negro." *Jour. Infect. Dis.,* 21 (1917):265–268.
"Cancer as it affects the Negro." *Opportunity,* 6 (1928):169.

ZIMMERMANN, E. L.
"A comparative study of syphilis in whites and Negroes." *Arch. Dermat. and Syph.,* 14 (1921):75.

ZINGHER, A.
"Diphtheria prevention work in the public schools of New York City." *Jour. Am. Med. Assoc.,* 77 (1921):835–842.

CHAPTER VI

INFANT MORTALITY

BAKWIN, H.
"The Negro infant." *Human Biol.,* 4 (1932):1–33.

BALDWIN, B. T.
The physical growth of children (Univ. of Iowa, *Studies in Child Welfare,* Series 1, No. 50, 1921), 411 pp.

CLARK, T., SYDENSTRICKER, E., AND COLLINS S. D.
    "Heights and weights of school children." *Pub. Health Repts.*, 37 (1922): 1185–1207.
COLLINS, S. D.
    "Past incidence of certain communicable diseases common among children." *Pub. Health Repts.*, 39 (1924):1553–1567.
DePORTE, J. V.
    "Inter-racial variation in infant mortality." *Am. Jour. Hyg.*, 5 (1925): 454–496.
DODGE, C. T. J.
    "Weight of colored infants. Growth during the first eighteen months." *Am. Jour. Phys. Anthrop.*, 10 (1927):337–365.
GRAHAM, V. T.
    "Health studies of Negro children." *Pub. Health Repts.*, 41 (1926):2759–2783.
HOLMES, S. J.
    "The low sex ratio in Negro births and its probable explanation." *Biol. Bull.*, 52 (1927):325–329.
HRDLIČKA, A.
    "Anthropological investigations on one thousand white and colored children of both sexes." *Forty-seventh Ann. Rept.*, New York Juv. Asyl. (New York and Albany, 1899), 86 pp.
JEANS, P. C.
    "Syphilis in its relation to infant mortality." *Trans. Am. Assoc. Prev. Inf. Mort.*, 9 (1918):146–156.
KNOX, J. H. M.
    "Morbidity and mortality in the Negro infant." *Arch. Pediat.*, 42 (1925): 242–247.
KNOX, J. H. M., AND ZENTAI, P.
    "The health problem of the Negro child." *Am. Jour. Pub. Health*, 16 (1926):805–809.
MITCHELL, MARY V.
    "Clinical notes from diseases among colored children." *Rept. Proc. Alum. Assoc.*, Women's Med. Coll. Penn. (Philadelphia, 1891), pp. 50–58.
MUSTARD, H. S., AND WARING, J. I.
    "Heights and weights of colored school children." *Am. Jour. Pub. Health*, 16 (1926):1017–1022.
PEARL, R.
    "Biometric data on infant mortality in the United States Birth Registration Area, 1915–1919." *Am. Jour. Hyg.*, 1 (1921):419–439.
    "Biological factors in Negro mortality." *Human Biol.*, 1 (1929):227–249.
PORTER, W. T.
    "The growth of St. Louis children." *Trans. Acad. Sci. St. Louis*, 6 (1894): 263–380.
ROYSTER, L. T., AND HOLVEY, C. N.
    "Relations of weight, height and age in Negro children." *Am. Jour. Dis. Child.*, 38 (1929):1222–1230.
SMILLIE, W. S., AND AUGUSTINE, D. L.
    "Vital capacity of the Negro race." *Jour. Am. Med. Assoc.*, 87 (1926): 2055–2058.

STERLING, E. B.

　"Health studies of Negro children, II. The physical status of the urban Negro child." *Pub. Health Repts.*, **43** (1928):2713–2774.

STOUGHTON, A. L., AND GOVER, M.

　"A study of Negro infant mortality." *Pub. Health Repts.*, **44** (1929): 2705–2731.

TANDY, E. C.

　"Infant and maternal mortality among Negroes." *Jour. Negro Education*, **6** (1937):322–349.

TEWKSBURY, R. B.

　"A biometric study of infant mortality in the United States Birth Registration Area, 1919–1922." *Am. Jour. Hyg.*, **6** (1926):32–73.

CHAPTER VII

THE NEGRO BIRTH RATE

ALEXANDER, W.

　"Birth control for the Negro—Fad or necessity." *Jour. Nat. Med. Assoc.*, **24** (1932):34–39.

　"A medical viewpoint." *Birth Control Rev.*, **16** (6) (1932):175.

BOUSFIELD, M. O.

　"Negro public health work needs birth control." *Birth Control Rev.*, **16** (1932):170–171.

BRYANT, CARYLYN

　"Clinical service for the Negro." *Birth Control Rev.*, **16** (1932):176–177.

CARTER, ELMER A.

　"Eugenics for the Negro." *Birth Control Rev.*, **16** (1932):169–170.

DuBOIS, W. E. B.

　"Black folk and birth control." *Birth Control Rev.*, **16** (1932):166–167.

FISHER, CONSTANCE

　"The Negro social worker evaluates birth control." *Birth Control Rev.*, **16** (1932):174–175.

FRAZIER, E. F.

　"Family life of the Negro in the small town." *Proc. Nat. Conf. Soc. Work*, **53** (1926):384–388.

　"The Negro family." *Ann. Am. Acad. Polit. Soc. Sci.*, **140** (1928):44–51.

　"Changing status of the Negro family." *Social Forces*, **9** (1931):386–393.

　"An analysis of statistics of Negro illegitimacy in the United States." *Social Forces*, **11** (1932):249–257.

　The Negro family in Chicago (Univ. Chicago Press, 1932), xxv + 294 pp.

　"Children in black and mulatto families." *Am. Jour. Sociol.*, **39** (1933): 12–29.

GRAHAM, I.

　"The Negro family in a northern city." *Opportunity*, **8** (1930):48–51.

HOLMES, S. J.

　"The Negro birth rate." *Birth Control Rev.*, **16** (1932):172–173.

HOLMES, S. J., AND DEMPSTER, E. R.

　"The trend of the illegitimate birth-rate in the United States." *Population*, **2** (1936):6–22.

JOHNSON, CHAS. S.
"A question of Negro health." *Birth Control Rev.*, 16 (1932):167–169.

MILLER, K.
"Eugenics of the Negro race." *Scient. Mon.*, 5 (1917):57–59.

PEARL, R.
"Contraception and fertility in 4,945 married women; a second report on a study of family limitation." *Human Biol.*, 6 (1934):355–401.
"Third report of progress on a study of family limitation." *Milbank Memorial Fund Quarterly*, 14 (1936):1–27.
"Fertility and contraception in urban whites and Negroes." *Science*, n.s., 83 (1936):503–505.
"Fertility and contraception in New York and Chicago." *Jour. Am. Med. Assoc.*, 108 (1937):1385–1390.

REED, R.
"Illegitimacy among Negroes." *Jour. Soc. Hyg.*, 11 (1925):73–91.
The Negro women of Gainesville, Ga. (Univ. Ga. *Bull.*, 22, 1921), 61 pp.

SANDERS, W. B.
Negro child welfare in North Carolina (Chapel Hill, Univ. North Carolina Press, 1933), xiv + 326 pp.

SCHUYLER, GEORGE S.
"Quantity or quality." *Birth Control Rev.*, 16 (1932):165–166.

TERPENNING, WALTER A.
"God's Chillun." *Birth Control Rev.*, 16 (1932):171–172.

THOMPSON, W. S.
Ratio of children to women, 1920 (Washington, D. C., Gov't Printing Office, 1931), ix + 242 pp.

UNITED STATES BUREAU OF LABOR
"Condition of the Negro in various cities." *Bull.*, 10:257–369 (May, 1897).

WILBUR, R. L.
"The health status and health education of Negroes in the United States. A critical summary." *Jour. Negro Education*, 6 (1937):572–577.

WILLCOX, W. F.
"Birth rate and natural increase of whites and Negroes in the U. S." *Report* of Fifth Internat. Neo-Mal. and Birth Control Conference (London, Heinemann, 1922):138–154.
"Changes in Negro and white birth rates." *Birth Control Rev.*, 16 (1932): 179–180.

WINSTON, S.
Illiteracy in the United States (Chapel Hill, Univ. North Carolina Press, 1930), xii + 169 pp.

CHAPTER VIII

WILL THE WHITES ABSORB THE BLACKS?

BAKER, R. S.
Following the color line (New York, Doubleday, Page, 1908), xii + 314 pp.
See chap. 8.
"The tragedy of the mulatto." *Am. Mag.*, 65 (1908):582–598.

BAND, H. M.
 "Two racial islands in Alabama; creoles and Cayuns." *Am. Jour. Sociol.*, 36 (1931):552–567.

BARNES, IRENE
 "The inheritance of pigmentation in the American Negro." *Human Biol.*, 1 (1929):321–381.

BOAS, F.
 "Race problems in America." *Science*, n.s., 29 (1909):839–849.

CARTER, E. A.
 "Crossing over." *Opportunity*, 4 (1926):376–378.

DAVENPORT, C. B.
 Heredity of skin color in Negro-white crosses (*Publ. Carnegie Inst. Wash.*, 1913), 106 pp.
 "Race crossing in Jamaica." *Scient. Mon.*, 27 (1928):225–238.

DAY, C. B.
 "Race crossings in the United States." *Crisis*, 37 (1930):81.
 "Study of some Negro-white families in the United States." *Harvard African Studies*, 10 (1932), part 2.

DIXON, W. A.
 "The morbid proclivities and retrogressive tendencies in the offspring of mulattoes." *Med. News* (Philadelphia), 61 (1892):180–182. See also *Jour. Am. Med. Assoc.*, 20 (1893):1–2.

DODGE, E.
 "The mulatto problem." *Jour. Hered.*, 16 (1925):281–286.

DUNN, L. C.
 "A biological view of race mixture." *Publ. Am. Sociol. Soc.*, 19 (1925): 47–58.

EMBREE, E. R.
 Brown America (New York, Viking Press, 1931), vi + 311 pp.

ESTABROOK, A. H., AND McDOUGLE, I. E.
 Mongrel Virginians. The Win tribe (Williams and Wilkins Co., Baltimore, 1926), 205 pp.

FRAZIER, E. F.
 "Children in black and mulatto families." *Am. Jour. Sociol.*, 29 (1933): 12–29.

GANNETT, H.
 "Are we to become Africanized?" *Pop. Sci. Mon.*, 27 (1885):145–150.

GREGORY, J. W.
 The menace of colour (Lippincott, 1924), 264 pp.

HALE, A. K. "Why miscegenation flourishes in the North." *Pearson's Mag.*, 23 (1910):543–551.

HERSKOVITS, M. J.
 "A further discussion of the variability of family strains in the Negro-white population of New York City." *Jour. Am. Statist. Assoc.*, 20 (1925): 380–389.
 "Does the Negro know his own father?" *Opportunity*, 4 (1926):306–311.
 "Correlation of length and breadth of head in American Negroes." *Am. Jour. Phys. Anthrop.*, 9 (1926):87–97.
 "Social selection in a mixed population." *Proc. Nat. Acad. Sci.*, 12 (1926): 587–593.

"Some effects of social selection on the American Negro." *Proc. Am. Sociol. Soc.*, **20** (1926):77–82.

"The American Negro evolving a new physical type." *Current Hist.*, **24** (1926):898–903.

"Variability and race mixture." *Am. Nat.*, **61** (1927):68–81.

"Some physical characteristics of the American Negro population." *Social Forces*, **6** (1927):93–98.

"Physical form and growth of the American Negro." *Anthrop. Anz.*, **4** (1927):293–316.

The American Negro. A study in racial crossing (New York, Knopf, 1928), xiv + 92 pp.

"Social selection and the formation of human types." *Human Biol.*, **1** (1929):250–261.

Anthropometry of the American Negro. Columbia Univ. *Contributions to Anthropology* (New York, Columbia Univ. Press, 1930), **11**, xv + 283 pp.

"The Negro in the New World; statement of the problem." *Am. Anthrop.*, **32** (1930):145–155.

"The physical form of Mississippi Negroes." *Am. Jour. Phys. Anthrop.*, **16** (2) (1931):193–201.

"A critical discussion of the 'mulatto hypothesis.' " *Jour. Negro Education*, **3** (1934):389–402.

HILL, J. L.
When black meets white (Chicago, Argyle Publishers, 1922), 149 pp.

HOFFMAN, FREDERICK L.
"The problem of Negro-white intermixture and intermarriage." In *Eugenics in race and state* (Baltimore, Williams and Wilkins, 1923; 2 vols.), 175–189.

HOLM, J. J.
Holm's race assimilation; or, The fading of the leopard's spots (Naperville, Ill.; Atlanta, Georgia, Nichols, 1910), 526 pp.

HOLMES, S. J.
"The biological effects of race mixture." Chap. 15 of *Studies in evolution and eugenics* (New York, Harcourt, Brace, 1923).

HOOTON, E. A.
"Progress in the study of race mixtures with reference to the work carried on in Harvard University." *Proc. Am. Philos. Soc.* (Philadelphia), **65** (1926):312–325.

HRDLIČKA, A.
"Anthropology of the American Negro." *Am. Jour. Phys. Anthrop.*, **10** (1927):205–235.

"The full-blood American Negro." *Ibid.*, **12** (1928):16–33.

JENKS, A. E.
"The legal status of Negro-white amalgamation in the United States." *Am. Jour. Sociol.*, **21** (1916):666–678. See also *Yale Law Jour.*, **36** (1927):858–866.

"The 'half-breed' ascendant." *Publ. Am. Sociol. Soc.*, **12** (1917):101–107.

JOHNSON, C.
"Crossing the color line." *Outlook*, **158** (1931):526–528. See also *Am. Mercury*, **16** (1929):282–286; **17** (1930):150–152.

JOHNSON, J. E.
Selected articles on the Negro problem (New York, H. W. Wilson, 1921).
JORDAN, H. E.
"The biological status and social worth of the mulatto." *Pop. Sci. Mon.*, 82 (1913):573–582.
McCARTY, U. S.
"Improvability of social amalgamation." *Arena*, 21 (1899):446–449.
McKINNEY, E. R.
"Race solidarity an ideal of no importance." *World Tomorrow*, 12 (1929): 32–34.
MAYO-SMITH, R.
"Theories of mixture of races and nationalities." *Yale Rev.*, 3 (1894): 166–186.
MILLER, K.
"Is the American Negro to remain black or become bleached?" *South Atlantic Quart.*, 25 (1926):240–252.
NEFF, L. W.
Race relations at close range (Emery Univ., Ga., 1931), 35 pp.
NOTT, J. C.
"The mulatto a hybrid." *Am. Jour. Med. Sci.*, 6 (1843):252–256.
PARK, R. E.
"Racial assimilation in secondary groups." *Am. Jour. Sociol.*, 19 (1913–14):606–623.
"The mentality of racial hybrids." *Am. Jour. Sociol.*, 36 (1931):534–551.
PLECKER, W. A.
"Virginia's effort to preserve racial integrity." In *A Decade of Progress in Eugenics* (Baltimore, Williams and Wilkins, 1934), pp. 105–112.
REUTER, E. B.
"Superiority of the mulatto." *Am. Jour. Sociol.*, 23 (1917):83–106.
The mulatto in the United States (Boston, Badger, 1918), 417 pp.
The American race problem (New York, Crowell, 1926), xii + 448 pp.
"The American mulatto." *Ann. Am. Acad. Polit. Soc. Sci.*, 140 (1928): 36–43.
Race Mixture (New York, Whittlesey House, 1931), vii + 224 pp.
"Civilization and the mixture of races." *Scient. Mon.*, 31 (1930):442–449.
SHANNON, A. H.
The racial integrity of the American Negro (ed. 2; Nashville, Tenn., Smith and Lamar, 1927), 305 pp.
The Negro in Washington. A study in race amalgamation (New York, Neale, 1930), 332 pp.
STEGGERDA, M., AND DAVENPORT, C. B.
Race crossing in Jamaica (Carnegie Inst. Wash. Publ. No. 395, 1929), 483 pp.
"Physical development of Negro-white hybrids in Jamaica." *Am. Jour. Phys. Anthrop.*, 12 (1928):121–138.
STONE, A. H.
"The mulatto factor in the race problem." *Atlantic Mon.*, 91 (1903):658–662.
Studies in the American race problem (New York, Doubleday, Page, 1908), xxii + 555 pp.

TAEUBER, I. B.
"Assortative mating for color in the American Negro." In *A Decade of Progress in Eugenics* (Baltimore, Williams and Wilkins, 1934), pp. 124–128.

TILLINGHAST, J. A.
The Negro in Africa and America (New York, Macmillan, 1902), vi + 231 pp.

TODD, T. W.
"Entrenched Negro physical features." *Human Biol.*, 1 (1929):57–69.

VILLARD, O. G.
"The crumbling color line." *Harper's Mag.*, 159 (1929):156–167.

WAGNER, K.
"Variability of hybrid populations." *Am. Jour. Phys. Anthrop.*, 16 (1932):283–307.

WHITE, W.
"Solving America's race problem." *Nation*, 128 (1929):42–43.

WOOD, C. C.
"Alabama. A study in ultra-violet." *Nation*, 116 (1923):33–35.

WOODSON, C. G.
"The beginning of the miscegenation of the whites and blacks." *Jour. Negro Hist.*, 3 (1918):335–353.

CHAPTER IX

NEGRO MIGRATION AND ITS BIOLOGICAL EFFECTS

BODDY, J. M.
"Getting at true causes of the migration of Negro labor from the South." *Econ. World*, 15:335 (March 9, 1918).

BROWN, FR. W.
The northward movement of the colored population (Baltimore, Cushing, 1897), 50 pp.

DONALD, H. H.
"The Negro migration of 1916–18." *Jour. Nat. Hist.*, 6 (1921):383–499.

DUNCAN, H. G.
The changing race relationship in the border and northern states (Thesis, Univ. Pa., 1922), 127 pp.

DUTCHER, D.
The Negro in modern industrial society (Thesis, Columbia Univ., 1930), xiv + 137 pp.

EPSTEIN, A.
The Negro migrant in Pittsburgh (Pittsburgh, 1918), 74 pp.

FANNING, J. W.
Negro migration, a study of the exodus of the Negroes between 1920 and 1925 from middle Georgia counties, etc. (*Bull. Univ. Ga.*; *Phelps Stokes Fellowship Studies*, 9, June, 1930), 39 pp.

FELDMAN, H.
Racial factors in American industry (New York, Harper, 1931), xiv + 318 pp.

FRAZIER, E. F.
"Occupational classes among Negroes in cities." *Am. Jour. Sociol.*, 35 (1930):718–738.
"The changing status of the Negro family." *Social Forces*, 9 (1931):386–393.
The Negro family in Chicago (Univ. Chicago Press, 1932), xxv + 294 pp.

GEE, W., AND CORSON, J. J.
Rural depopulation in certain tidewater and piedmont areas of Virginia (Charlottesville, Univ. Virginia, 1929), x + 104 pp.

GRAHAM, IRENE
"The Negro family in a northern city." *Opportunity*, 8 (1930):48–51.

HARPER, R. M.
"Contrasts between northern and southern urban and rural Negroes in the United States." *Social Forces*, 12 (1934):576–578.

HAYNES, G. E.
"Conditions among Negroes in cities." *Ann. Am. Acad. Polit. Soc. Sci.*, 49 (1913):104–119.
"Migration of Negroes into northern cities." *Proc. Nat. Conf. Soc. Work*, 44 (1917):494–497.
"Negro migration and its effect on family and community life in the North." *Ibid.*, 51 (1924):62–75. See also Fisher, *op. cit.*, 75–82.

HEBERLE, R.
Ueber die Mobilität der Bevölkerung in den Vereinigten Staaten (Jena, Fischer, 1929), iv + 224 pp.

HERBST, A.
The Negro in the slaughtering and meat-packing industry in Chicago (Boston, Houghton Mifflin, 1932), xxiii + 182 pp.

HILL, JOS.
"The recent northward migrations of the Negro." *Publ. Am. Sociol. Soc.*, 18 (1924):34–46.

HOLMES, S. J.
"Will the Negro survive in the North?" *Scient. Mon.*, 27 (1928):557–561.
"Racial migration." *Southwest Rev.*, 17:110–118 (Oct., 1931).
"The effect of migration on the natural increase of the Negro." In *A decade of progress in eugenics* (Baltimore, Williams and Wilkins, 1934), pp. 119–123.

INGLE, C. L.
The Negro in the District of Columbia (Johns Hopkins Univ. *Studies, Hist., Pol. Sci.*, 11, ser. 3–4, 1893), 110 pp.

JOHNSON, C. S.
"Substitution of Negro labor for European immigrant labor." *Proc. Nat. Conf. Soc. Work*, 1926:317–327.
"The American Migrant: the Negro." *Ibid.*, 1927:554–558.
"Some economic aspects of northern migration." *Opportunity*, 5 (1927):297–299.
"The Negro and the depression." *Social Forces*, 12 (1933):103–115.

KENNEDY, L. V.
The Negro peasant turns cityward (New York, Columbia Univ. Press, 1930), 270 pp.

KLINEBERG, O.
Negro intelligence and selective migration (New York, Columbia Univ. Press, 1935), xii + 66 pp.

KNIGHT, C. L.
Negro housing in certain Virginia cities (*Publ.* Univ. Va., *Phelps-Stokes Fellowship Papers,* No. 8, 1927), 158 pp.

LEWIS, E. E.
The mobility of the Negro (Columbia Univ. *Studies in Hist., etc.,* No. 342; New York, 1931), 145 pp.
"Economic factors in Negro migration." *Jour. Am. Statist. Assoc.,* 27 (1932):47–53.
"The southern Negro and the American labor supply." *Pol. Sci. Quart.,* 48 (1933):172–183.

MARK, M. L.
"Negroes in Columbia." Ohio State Univ. *Contr. in Social Science,* No. 2 (1928):64 pp.

MILLER, K.
Race Adjustment (New York, Neale, 1908), 306 pp.

MOSSELL, S. T.
"The Standard of Living among 100 Negro migrant families in Philadelphia." *Ann. Am. Acad. Polit. Soc. Sci.,* 98 (1921):173–218.

MOTON, R. R.
"Migrations of Negroes from the southern to northern states, and its economic effects." *Econ. World,* n.s., 26 (1923):688–691. See also *New York Times,* May 6, 1923.
The Negro in Chicago (Chicago, Univ. Chicago Press, 1922), xxii+672 pp.

NEW YORK CHARITY ORGANIZATIONS
"The Negro in the cities of the north." *Charities* (New York), 15 (1905): 1–96.

O'KELLY, H. S.
"Sanitary conditions among the Negroes of Athens, Ga." *Bull.* Univ. Ga., 18 (1918):28 pp.

PENNSYLVANIA, STATE DEPARTMENT OF PUBLIC WELFARE
Negro Survey of Pennsylvania (Harrisburg, Pa., 1928), 97 pp.

POINDEXTER, H. A.
"Special health problems of Negroes in rural areas." *Jour. Negro Education,* 6 (1937):399–412.

ROSS, F. A., AND TRUXAL, A. G.
"Primary and secondary aspects of interstate migrations." *Am. Jour. Sociol.,* 37 (1931):435–444.

ROSS, F. A., AND KENNEDY, L. V.
Bibliography of Negro migrations (New York, Columbia Univ. Press, 1934), 251 pp.

SCOTT, E. J.
"Letters of Negro migrants of 1916–18." *Jour. Negro Hist.,* 4 (1919): 290–340.
"The migration." *Opportunity,* 2 (1924):1840–1845.
Negro migration during the war (*Prelim. Studies,* No. 16, Carnegie Endowment for Internat. Peace, New York, 1920), 189 pp.

SHAFFER, E. T. H.

"New South." *Atlantic Mon.*, **129** (1922):116–123.

"A new South—the Negro migration." *Ibid.*, **132** (1923):403–409.

SHANNON, A. H.

The Negro in Washington (New York, Neale, 1930), 332 pp.

SOZINSKY, T. S.

"Medical aspects of Negro exodus." *Pennsylvania Mon.*, **10** (1879):529–538.

SPERO, S. D., AND HARRIS, A. L.

The black worker (New York, Columbia Univ. Press, 1931), 509 pp.

THAYER, A. C.

"Trends in Negro occupations." *Southern Workman*, **58** (1930):449–453.

THORNTHWAITE, C. W.

Internal migration in the United States (Philadelphia, Univ. of Pa. Press, 1934), x + 52 pp.

TIBBITTS, C.

"The socio-economic background of Negro health status." *Jour. Negro Education*, **6** (1937):413–428.

UNITED STATES DEPARTMENT OF LABOR

Negro migration in 1916–17 (*Bull.* Div. of Negro Economics, Washington, D. C.).

VANCE, R. P.

Human factors in cotton culture (Chapel Hill, Univ. North Carolina Press, 1929), xi + 346 pp.

Human geography of the South (Chapel Hill, Univ. North Carolina Press), 1932), xiv + 596 pp.

WESLEY, C. H.

Negro labor in the United States (New York, Vanguard Press, 1927), xiii + 343 pp.

WILLETS, J. H.

"Some aspects of the depression upon the Negro in Philadelphia." *Opportunity*, **11** (1933):200, 204.

WOODSON, C. G.

A century of Negro migration (Washington, D. C., Assoc. for Study of Negro Life and History, 1918), vii + 221 pp.

The rural Negro (Washington, D. C., Assoc. for Study of Negro Life and History, 1930), xvi + 265 pp.

WOOFTER, T. J.

Negro problems in cities (New York, Doubleday, Doran, 1928), 285 pp.

Negro migration (New York, W. D. Gray; Columbia Univ. Thesis, 1920), 95 pp.

"Negro migration to cities." *Survey*, **59** (1928):647–649.

"Southern population and social planning." *Social Forces*, **14** (1935):16–22.

WRIGHT, R. R.

"The migration of Negroes to the North." *Ann. Am. Acad. Polit. Soc. Sci.*, **27** (1906):543–609.

ZIMMERMANN, C. C., AND SMITH, L.

"Migration to towns and cities." *Am. Jour. Sociol.*, **35** (1930):41–51.

INDEX

Abdominal tuberculosis, 80
Abortion, 74, 127, 128
Acker, G. N., 268; on rickets, 121
Age groups, 20–24
Alexander, W. G., 282
Allen, F. J., 268
Allen, F. P., on heart disease, 114, 268
Alsobrook, H. B., on fibroid growths, 118, 268
Amalgamation, 167 ff.
Anderson, W. T., 275
Aronson, J. D., prevalence of tuberculosis, 83, 268
Arteriosclerosis, 113, 114
Asserson, M. A., 83, 84
Augustine, D. L., 281; on vital capacity, 86, 87; on hookworm, 120

Bacon, A. L., 277
Baker, G. W., on mortality from tuberculosis, 42, 89, 272
Baker, O. E., 216
Baker, R. S., 283; on miscegenation, 168
Bakwin, H., 280
Baldwin, B. T., 280
Band, H. M., 284
Barker, J. E., 268
Barnes, I., 269, 284
Beales, LeV., on Negro population, 19, 265
Beals, C., 264
Bell, F. K., 275
Bertram, N. W., 269
Billings, J. S., Negro mortality, 40, 48; Negro birth rate, 143, 144
Birth control in Negroes, 162–166
Birth rates, 2, 5, 8, 32 ff., 215, 218, 220, 221, 256–262
Bishop, E. L., 270
Black, J. B., 269
Blanc, H. W., 269
Boas, E. P., 269
Boas, F., 282
Boddy, J. M., 287.
Bogen, E., 269
Boinet and Isemein, 269
Borrell, A., 269
Bousfield, M. O., 269, 282
Bowcock, H. M., 269; reactions to insulin, 111
Breast, cancer of, 108
Britten, R. H., 269

Brock, B. L., and Black, H., 269
Bronchitis, 100, 101
Broncho-pneumonia, 91 ff.
Brown, F. W., 287
Brumfield, W. A., 71, 275
Bryant, C., 282
Bryce, J., 264
Buckner, Dr., on tuberculosis, 75
Bull, on Schick test, 63
Buller, Sir Wm., on extinction of Maoris, 6
Buller, V. W., on fibroids, 118, 119
Bulloch, E., 269
Burnett, S. M., 123
Burrat, W. J., 5
Bushnell, G. E., 269; Negro immunity to tuberculosis, 88

Calmette, L. C. A., on immunization to tuberculosis, 88
Cancer, 105–109, 238–246
Carley, P. S., and Wenger, O. C., syphilis in Negroes, 70, 71, 269
Carter, E. A., 282, 284; on birth restriction in Negroes, 162, 163
Carter, H. G., on tuberculosis in Negroes, 89, 270
Cason, T. Z., on syphilitic heart disease, 114, 270
Castle, W. E., on effects of race crossing, 177
Chadwick, H. D., 270
Chandler, A. C., on hookworm in Negroes, 120
Chase, T. N., 267
Churn, W. P., 270
Clark, G. C., 270
Clark, T., 281
Clements, F., 270
Cobb, W. M., 270
Cobbett, L., 270
Cohen, J., 270
Colds, 104
Collins, S. D., 270, 281; on respiratory diseases, 99, 104
Congenital debility, 126
Convulsions, 122
Cormia, F. E., 120, 279
Corson, E. R., on vitality of Negroes, 76, 270
Cort, W. W., on hookworm infestation, 121
Crabtree, J. A., 87, 270
Craig, J. D., and Dublin, L. I., 270